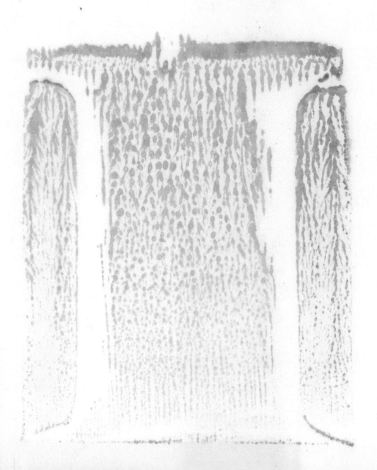

Introduction to

ATOMIC AND
NUCLEAR PHYSICS

Series in Physics

Richard M. Sutton
Editor

Introduction to
ATOMIC AND NUCLEAR PHYSICS
Second Edition

Rogers D. Rusk
MOUNT HOLYOKE COLLEGE

New York

APPLETON-CENTURY-CROFTS

DIVISION OF MEREDITH PUBLISHING COMPANY

PREFACE

This book represents an extensive rearrangement and rewriting of the author's previous book on atomic and nuclear physics, and it covers significant recent work which should stimulate the student's interest. The aim is to introduce the student to the concepts and methods underlying the fields of quantum physics and relativity. By reducing the total number of subjects covered it has been possible to give more depth of treatment and more emphasis on fundamentals at many points while preserving in general the elementary level of the work.

The book is chiefly intended for students of science and engineering who are completing a third or fourth semester of physics. However, it may be of equal value for the general student who is rounding out his knowledge of physics on an elementary or intermediate level. All of this is in keeping with the growing need to introduce the student to the basic ideas of much of what is called "modern physics" as early as possible and to enable him to learn how quantum physics and relativity have succeeded where classical physics failed.

It is assumed that the student has had a good general course in college or university physics and some acquaintance with calculus. For those who wish a shorter and simpler course a few chapters such as those on wave mechanics, molecular spectra, and quantum statistics may either be omitted or referred to briefly. Some teachers may prefer to introduce the last chapter on particle accelerators at an earlier point whereas others may wish to assign it merely as supplementary reading. Despite its great interest it was placed last because it does not represent basic theory but rather large-scale "hardware."

Numerous problems are included at the end of each chapter. Some of these illustrate the application of basic principles in a more or less simple form while others are designed to challenge the student. For a shorter course the starred problems should be omitted as they are either of greater difficulty or else are on more specialized subjects. Answers to odd-numbered problems are at the back of the book. For the most part rationalized mks units are used throughout the book but references are sometimes made to cgs units and a convenient table of conversion factors for common units is given in Appendix 2.

A list of recommended reading at the end of each chapter will enable the student to pursue in more detail subjects of special interest or those but briefly mentioned in the text.

The author is indebted to many teachers, friends and physicists who have given helpful suggestions and who have furnished interesting photographs with permission to publish them. He is particularly indebted to Sarah E. Rusk for the many arduous hours spent in typing and preparing the manuscript.

R. D. R.

CONTENTS

3. Positive Rays and Mass Spectroscopy   35

4. X-rays and Crystal Structure   48

5. Quantum Properties of Waves and Particles   76

6. Relativity

7. The Nuclear Atom; Hydrogen Spectrum

8. Wave Mechanics and the Hydrogen Atom

14. Nuclear Structure and Nuclear Forces   316

15. Nuclear Processes   345

16. Neutron Physics   363

17. High-Energy Rays and New Particles   389

18. Particle Accelerators   420

Appendix   445

Answers to Odd-Numbered Problems   457

Index   461

Introduction to

ATOMIC AND
NUCLEAR PHYSICS

1

From Classical Physics to Quantum Physics

1-1. Classical Physics

The nineteenth century was preeminently the period of rise to maximum usefulness of what we now call *classical physics*, the physics based on the Newtonian mechanics and extended during the last half of the century to include the electromagnetic theory of Maxwell. Toward the end of the century it had seemed to many as if physical theories were almost complete. Although the more far-sighted scientists saw some disturbing difficulties it was the general idea that there remained little to be discovered and little to be done except by way of greater precision of measurements together with refinement of existing theories.

However, just at the close of the century this smug little world practically "blew up" with a series of discoveries, some of them so startling and revolutionary that they were headlined in the newspapers, others announced with less fanfare but of equal or even greater significance.

Chief among these discoveries near the beginning of the present century were: *x-rays* (1895); *radioactivity* (1896); *the electron* (1897). On the theoretical side came Planck's *quantum theory* of radiation (1900) and Einstein's special *theory of relativity* (1905). These developments were preceded by Maxwell's formulation of the *electromagnetic theory of light* (1862–64) and by the discovery of the *photoelectric effect* by Hertz in 1887 which was shown by Einstein (1905) to require the quantum theory for its explanation. Such developments opened vast new fields of investigation in atomic physics and they led to the more recent achievements in nuclear physics. Along with such experimental developments it was inevitable that revolutionary viewpoints and concepts would arise involving radically different methods of thought and theory.

It must not be concluded that in its day the Newtonian theory was not revolutionary. It represented an extraordinary change in man's view of his world. Kepler had announced his laws of planetary motion and this was a monumental advance. Until that time it had not been recognized that the so-called *heavenly bodies* were subject to natural law, and in particular it was not known that the laws of planetary motion had any direct connection to the laws of motion of terrestrial objects. By clearly formulating the laws of motion of terrestrial objects, and by deducing the universal law of gravitation Newton was able to show that Kepler's laws of planetary motion followed directly from these. Thus Newton created a great synthesis by bringing both types of motion under the rule of law and order in a single system. This is what is known as the *Newtonian synthesis*, an achievement unparalleled in the history of science, and its significance can scarcely be overestimated.

The successes of the Newtonian mechanics were extended by many others including Laplace, Lagrange and Hamilton, and in the form of the more generalized Hamiltonian mechanics it has become the basis for much in the newer physics which despite its revolutionary character has never broken completely with classical physics as will become evident in later pages. Indeed the fundamental *conservation laws* of classical physics have become the canonical guiding principles throughout all of physics, even in the realm of quantum physics. We refer of course to the laws of conservation of *energy* and *mass* (or *energy-mass* in more modern relativistic terminology), the conservation of *electric charge*, and the conservation of both *linear* and *angular momentum*. In the atomic realm other conservation laws will be added as needed.

1-2. The Failure of Classical Mechanism: Probability

The attempts to apply classical mechanics to matter in a more and more finely divided state met with increasing difficulties. When objects could be observed directly there were no real difficulties. This is the realm of *macrophysics* based on the physics of everyday objects and common phenomena. But the application of the same laws to atoms, or for instance to the molecules of a gas, was different. This is the realm of *microphysics* and detailed observations on the individual molecules of a gas were impossible for two reasons: they were too small to be seen and there were too many of them.

Nevertheless faith in the classical mechanics was such that it was believed that if a molecule of mass m were subjected to a force F, it would experience an acceleration a given by the classical relation $F = ma$. Many more or less indirect measurements successfully bore this out as, for instance the computation of the macroscopic pressure P of a gas ($P = \frac{1}{3}nmv^2$). P is given in terms of the microscopic quantities, m the mass of each particle, v the velocity, and n the number of particles per unit volume. These extensions of classical theory marked its further successes. However, statistical theory had to be resorted to by Maxwell and by Boltzmann in the latter part of the 19th century in order to obtain the *velocity distribution* resulting from collisions of gas molecules with one another. It then became apparent that despite the deterministic character of classical mechanics no one could follow the individual molecules of a gas and say that any one molecule must be at a certain place at a certain time. It could only be said that a certain number of molecules would *most probably* be found in a particular element of volume at a particular time and that they would *most probably* have a particular range of velocities.

The full significance of the entrance of probability theory into physics at that time was certainly not dreamed of. However, with the development of quantum statistics, the deep involvement of statistical theory in the realm of the atom and the nucleus soon became apparent. At the same time it became clear that not only was it impossible to apply classical deterministic methods throughout the atomic realm but when applied they usually gave the wrong answers, whereas *quantum methods* which were developed after the discovery of quantum phenomena gave the correct answers. Thus arose a fundamental distinction between the realms of classical physics and quantum physics.

1-3. Radiant Energy and the Planck Quantum Hypothesis

The quantum theory originated when Max Planck advanced the hypothesis that radiant energy is absorbed or emitted by "quantized oscillators" in definite units called *quanta*. Planck had been forced to this conclusion when he attempted to reconcile conflicting theories of thermal radiation (Chap. 11). On this new assumption, radiation and absorption processes instead of being continuous, as had been supposed, were found to be discontinuous. This in turn led Einstein to the conclusion that the radiant energy is itself quantized. The discontinuous or "atomic" character of radiation is in many ways similar to the atomic character of matter and of electricity. Ordinary matter exists in "quanta" which we call atoms.

Electricity is "quantized" in the form of electrons. With the acceptance of the quantum theory we see that not only matter and electricity but also radiant energy (at least in its interactions with atoms and electrons) is essentially discontinuous and atomic in nature.

Planck assumed that the energy E_q represented by one quantum of electromagnetic radiation was given by the relation

$$E_q = h\nu \qquad\qquad [1\text{–}1]$$

where h is now called the *Planck constant* (§5-2) and ν is the frequency of the radiation. The application of this idea of quantization of radiant energy to the photoelectric effect and the production of x-rays (Chaps. 4 and 5) and to successive problems of atomic physics led to explanations of phenomena which could not satisfactorily be made on any other basis. These ideas led in time to the more all-embracing theories of present-day quantum physics which are summarized under the name *quantum mechanics*, or in its most common form, *wave mechanics*. We shall therefore accept $E_q = h\nu$ as a fundamental relation just as basic in the atomic realm as Newton's second law of motion represented by $F = ma$ is in the realm of everyday phenomena, and to this we shall add the equally important defining equation for the wavelength of a particle (§5-7).

1-4. Relativity: Relativistic Quantum Mechanics

Five years after the birth of the quantum theory at the beginning of the century Einstein proposed his *restricted or special theory of relativity* which revolutionized ideas of the measurement of basic physical quantities and critically examined concepts which had been taken for granted without adequate definition. Again as with Planck's quantum theory the Einstein theory arose from a deep conflict in both theory and experiment (Chap. 6) involving classical mechanics and electromagnetic theory. Einstein resolved this conflict with unexpected results. Among other things he showed that Newton's laws of motion though apparently valid for everyday phenomena cannot be considered valid for bodies moving at high speeds, and that a more general form of such laws is required which reduces for all practical purposes to the Newtonian form for low speeds. Classical concepts of absolute rest or motion were overthrown and physical measurements were found to depend in a new way on the state of rest or motion of the observer.

At first it appeared that the Einstein theory of relativity belonged to the realm of large-scale events and that if it had anything to do with atomic structure it would be of the nature of a small "relativistic" correction. However, in 1928 a major step forward in atomic theory was taken by Dirac who made a complete break with classical methods in the form of a quantum mechanical theory into which he put relativity as a fundamental part of the theory, not just a mere correction. This led Dirac to a far more complete mathematical description of the atom involving both quantum physics and relativity physics in which it was unnecessary to start with an incomplete theory and then patch it up with *ad hoc* assumptions. Although most of the mathematics will be beyond the scope of this book, the over-all picture will show Dirac's great success.

1-5. The Particles of Physics

With the discovery of cathode rays, the electron, the proton, and radioactivity the Newtonian picture of a solid "lifeless" everlasting atom was demolished for all time. Now began the study of the particles of which the atom and its nucleus are composed. As will be seen, the hope of finding a small number of indivisible particles from which all atoms (and their nuclei) could be constructed according to some fairly simple system has not been achieved. Although the growing number of particles and the complexity of the atomic nucleus will be dealt with in later chapters, it is desirable at this point to summarize the chief characteristics of some of the more common particles with which we will be concerned in the earlier portions of this book.

1-6. Cathode Rays and the Discovery of the Electron

The electron is commonly said to have been *discovered* by J. J. Thomson of the Cavendish Laboratory in England in 1897 because he made convincing measurements and demonstrated conclusively that these tiny units of electric charge actually exist and are found in all forms of matter. The later more precise measurement of the charge of the electron by R. A. Millikan extended and confirmed Thomson's work.

Actually the discovery of the electron is an interesting example of how such discoveries are often the culmination of the work of many investigators. In 1859 Plücker noted fluorescence of the glass of a highly evacuated discharge tube and attributed it to "rays" from the cathode. He found he could deflect the rays with a magnetic field. His pupil, Hittorf, confirmed that the rays came from the cathode and showed that a solid object in the path of the rays would cast a shadow. Goldstein made further studies and called the rays *cathode rays*. The experiments of Sir William Crookes led him to believe the rays were particles rather than waves, and with considerable weight he advanced the idea that they were not ordinary particles but matter in a new form.

Perrin in 1895 deflected the rays into a cup inside a discharge tube and showed that the cup acquired a negative charge. J. J. Thomson carefully measured the deflection of the rays by both electric and magnetic fields. Although he could not measure the mass of each particle he did measure the ratio of charge to mass, e/m. On the assumption, not immediately confirmed, that the charge e of a cathode-ray particle was the same as that carried by a singly-charged ion in a liquid, he found that the mass must be far less than that of any known particle. He further showed that the same cathode-ray particles were always present regardless of the material of the cathode or of the gas in the tube. Thus came about the *discovery* of the electron and the ultimate recognition that electrons are all alike.

MILLIKAN'S DETERMINATION OF THE CHARGE OF THE ELECTRON

The precise measurement of the electronic charge e was accomplished by R. A. Millikan in his famous "oil-drop experiment." In its simplest form the experiment consisted of balancing a tiny negatively charged oil droplet between the two horizontal plates of a charged capacitor. When the upper plate was positive and the lower plate negative the electric field intensity $\mathcal{E}$ between the plates could be adjusted so that the upward force $\mathcal{E}q$ of the field on the charge q of the droplet was just equal to the net downward force. This is the force of gravity mg less the buoyant force $m'g$ of the air displaced by the droplet, where m is the mass of the droplet and m' is the mass of the displaced air. Then

$$\mathcal{E}q = mg - m'g \qquad [1-2]$$

The electric field intensity $\mathcal{E}$ was given by $\mathcal{E} = V/d$ where V was the voltage on the plates and d was the distance between. The mass of the drop could be determined indirectly by observing the rate of free fall when the field was removed and applying "Stokes' law" (see problems) for the rate of fall of a sphere in a resisting medium (air). Since the field intensity $\mathcal{E}$ was known and $g = 9.8$ m/sec^2 the unknown charge q could be obtained. After many precise determinations of different charges on different drops Millikan found that there was a minimum charge e, the charge of one electron, which was always the same and that all other charges q were integral multiples $q = ne$ of this fundamental unit.

The presently accepted values of the charge e and the mass m_e of the electron to five significant figures are

$$e = -1.6021 \times 10^{-19} \text{ coulomb}$$
$$= -4.8029 \times 10^{-10} \text{ esu}$$
$$m_e = 9.1091 \times 10^{-31} \text{ kilogram}$$

THE POSITRON

Thirty-five years later came the discovery of the *positive electron* or *positron*, the *antiparticle* of the electron. It is the "twin" of an ordinary negative electron except that the charge is positive. This particle occurs most frequently in nuclear transformations and not at all in ordinary gas discharges. It is only mentioned at this time because of its general importance and because it was first detected by the method of magnetic deflection discussed in the next chapter. In observing tracks of cosmic-ray electrons by means of a cloud chamber (§13-15), Anderson in 1932 noted one track bent by the magnetic field in exactly the opposite direction. It was obvious that the charge must be positive, and thus the world of physics acquired its first antiparticle. (See Plate 3 in the plate section preceding Chap. 13.)

1-7. The Proton

The charged particles of a gas or liquid, the motion of which in a given direction constitutes a current of electricity through the gas or liquid, are either electrons or charged atoms (or groups of atoms) called *ions*. The positive gas ion of smallest known mass (largest q/M) is found in a discharge tube containing hydrogen. From the vantage point of present knowledge we know that atoms consist of extremely small, but relatively massive, positively charged nuclei surrounded by the same number of electrons as there are similar positive charges on the nucleus.

According to this picture a hydrogen atom, the lightest of all, consists of a singly charged nuclear particle plus one external electron. Removal of the electron from a neutral hydrogen atom results in *ionization* of a hydrogen atom and leaves only a bare nucleus of hydrogen. This bare nucleus is called the *proton* and it is a basic sub-atomic particle now known to be involved in the structure of the nuclei of all atoms. By the law of conservation of charge the charge of the proton is of the same magnitude as that of the electron but opposite in sign (positive). The mass of a proton is

$$M_p = 1.6725 \times 10^{-27} \text{ kg}$$

The discovery in 1955 of the negative proton or *antiproton*, a particle having the same mass as a proton but possessing a negative charge, was a remarkable development giving added confirmation to the theory that for every particle there is an *antiparticle* (Chap. 17) even though the antiparticle may be short-lived. The antiproton and other antiparticles will be discussed later but the creation of a particle pair, that is a particle and its antiparticle, will be discussed in §6-11.

1-8. The Neutron and the Nuclear Atom; Mass Number

The three most important sub-atomic particles of which we may consider all atoms to be composed are the electron, the proton and the neutron.

The neutron was discovered in 1932 by Chadwick and its properties will be discussed more fully later (Chap. 16). The neutron is a neutral particle possessing zero net charge and consequently it is unaffected by an electric field. It has a mass only slightly larger than that of the proton.

$$M_n = 1.6748 \times 10^{-27} \text{ kg}$$

The neutron does, however, possess magnetic moment and it is therefore affected by a magnetic field. This may mean that although any positive and negative charges in the neutron add to a net charge of zero, the effects of the motions of these charges upon which the magnetic moment of the neutron depends do not add to zero.

The discovery of the neutron made it possible to simplify the structure of atomic nuclei and consequently of atoms themselves. Experimental evidence indicates that from the simplest viewpoint all nuclei of atoms are composed of a number of protons equal to the nuclear charge and the proper number of neutrons required to account for the remaining mass of the nucleus. Thus the nucleus of the most common type of oxygen atom, O^{16}, must possess 8 protons and 8 neutrons to give it an approximate mass of 16 units. The total number of nuclear particles (*nucleons*) is then 16 and this is called the *mass number* of the nucleus. Because of its 8 protons the nucleus of an O^{16} atom has a net positive charge of 8 electronic units. In the neutral atom these will be balanced by 8 external electrons. Since the characteristic behavior of an atom of any element depends on the number of external electrons which in turn depends upon the number of protons in the nucleus this number will be constant for all the atoms of a given element regardless of the mass or the mass number.

1-9. Other Common Particles

THE DEUTERON

The atomic nucleus of next larger mass to that of the proton is called the *deuteron*. It is the nucleus of a *heavy hydrogen* atom, and it is what remains when an atom of heavy hydrogen (deuterium) is ionized by removal of its single electron. The mass of a heavy hydrogen atom (H^2 or D) is approximately twice that of an ordinary hydrogen atom.

$$M_D = 3.34355 \times 10^{-27} \text{ kg}$$

The deuteron is not a single particle but is composed of one proton plus one neutron. Evidently it must carry a single positive charge just as the proton does. More will be said of it in §3-6, where the mass of the deuteron will be given in *atomic mass units* and it will be compared with the proton and neutron. The deuteron is often used as the bombarding particle to produce nuclear transformations, and the study of the deuteron itself furnishes important information about the forces holding nuclear particles together. It may be found in an electric discharge when deuterium is present.

THE ALPHA PARTICLE

The next most common nuclear particle in the scale of ascending masses is the *alpha particle*. It is the nucleus of a helium atom and it is composed of two protons and two neutrons. Since a helium atom has two electrons, loss of one of these would result in a singly charged (positive) helium atom. Loss of both electrons leaves only the doubly charged bare nucleus of helium, an alpha particle. The alpha particle plays an important role in radioactivity and nuclear physics, as will be seen later, but it may be found in an electric discharge when helium is present.

1-10. Avogadro's Number

In 1811, nine years after Dalton had introduced the concept of atoms into chemistry as a working hypothesis, Avogadro pointed out that current thinking led to the conclusion that *equal volumes of different gases at the same temperature and pressure contain equal numbers of molecules.* Although slow in gaining general acceptance, this principle has now been amply confirmed by many experiments.

The term *gram-atomic weight* (or gram-atom) has long served to represent the number of grams of any substance equal numerically to its atomic weight. A *gram-molecular weight* or *mole* (now called a *gram-formula weight*) is the number of grams equal to its formula weight. The number of atoms in a mole (or in a gram-atomic weight) is an important constant called *Avogadro's number*. In mks units it is the number in a *kilogram-atomic weight*.

The quantity of electricity required to deposit 1 gram-atomic weight of any monovalent element (an element forming singly charged ions) can be directly measured and is 96,522 coulombs. This quantity of electricity is called the *faraday*.

$$1 \text{ faraday} = 96,487 \text{ coulombs}$$

In depositing 1 gram-atomic weight of any monovalent substance, Avogadro's number or N_0 atoms are deposited. If each carries a charge e, the total quantity of charge Q per gram-atomic weight is $N_0 e$. But this is the faraday F. Consequently

$$N_0 e = F \quad \text{and} \quad N_0 = \frac{F}{e} \qquad [1\text{--}3]$$

Since F and e could be determined with much precision except for some difficulty in measuring the viscosity of air, this led to a similarly precise value for Avogadro's number.

With the introduction of very precise methods of determining the spacing of atoms in a crystal by means of x-rays (Chap. 4) it became possible to obtain an even better value of Avogadro's number in a more direct manner. Putting this and the value of F into Eq. 1–3 enabled a new determination of the charge e to be made (see Problem 7) and led to a small correction of the earlier work by Millikan (§4-11). The corrected value was given in §1-6 and since this is one of the most useful constants of nature a dependable and precise value is of utmost importance. The accepted value of Avogadro's number is

$$N_0 = 6.0252 \times 10^{23} \text{ (per gram-atomic weight)}$$
$$= 6.0252 \times 10^{26} \text{ (per kilogram-atomic weight)}$$

The uses of Avogadro's number are manifold. Since a gram-molecule of any gas occupies a volume of 22,415 cm^3 (or 0.022415 m^3) at 0°C and 76 cm mercury pressure and a kilogram-molecule occupies a volume of 22.415 m^3, it is a simple matter to find the number of molecules per unit volume of a gas under standard conditions. This is the prodigious number 2.68×10^{25} per m^3.

1-11. Some Particle-Like Properties of Electrons

What do we know about electrons? The answer is that we know a very great deal. In the earlier experiments the electron was observed to behave like any charged particle even though of extremely small (sub-atomic) size. Later experiments revealed the wave-like behavior under certain conditions and this wave-like character led to the development of present-day *wave mechanics*. Some of the principal particle-like properties of the electron as revealed by the early experiments are as follows, whereas the wave-like character will be discussed in Chapter 5.

1. The electron is the fundamental atomic unit of electricity.

2. Its mass is 1/1837 that of a hydrogen atom.

3. It has a negative charge of 4.803×10^{-10} esu or 1.602×10^{-19} coulomb.

4. It is extremely small in size, its diameter being about 10^{-5} that of a hydrogen atom which is the smallest atom.

5. The effective mass of an electron moving in a vacuum increases with increasing speed, approaching infinity as the speed approaches the speed of light in accordance with relativity theory.

6. If moving with sufficient energy it will *ionize* gas molecules (or *excite* them) and produce a luminous glow.

7. In an electric field it behaves like any negatively charged particle.

8. A moving electron is deflected by a magnetic field like any moving particle with a negative charge.

9. The spot where electrons strike a photographic plate will be "exposed" and appear black after development.

10. When electrons of sufficient speed strike a fluorescent screen a luminous spot will appear.

Problems

Note: In the Millikan "oil-drop experiment" neither the mass of the droplet m nor its radius a can be measured directly. However, the radius can be computed by measuring the constant "terminal velocity" which is very quickly attained by the droplet falling in air, since the air acts as a resisting medium. The terminal velocity is attained when the resisting force ("drag") caused by the viscosity of the air is equal in magnitude to the net downward force. By Stokes' law the magnitude of this drag on a sphere is $F = 6\pi\eta a v$ where a is the radius of the sphere, η is the viscosity of the medium and v is the terminal velocity. For the highest precision a correction is made for very small drops but need not concern us here.

1. The net downward force on a droplet is $F = (m - m')g = (4\pi a^3/3)(\rho - \rho')g$ where ρ is the density of the oil and ρ' is the density of the displaced air. Find the radius of a droplet for which the terminal velocity is 5×10^{-5} m/sec. Take $\rho = 850$ kg/m³ at room temperature, $\rho' = 1.20$ kg/m³, and $\eta = 1.80 \times 10^{-5}$ kg/(m/sec).

2. Find the mass of an oil drop which is observed to fall at a constant rate in air for a distance of 0.0050 m in 20 sec. Take pertinent data from previous problem.

3. The horizontal plates for determining the charge of an electron by the oil-drop method are 1.5 cm apart and are kept at a potential difference of 1500 volts. What is the electric field intensity between the plates? What is the force of the field on a droplet carrying a charge of 1 electron?

4. A droplet of 10^{-12} gm mass and charge e is held balanced in a vacuum between parallel plates by an electric field which opposes the pull of gravity. If the plates are 2 cm apart, what potential difference between the plates is required to balance the pull of gravity exactly?

5. In a variation of the simplest method of determining e Millikan measured the terminal velocity of free fall v_d and the terminal upward velocity v_u when a sufficiently strong field $\mathcal{E}$ was applied. Show that the charge q on the oil drop is given by

$$q = \frac{k}{\mathcal{E}}(v_u + v_d)$$

if $k = 6\pi\eta a$ from Stokes' law and the buoyant force of the air is omitted.

6. What would be the advantages and disadvantages of observing relatively large or relatively small oil drops in the Millikan experiment?

7. Careful work by Bearden in determining the precise spacing of atoms in a crystal by x-ray methods (Chap. 4) led to a small correction of the charge of the electron as measured by Millikan. To determine the charge e by this method it was necessary to dissolve certain crystals and measure the charge carried per atom in electrolysis. Explain how e can be measured in this fashion.

8. Find the number of atoms in 10^{-2} kg of silver.

9. A gold coin weighs 0.0225 kg. How many atoms of gold does it contain? If the density of gold is 19300 kg/m³ what is the average separation between centers of the atoms?

10. An oxygen tank having a volume of 4 liters contains oxygen at a pressure of 40 lb/in² above atmospheric pressure. How many oxygen molecules are in the tank?

Recommended Reading

Richtmeyer, F. K., E. H. Kennard, and T. Lauritsen, *Introduction to Modern Physics*. New York: McGraw-Hill Book Company, Inc., 1955.

De Broglie, L., *Physics and Microphysics*. New York: Torchbooks, Harper and Row, Publishers, 1960.

Crowther, J. A., *Ions, Electrons and Ionizing Radiations*, 8th ed. London: Edward Arnold, 1949.

Massey, Sir Harrie, *The New Age in Physics*. New York: Harper & Row, Publishers, 1960.

Fretter, W. B., *Introduction to Experimental Physics*. Englewood Cliffs, N. J.: Prentice-Hall, Inc., 1954.

Cohen, E. R., K. M. Crowe, and J. W. M. DuMond, *The Fundamental Constants of Physics*. New York: Interscience Publishers, Inc., 1957.

Early Work

Millikan, R. A., *Electrons (+ and −), Protons, Photons, Mesotrons, and Cosmic Rays*. Chicago: University of Chicago Press, 1947.

Electric and Magnetic Fields: Effects on Moving Charges

2-1. The Concept of a Force Field

There are two primary ways in which a force can be exerted on an object, either by contact with another object or by the action of a force field. When an object not in contact with another object is accelerated without visible cause for such acceleration (or requires the application of a force to prevent its being accelerated) we conceive that it has been acted upon by some *field of force*.

The fields of force with which we are most familiar are *gravitational fields, electric fields, magnetic fields,* or a combination of the latter two in an *electromagnetic field*. The concepts of electric and magnetic fields arose with the work of Faraday who first represented such fields by *lines* (or *tubes*) *of force*. The total number of these issuing from a given region or passing through a given region is called the *flux*. The number per unit area cutting across any surface at right angles to the field is called the flux density and measures the intensity of the field. It is better to think of flux and flux density as symbols directly representing the field and field intensity respectively than to think of them as representing a mechanical model in terms of lines or tubes.

The intensity ε of an electric field is measured by the *force per unit charge* exerted on a small test charge Δq placed in the field. The test charge

13

must be small in order not to distort the field being measured. The force **F** exerted on any similar charge Δq is then

$$\mathbf{F} = \mathcal{E}\Delta q \qquad [2\text{-}1]$$

If q is in *coulombs* and the force is in *newtons* the electric field intensity $\mathcal{E}$ is in *newtons per coulomb* (mks units). This force is a vector quantity and the direction of the force is taken to be the direction of the field. Such a field can be thought of then as a region at each point of which the field can be represented by a vector and the field is called a *vector field* (Fig. 2-1).

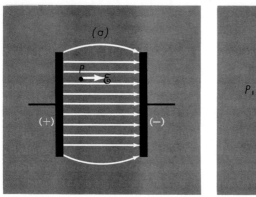 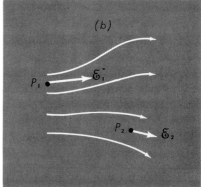

Fig. 2-1.   *a,* The field between charged parallel plates (uniform except at edges). The vector $\mathcal{E}$ represents the electric field intensity at the point P. *b,* A more general type of field (non-uniform) showing how the vector field at P_2 may differ from that at P_1 in both magnitude and direction.

Since the potential difference in volts between any two points A and B is defined as the number of joules per coulomb required to move a small test charge Δq from A to B against the force **F** of the field, the work done is $\Delta q(V_A - V_B)$ or ΔqV where $V = V_A - V_B$ is the difference of potential. In a uniform field this work is the force **F** on the charge times the component of the displacement **s** in the same direction, or in vector terminology

$$\mathbf{F} \cdot \mathbf{s} = \Delta q \mathcal{E} \cdot \mathbf{s} = \Delta q(V_A - V_B) \qquad [2\text{-}2]$$

where **F** · **s** and $\mathcal{E}$ · **s** are each the *scalar* or *dot products* of two vectors which may be at any angle θ. By definition

$$\mathbf{F} \cdot \mathbf{s} = Fs \cos \theta$$

and

$$\mathcal{E} \cdot \mathbf{s} = \mathcal{E}s \cos \theta$$

where F, $\mathcal{E}$ and s are the magnitudes of the corresponding vectors. The field intensity $\mathcal{E}$ or force per unit charge in *newtons per coulomb* is also measured in the units *volts per meter* since from Eq. 2–2 the magnitude of $\mathcal{E}$ is

$$\mathcal{E} = \frac{V_A - V_B}{s} \qquad [2\text{–}2a]$$

Since work must be done to establish an electric field, the field is considered to possess energy. For instance, if the two plates of a parallel plate capacitor are pulled apart when the plates are oppositely charged, work must be done because the plates attract each other. This work may be considered as energy stored in the field between the plates when the plates are separated and the field is established.

By electrical theory the magnitude of the force of attraction per unit area of one plate for the other (assuming uniform field) is $F = \frac{1}{2}\epsilon_0\mathcal{E}^2$ where ϵ_0 is the required constant of proportionality in mks units (called the *permittivity* of free space).

$$\epsilon_0 = 8.85 \times 10^{-12} \text{ coul}^2/\text{n m}^2$$

The force on area A is then $\frac{1}{2}\epsilon_0\mathcal{E}^2 A$ and the work done in separating the plates an amount Δs is,

$$\text{work done} = \frac{1}{2}\epsilon_0\mathcal{E}^2 A \Delta s = \frac{1}{2}\epsilon_0\mathcal{E}^2 \Delta v$$

where Δv is the change in volume between the plates. From this the energy density or energy per unit volume E_e of the electric field in a vacuum is

$$E_e = \frac{1}{2}\frac{\epsilon_0\mathcal{E}^2\Delta v}{\Delta v} = \frac{1}{2}\epsilon_0\mathcal{E}^2 \qquad [2\text{–}3]$$

In a somewhat similar manner the energy density E_m of a magnetic field in free space may be shown to be

$$E_m = \frac{1}{2}\mu_0\mathcal{H}^2 = \frac{1}{2}\frac{B^2}{\mu_0} \qquad [2\text{–}4]$$

where the magnitude of the intensity of the magnetic field in free space is $\mathcal{H}$. In any magnetic medium it is customary to make use of what is called the magnetic flux density **B**. In free space this is defined in the mks system as

$$\mathbf{B} = \mu_0\mathcal{H} \qquad [2\text{–}5]$$

or in scalar terms $\qquad\qquad B = \mu_0\mathcal{H}$

where μ_0 is the required constant called the *permeability of space*.

$$\mu_0 = 4\pi \times 10^{-7} \text{ weber/amp m}$$

In an electromagnetic field both electric and magnetic fields are present simultaneously. In 1864 James Clerk Maxwell investigated the theory of the electromagnetic field and obtained a wave equation indicating that when both fields are present a disturbance in the field will be propagated as a wave. His equations indicated the speed of propagation v of such a wave would be given by

$$v = \frac{1}{\sqrt{\epsilon_0 \mu_0}} \qquad [2\text{--}6]$$

Putting in the numerical values of ϵ_0 and μ_0 we have

$$v = \frac{1}{\sqrt{(8.85 \times 10^{-12})(4\pi 10^{-7})}} \cong 3 \times 10^8 \text{ m/sec} \qquad [2\text{--}7]$$

This agrees closely with the best experimentally measured value for the velocity of light c in free space where

$$c = 2.997925 \pm 0.000008 \times 10^8 \text{ m/sec}$$

but we shall use the approximate value 3×10^8 m/sec in all computations. The fact that the velocity of such an electromagnetic wave is the same as the velocity of light led Maxwell to conclude that light waves are electromagnetic in nature. In 1887 Hertz succeeded in confirming Maxwell's theory by producing electromagnetic waves in the laboratory. Since then many experiments have confirmed the electromagnetic nature of light and have extended to wide limits the known range of electromagnetic radiations (§4-12).

Since the electric and magnetic components of the electromagnetic field each possess energy, the electromagnetic wave represents energy in transit. It must also be considered to possess momentum and such waves should exert a pressure when they are incident on a surface. The momentum of electromagnetic radiation as deduced by classical theory is

$$\text{momentum of radiation} = \frac{E}{c} \text{ (in a vacuum)} \qquad [2\text{--}8]$$

where E is the energy per unit volume of the moving field. Though difficult to prove for radio waves the idea was confirmed when Lebedev in Russia measured the pressure of light by delicate experiments in 1900, followed shortly by similar work of Nichols and Hull in this country.

2-2. Effect of an Electric Field on a Charge, Classical Theory

Two ideal point charges q_1 and q_2 separated by a distance r attract (or repel) each other according to the Coulomb inverse square law with a force F given by

$$\mathbf{F} = k \frac{q_1 q_2}{r^2} \mathbf{r} \qquad [2\text{--}9]$$

where $\hat{\mathbf{r}}$ is a unit vector in the direction r, and k is a constant depending on the units used.

If this force is divided by q_2 there results the force per unit charge $(kq_1/r^2)\hat{\mathbf{r}}$ which defines the intensity of the electric field at a distance r from the charge q. The direction in which a positively charged particle is accelerated by an electric field defines the direction of the field, whereas an electron because of its negative charge is accelerated in the opposite direction. In the mks system q is in coulombs, r is in meters (m), F is in newtons (n) and $k = 8.98 \times 10^9$ n m^2/coul^2. In the rationalized form of the mks system, in order to cancel out the factor 4π in many equations, k is written as $1/4\pi\epsilon_0$ where ϵ_0 has the value given in Eq. 2–7. Eq. 2–9 is similar to Newton's law of gravitation for ideal point masses $m_1 m_2$ separated by a distance r,

$$\mathbf{F} = -G\frac{m_1 m_2}{r^2}\hat{\mathbf{r}} \qquad [2\text{--}10]$$

where G is called the *gravitational constant*. One difference must be noted. In the gravitational case all bodies attract one another and the sign of the force is always negative. In the electrical case only charges of opposite sign attract, their product being negative, whereas a positive sign indicates repulsion of like charges. In a manner similar to that for the electric field intensity the quantity GM/r^2 represents the *intensity* of the gravitational field of the earth (force per unit mass) at any point distance $r = R + h$ from the center of the earth if M is the mass of the earth, R is the radius of the earth and h is the elevation above the earth's surface.

When a free electron is acted on by an electric field the electron behaves as a classical Newtonian particle and Newton's second law of motion $\mathbf{F} = \Delta(m\mathbf{v})/\Delta t$ can be applied to find the rate of change of momentum. In a uniform electric field at low velocities (when the mass is essentially independent of the velocity) $\mathbf{F} = m\mathbf{a}$ and the acceleration $\mathbf{a}$ of the electron in such a field is given by putting the value of the force from Eq. 2–1 into the equation $\mathbf{F} = m\mathbf{a}$. Then writing $-e$ for the charge of the electron

$$\mathbf{a} = \frac{\Delta\mathbf{v}}{\Delta t} = \frac{\mathbf{F}}{m} = \frac{-\mathcal{E}e}{m} \qquad [2\text{--}11]$$

The displacement $\mathbf{s}$ of the electron in time Δt is therefore the vector sum.

$$\mathbf{s} = \mathbf{v}_0(\Delta t) + \frac{1}{2}\mathbf{a}(\Delta t)^2$$

$$= \mathbf{v}_0(\Delta t) - \frac{1}{2}\frac{\mathcal{E}e}{m}(\Delta t)^2 \qquad [2\text{--}12]$$

where $\mathbf{v}_0$ is the initial velocity of the electron at the beginning of the time interval Δt. If the direction of the electric field is at right angles to the direction of the initial velocity, the electron will be deflected from its initial path by an amount given by the second term of Eq. 2–12.

2-3. The Deflection of Electrons by a Transverse Electric Field

A simple type of cathode-ray tube such as that in an oscilloscope affords a ready method of studying electron deflections by an electric field. The tube, as shown in Fig. 2-2, includes at one end a source of high-speed electrons known commonly as an *electron gun*. This consists of a hot cathode C which emits electrons and, some distance in front of the cathode, an anode A with a tiny hole in it. Since the anode is made positive with respect to

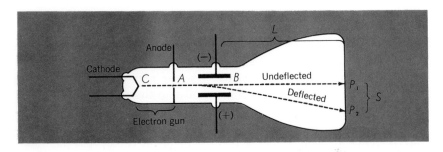

Fig. 2-2. Deflection of electrons by an electric field. Electrons from hot cathode C pass through a hole in anode A and are deflected by electric field between plates at B.

the cathode, electrons are accelerated toward the anode and will gain velocity continually until they either strike the anode or pass through the small hole. Electrons passing through such a hole behave in a manner similar to a stream of bullets emerging from the muzzle of a gun. Since they have left the region of an accelerating field they now travel forward with uniform velocity or speed unless interfered with by collision with gas molecules. They then strike the end of the tube at P_1 if not deflected. If they are deflected by an electric field between the plates at B they may strike at P_2.

Electrons travel so fast that in their brief transit time the distance they fall under the action of gravity is not appreciable and they travel through a discharge tube in almost straight lines. If the opposite end of such a tube is coated with fluorescent material, the position at which the electrons strike can be observed directly as a luminous spot on the fluorescent screen. If electrons pass between two deflecting plates D_1D_2 (Fig. 2-3) with the lower plate positively charged, they will be accelerated downward by the field between the plates in much the same way as a rifle bullet is accelerated downward by the force of gravity.

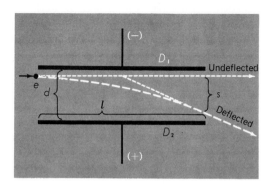

Fig. 2-3. When electron e enters field between deflecting plates D_1D_2 it is accelerated toward the positively charged plate. The deflection s can be computed (see text). Correction should be made for nonuniformity of field at edge of plates.

The distance s that the electron falls while in the accelerating field between the plates at B is given in scalar terms by the relation

$$s = \frac{1}{2} at^2 = \frac{1}{2} \frac{e\mathcal{E}}{m} t^2 = \frac{1}{2} \frac{e\mathcal{E}}{m} \left(\frac{l}{v}\right)^2 = \frac{1}{2} \frac{eV}{md} \left(\frac{l}{v}\right)^2 \qquad [2\text{--}13]$$

where l is the length of path of the particle in the field and v is its average velocity. The amount of deflection s may be readily computed if e/m and the electric field intensity $\mathcal{E}$ are known, provided the time during which the electron is in the field between the deflecting plates is also known. The magnitude of the field intensity $\mathcal{E}$ is equal to the difference in potential V between the plates divided by their distance d apart. The time the electron spends between the deflecting plates when moving with a known speed v is l/v and to obtain t the speed must be known or derived by Eq. 2–16 (next section). Actually J. J. Thomson used this type of tube (but with a cold cathode) to compute e/m by Eq. 2–13.

The deflection s on a screen at a distance L from the middle of the deflecting plates (Fig. 2-2) is readily determined by recognizing the similar triangles involved. Although the path of the electron beam between the plates is a parabola, the direction of the beam upon leaving the field at the edge of the plates can be shown to be the same as if the path of emergence were a straight line beginning at the center of an undeviating path between the plates as indicated in Fig. 2-3. (See Problem 16).

2-4. Non-relativistic Computation of Speeds of Charged Particles

The speed of a moving electron was first measured experimentally by the method to be given in §2-10. However, it is usually simpler to compute it from classical energy relations when it is accelerated by passing through a region in which there is a known difference of potential. If we neglect the relatively small speeds with which electrons are emitted from a hot cathode we may assume an electron in an electron gun starts from rest at the cathode and is accelerated toward the anode by a known potential difference V. If it gains a speed v, its kinetic energy is then $\frac{1}{2}mv^2$. The problem is similar to that of a body falling from a height h. A body of mass m raised to a height h possesses potential energy mgh. On falling to its initial level the potential energy is converted into kinetic energy and $mgh = \frac{1}{2}mv^2$. In the electrical case the work done by a uniform field ε on the electron is $e\varepsilon \cdot l$ where l is the vector distance from cathode to anode and the magnitude of the field intensity ε is V/l volts per meter. Then

$$\text{the work done on electron by field} = e\,\frac{V}{l}\,l = eV \text{ (joules)} \qquad [2\text{--}14]$$

but this appears as kinetic energy and

$$eV = \frac{1}{2}mv^2 \qquad [2\text{--}15]$$

from which in mks units (e in coulombs, V in volts, and m in kg) the speed of an electron in the non-relativistic range is given by

$$v = \sqrt{\frac{2eV}{m}} \text{ (m/sec)} \qquad [2\text{--}16]$$

or

$$v(\text{m/sec}) = 5.93\,\sqrt{V(\text{volts})} \qquad [2\text{--}16a]$$

Note: If e and m are measured in cgs units, e is in statcoulombs (coulombs $\times$ 10^{-9}) m is in grams, and V must be in statvolts. The speed is then given in cm/sec. It is convenient to remember that volts/300 = statvolts.

Since positively charged particles are of atomic mass, far more massive than an electron, they move much more slowly and gain much less speed in the same time. Eq. 2–16 may be written in more general form for any particle of mass M and charge q as

$$v = \sqrt{\frac{2qV}{M}} \qquad [2\text{--}17]$$

Although eV is always the electron energy regardless of the magnitude of V, both Equations 2–16 and 2–17 are only sufficiently good approximations for speeds low enough that the relativistic increase in mass (§2-6) can be neglected and the mass considered constant. For electrons the error is small below 10^4 volts (§2-6).

2-5. Electron Energies and the Electron Volt

From Eq. 2–16 it is seen that the speed of the electron is proportional to the square root of the accelerating potential and also to the square root of the ratio of charge to mass. A "1-volt electron" has a velocity of 5.93×10^5 m/sec (368 mi/sec) and, by Eq. 2–16, a "100-volt electron" would then have 10 times this velocity. The energy of the electron on being accelerated by a difference of potential of V volts is conveniently specified in terms of the unit, the *electron volt*. For instance, in "falling through" a potential difference of 100 volts an electron is said to gain an energy of 100 *electron volts* (100 eV). For electrons of higher energies the units are 10^6 electron volts (1 meV) and 10^9 electron volts (1 beV).

$$1 \text{ electron volt} = 1.602 \times 10^{-19} \text{ joule}$$
$$= 1.602 \times 10^{-12} \text{ erg}$$

The term *electron volt* is a unit of energy and should not be used loosely as a unit of velocity or speed. All particles having the same charge acquire the same energies in being accelerated by a given difference of potential regardless of mass, but if they have different masses they acquire different speeds.

As can be seen from Eq. 2–16 acquired speed is inversely proportional to the square root of the mass, and the speeds v_1 and v_2, acquired by two particles of the same charge but different masses m_1 and m_2, are in the inverse ratio of the square roots of their masses. Thus

$$\frac{v_1}{v_2} = \sqrt{\frac{m_2}{m_1}} \qquad [2\text{–}18]$$

Since a proton is 1836 times more massive than an electron it moves much more slowly in an electric field. A proton of the same energy in electron volts as an electron moves with a speed inversely proportional to the square root of the mass ratio 1836 or approximately with a speed $\frac{1}{43}$ that of the electron. A still more massive particle such as, for instance, an ionized mercury atom would acquire a still smaller speed in falling through the same potential difference.

2-6. Relativistic Electron Speeds: Variation of Mass with Speed

Classical physics had long clung to the idea of the invariance of the mass of a body under all conditions of motion. This led to the law of conservation of mass. But before the advent of the Einstein theory of relativity Lorentz in Holland concluded from somewhat involved reasoning that the apparent mass of a moving charge should increase with increasing speed. Einstein obtained the same equation as Lorentz but as a logical consequence of his theory of relativity from a quite different viewpoint and for the motion of any particle. It was confirmed experimentally for electrons when it was observed that a high-speed electron is accelerated less by an electric field than a low-speed electron, thus indicating that e/m decreases with increasing speed. Since there are experimental and theoretical reasons for believing the charge is constant, it was necessary to conclude that the mass increases with increasing speed in agreement with the prediction of relativity theory. Measurements by Kaufmann and Bucherer and others gave experimental values of the mass lying close to the theoretical curve (Fig. 2-4).

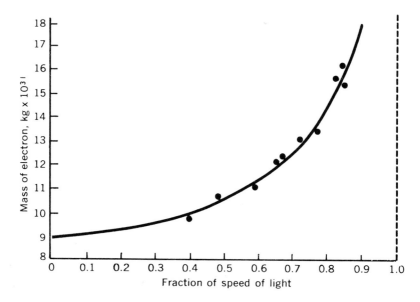

Fig. 2-4. Variation of mass of electron with speed. Experimental points lie close to theoretical curve, and curve approaches infinity as speed approaches that of light.

If the mass of a particle such as an electron at rest is m_0 (called the rest mass), the mass m_v at any speed v is given by the Einstein and Lorentz equation

$$m_v = \frac{m_0}{\sqrt{1 - \dfrac{v^2}{c^2}}}$$ [2–19]

where c is the velocity of light. This equation indicates that at ordinary speeds the variation of mass is too small to be detected. However, the mass of the particle would approach infinity as its speed approaches the speed of light (Fig. 2-4).

Equation 2–14 ($eV = \frac{1}{2}mv^2$) for computing the velocity of an electron accelerated through a potential difference of V volts is thus only valid with small voltages or low velocities where the variation in mass is inappreciable. For large voltages the variation of mass must be considered. Up to 7000 volts, the error is less than 1 per cent. At larger voltages the error rises rapidly. However, Eq. 2–19 cannot be put directly into Eq. 2–16 to obtain the speed of an electron at any voltage. The reason is that not just the mass but the total energy as well must be considered. Einstein has shown (Chap. 6) that the energy equivalent of any mass m is mc^2 where c is the velocity of light. This is the famous *energy-mass relation*.

The energy equivalent of the mass of an electron at rest is m_0c^2 whereas the energy equivalent of the electron moving with speed v and possessing mass m_v is

$$E(\text{energy}) = m_vc^2 = \frac{m_0}{\sqrt{1 - \dfrac{v^2}{c^2}}}c^2 \qquad [2\text{–}20]$$

The kinetic energy E_k gained by an electron in being accelerated from rest to a velocity v is $E_k = m_vc^2 - m_0c^2$ and this must equal the energy eV supplied by the field. Therefore for an electron accelerated from zero to the maximum obtainable for a potential difference V the following equation is required to compute the speed or velocity v.

$$m_0c^2\left(\frac{1}{\sqrt{1 - \dfrac{v^2}{c^2}}} - 1\right) = eV \qquad [2\text{–}21]$$

It is often convenient to use this equation to obtain the ratio v/c, the speed of the electron as a fraction of the speed of light c, a few examples of which are given in Table 2-1. It will be noted that the speed of light is always approached but never reached. It is evident from Eq. 2–17 that since in a given field the speeds acquired by positive ions are much less than those of electrons the relativistic change in mass of the positive particles only becomes appreciable at much higher energies.

TABLE 2-1. RELATIVISTIC ELECTRON SPEEDS AND MASSES

Electron Energy (eV)	Electron Speed	Mass
1,000	0.063c	1.00 m_0
10,000	0.196c	1.02 m_0
100,000	0.534c	1.19 m_0
1,000,000	0.942c	2.95 m_0
10,000,000	0.998c	20.50 m_0
100,000,000	0.999c	196.00 m_0
1,000,000,000	0.9998c	1951.00 m_0

(speeds are in fractions of the speed of light, c)

2-7. The Deflection of Charged Particles in a Magnetic Field

A magnetic field exerts no force on an electrically charged particle in the field if the particle is at rest in the field, but if the charged particle is in motion with respect to the field it also possesses a magnetic field and the two magnetic fields may interact. If the particle is not moving parallel to the field it will be deflected.

The magnitude of force per unit length on a conductor carrying a current i at right angles to a magnetic field of flux density B is $F = Bi$. If the equivalent current qv of a charge q moving with velocity v is substituted for i the magnitude of the force on the moving charge is

$$F = Bqv \text{ (or } -Bev \text{ for a moving electron)} \qquad [2\text{--}22]$$

If the charge is in coulombs, the velocity in meters per sec, and B in webers per meter squared, the force is in newtons. If the direction of the moving charge makes an angle θ with the direction of the field, the force is $F = Bqv \sin \theta$. The direction of the force is always at right angles to the direction of field and to the direction of motion of the charge. If the charged particle crosses a constant field at right angles the path will be circular. If it crosses the field at some other angle (not zero) the path will be a spiral.

In general the force on a charge q which moves across a magnetic field B with velocity v is given both in magnitude and direction by the vector equation

$$\mathbf{F} = q(\mathbf{v} \times \mathbf{B}) \qquad [2\text{--}23]$$

where $\mathbf{v} \times \mathbf{B}$ is called the *vector cross product*. The magnitude of such a vector cross product is defined as $vB \sin \theta$ where θ is the angle between $\mathbf{v}$

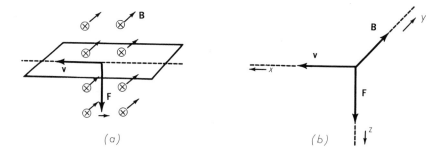

Fig. 2-5. a, A positive charge q moving in direction v at right angles to magnetic field B experiences a force F at right angles to both. (Crosses in circles indicate field is directed away from the reader.) b, Vector representation in conventional right-hand system.

and **B**. The direction of the cross product **v** $\times$ **B** is at right angles to **v** and to **B**, and by convention the vector representing the product points in the direction in which a right-hand screw would move if **v** were turned toward **B**. This is represented by **F** in Figs. 2-5a and 2-5b for the case where **v** and **B** are at right angles and these vectors are represented for simplicity along the x, y, z axes of a right-hand system of coordinates such that positive x turned into positive y would indicate the positive z direction.

The resultant force on a moving charge in combined electric and magnetic fields is given by the well-known Lorentz equation

$$\mathbf{F} = q\mathbf{\varepsilon} + q(\mathbf{v} \times \mathbf{B}) \qquad [2\text{--}24]$$

This is a vector equation in which **F** is the vector sum of the forces resulting from the separate effects of the superposed electric and magnetic fields.

When two particles of similar charge move in the same direction the magnetic fields of the particles interact to produce a force of attraction between them. At the same time their electrostatic fields repel one another. If the speeds are large enough the attraction will predominate. This leads to the so-called "pinch effect" which is important in the study of high-current plasmas (regions of uniform and intense ionization in a gas or vapor). For instance in a mercury arc rectifier under certain conditions the current may cease ("pinch off") and interrupt the action of the rectifier. In the more recent studies of high-temperature plasmas which have been made in the attempt to liberate nuclear energy this effect has been tried in efforts to contain the plasma without pinching it off.

2-8. Ratio of Charge to Mass: *e/m* for the Electron

Experimental determinations of e/m for the electron may be made in various ways. For instance, the deflection obtained in a cathode-ray tube of the type shown in Fig. 2-2 may be measured and e/m may be computed from Eq. 2–13 as Thomson did.

A common experimental arrangement is to bend a stream of electrons in a circular path (or an arc of a circle) in an evacuated tube by a magnetic field. If an object of mass m moving with constant speed experiences a force of constant magnitude always acting at right angles to the direction of motion, the moving object is then constrained to move in a circular path and the magnitude of the required centripetal force is $F = mv^2/r$.

For an electron moving with constant speed the force is directed as shown in Fig. 2-6. After leaving the region of the accelerating potential the electrons travel with constant speed and if they cross the field at right angles to the field they experience a force of constant magnitude at right angles to the direction of motion and to the direction of the field according to the second term on the right of Eq. 2–24. The direction of the deflecting force

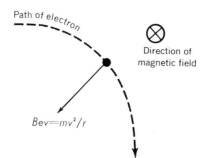

Path of electron

Direction of magnetic field

$Bev = mv^2/r$

Fig. 2-6. A uniform magnetic field exerts a deflecting force *Bev* on an electron moving at right angles to the field, the force being at right angles to the field and to the direction of motion. The cross in the circle stands for the feather end of an arrow and represents a field directed away from the observer. A dot in a circle represents a field directed toward the observer.

(and the deflection) is given by proper application of the foregoing rules for the vector product, remembering that the charge is negative. For circular motion under these conditions, equating magnitudes only,

$$\frac{mv^2}{r} = Bev \qquad\qquad [2\text{--}25]$$

From this the ratio of charge to mass for an electron is

$$\frac{e}{m} = \frac{v}{Br} \qquad\qquad [2\text{--}26]$$

If the accelerating potential is known the speed of the electron can be computed by Eq. 2–16. The flux density of the field can be readily obtained by standard methods and it only remains to find the radius of path. In a simple form of the apparatus a small amount of gas is left in the discharge tube. Some of the electrons will hit gas molecules and excite them to emit visible radiation. The radius of path can then be measured directly.

Accepted values of e/m are

$$e/m = 1.759 \times 10^{11} \text{ coulombs/kg}$$
$$= 1.759 \times 10^7 \text{ abcoulombs/gm}$$
$$= 5.273 \times 10^{17} \text{ statcoulombs/gm}$$

It is often desired, particularly in mass spectroscopy (next chapter), to find the radius of curvature of the path of a positively charged particle in a magnetic field of uniform flux density B when the charge q and the mass M are known, and when the speed of the particle is known. This is readily obtained from Eq. 2–25 which may be conveniently solved for the radius of path, giving

$$r = \frac{Mv}{Bq} \qquad\qquad [2\text{--}27]$$

From this equation it is apparent that the radius of curvature of path is directly proportional to the speed, at those speeds for which the mass may be taken as constant, and it is inversely proportional to B and q.

2-9. Mass and Size of an Electron

After the charge of an electron was accurately measured the value could be substituted in e/m to give the mass of the electron, or Eq. 2–26 can be solved explicitly for the mass in terms of experimentally measurable quantities, giving

$$m_e = \frac{B^2 r^2 e}{2V} \qquad [2\text{–}28]$$

From this the accepted value of the mass of the electron is

$$m_e = 9.11 \times 10^{-31} \text{ kg}$$
$$= 9.11 \times 10^{-28} \text{ gm}$$

This is $1/1837$ the mass of the lightest known atom (hydrogen), and the value makes us realize that we are dealing with a subatomic particle.

The size of the electron is a more debatable matter, and it can only be estimated indirectly, since there is no experiment which gives the size in a forthright manner as the mass is given. One method of estimation is based on a possible relation between mass and size. In the latter part of the nineteenth century it was shown that an electric charge should possess inertia, and by classical theory J. J. Thomson showed that the electromagnetic mass or inertia of a spherical charge should be inversely proportional to its radius. For the electromagnetic inertia of such a spherical charge to be equal to that of an electron the diameter would have to be in the neighborhood of 10^{-13} cm. Experimental evidence indicates that this is probably the correct order of magnitude for the diameter of the electron, and consequently the assumption of electromagnetic mass became plausible. However, there remained unexplained difficulties, and serious objections to considering the mass as a purely electromagnetic effect have arisen. Unfortunately, we do not understand the nature of the inertia of ordinary objects and our choice of probable explanations is decidedly limited.

2-10. Experimental Determination of the Speed of an Electron by Balanced Electric and Magnetic Deflections

It was J. J. Thomson who showed that the speed of an electron may be obtained by a comparatively simple experiment. When one considers that the problem is to measure the speed of a particle far too small to be directly observed and that this speed may be many thousands of miles per second, the idea of measuring it presents an intriguing problem. Thomson found that, if an electron stream is passed through a region in which magnetic and electric fields are superposed in such a manner as to produce deflections in opposite directions, the fields can be so adjusted that the effect of one just cancels the effect of the other. The electrons for which the fields are thus balanced would go through undeflected (Fig. 2-7). For such a balance the

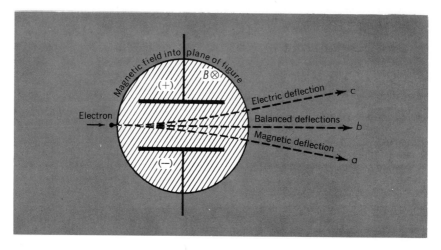

Fig. 2-7. Method of determining electron speed by balancing electric and magnetic deflections. The symbol ⊗ indicates the magnetic field *B* is directed away from the observer.

magnitude of the force $\mathcal{E}e$ of the electric field $\mathcal{E}$ on the electron must be equal to the magnitude of the force of the magnetic field Bev, or

$$\mathcal{E}e \,=\, Bev \qquad\qquad [2\text{--}29]$$

and the fields must be at right angles to each other. The charge of the electron cancels on the two sides of the equation, and the speed v is given by

$$v(\text{m/sec}) \,=\, \frac{\mathcal{E}\ (\text{volts/m})}{B\ (\text{web/m}^2)} \qquad\qquad [2\text{--}30]$$

Thus to obtain the speed of the electron it is only necessary to measure the magnetic flux density and the electric field intensity and take their ratio. This is called the method of *balanced deflections*.

2-11. Electron Optics and Electron Lenses

Electrons may be reflected, refracted, and focused by means of electric and magnetic fields very much as light may be. In Fig. 2-8, an electron is represented approaching a negatively charged plate. If the field in front of the plate is sufficiently intense the direction of motion of the electron will

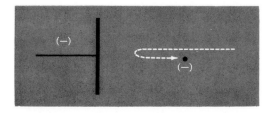

Fig. 2-8.   Reflection of electron from negatively charged plate.

be reversed, and *reflection* occurs. The path of an electron on passing into an electric or magnetic field may be bent, and *refraction* occurs.

If a divergent beam of electrons is passed through a properly shaped electric or magnetic field it may be brought to a focus in much the same way as divergent light rays are brought to a focus by means of a lens. The electric or magnetic field, so shaped as to accomplish this, is called an *electrostatic* or *magnetic lens*, or simply an *electron lens*. Such lenses suffer from defects similar to those of optical lenses and the sharpness of the focus ultimately depends on a number of factors, but the ultimate limit depends upon the speed of the electron and its wave character as will be explained in §5-14.

An electrostatic electron lens, formed by arranging electrodes so as to give a symmetrical field that will focus a diverging beam of electrons, is called a converging lens. If the lines are drawn to represent points of equal potential in the electric field, these lines make the appearance of the field more like that of an optical lens. Actually electrons moving through this field are so affected by it as to tend to move in a direction at right angles

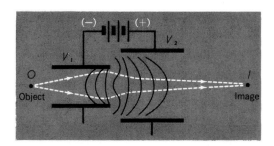

Fig. 2-9.   Electrostatic electron lens formed by electric field between two coaxial cylinders. Fine lines are equipotential lines (at right angles to the electric field). This is a long focus lens, equivalent to a strong converging lens plus a weak diverging lens.

to the equipotential line. For instance, in the electrostatic field between metal-ring electrodes (Fig. 2-9) electrons from point O may be focused at point I. The analogy between electron lenses and optical lenses may be pushed further, and an expression may be obtained for the focal length of an electron lens and for the index of refraction for electrons considered as waves.

A divergent electron beam may also be focused by a properly shaped magnetic field (magnetic lens). A coil of wire A (Fig. 2-10), in which a current is flowing, has a magnetic field, as indicated by the dashed lines *H*. Electrons in passing through this coil are deflected in such a way as to focus at point *I*. The actual motion of electrons in such a magnetic field is more complicated than is indicated in Fig. 2-10. Instead of traveling along a line curved in a single plane, an electron possessing a component of velocity at

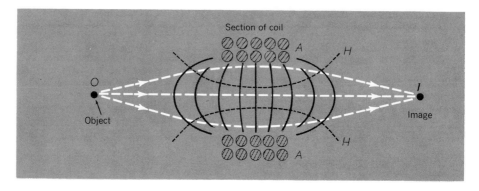

Fig. 2-10. Magnetic electron lens. The fine vertical lines are lines of equal magnetic potential (at right angles to the magnetic field *H, H*). Electron paths are actually spirals which cannot easily be represented in two dimensions.

right angles to the field tends to spiral about the lines representing the magnetic field. However, mathematical analysis shows that a divergent beam of electrons can still be made to focus at the point *I*. Such electron lenses have many applications, one of the most important of which is the electron microscope.

2-12. The Electron Microscope

From classical theory it has long been known that the useful magnification by an optical instrument is limited by the resolving power of that instrument. The resolving power of any optical instrument is inversely proportional to the wavelength of light. The shorter the waves are the more distinct will be the magnified image, and hence the larger will be the magnification that is effective. The limit of magnification of an ordinary microscope using visible light is in the neighborhood of 2000 diameters. This extreme limit is independent of the degree of perfection of the lenses and depends only upon the wavelength of the light when the other optical dimensions are unchanged. Enlargement of the image beyond this point merely produces a fuzzy and less distinct image. Since x-rays have far shorter wave-lengths than ordinary light, a microscope using x-rays could give much greater magnification. Owing to the difficulty of bending or refracting x-rays such applications have only been possible in extremely limited cases.

The very small size of the electron, however, indicates that if it could be used to form enlarged images of objects it would give enormous magnifications, and electrons are relatively easy to control by means of suitable fields. Either the electrons forming the image must be emitted by the specimen to be observed, as in the "field emission electron microscope" by which the surface structures of some metallic crystals have been studied, or else the specimen must be thin enough for electrons from another source to be able to pass through it. Since electrons, like x-rays, produce fluorescence on a suitable screen, an electron image falling on such a screen can be transformed into a visible image to be observed directly or photographed.

In the design of an electron microscope the electron is usually treated as a particle deflected by electric and magnetic fields. However, as will be seen in Chap. 4, the electron also has wave-like properties and an effective wavelength can be assigned to it which varies inversely as the speed. If the speeds are large enough the electron may have a wavelength shorter than an ordinary x-ray. The computation of the resolving power of an electron microscope will be given in Chap. 4 after the wave properties of the electron have been studied, but it may be said here that the electron microscope far surpasses in resolving power any other instrument and is theoretically capable of magnifications approaching a million diameters.

The principle of the electron microscope is shown in Fig. 2-11. Electrons from a hot cathode are accelerated by a positive potential on an anode and are focused so as to form a beam of high-speed electrons which fall upon a sample to be observed. Electrons emerging from this sample are focused

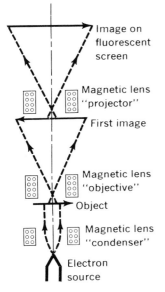

Fig. 2-11.   Principle of two-stage electron microscope with magnetic lenses. Unlike an optical microscope, the second lens projects a magnified image on a fluorescent screen.

by another electron lens and may form a magnified image on a fluorescent screen. In a compound electron microscope, a second lens is placed in the path of the electron beam so that electrons diverging from the plane of the first image will focus at a second plane in such a way as to magnify the already magnified image. The fluorescent screen is now placed at the plane of the second image, and the image may be observed directly or photographed (Fig. 2-12).

Fig. 2-12. Electron-microscope photo of influenza virus *A* and *B* vaccine, magnification 11,500. The white squares are small crystals of magnesium oxide. (Courtesy, Dr. F. Heinmetz, University of Pennsylvania.)

Problems

1. An electron having an energy of 1000 eV crosses (perpendicularly) a magnetic field of flux density 10^{-3} weber/m². How long does it take to traverse a complete circle?

2. A 100-eV electron crosses (at right angles) a magnetic field of flux density equal to 0.25 weber/m². What is the radius of its path? What is its momentum?

3. Why is it that a constant magnetic field cannot do work on a moving electric charge that crosses the field?

4. Two identical spherical particles have charges of one electron each. What mass would each require in order that gravitational attraction exactly balance the Coulomb repulsion of their charges?

5. Compute the number of joules equal to one electron volt.

6. To escape from the earth a rocket must be fired upward with a speed of 7 mi/sec. What energy in eV would this amount to for an aluminum atom in the rocket shell?

7. The electrons in a radio tube are accelerated toward the anode (plate) by a uniform field produced by 300 volts potential difference. With what velocity will they arrive at the anode? What will be the average velocity during flight from cathode to anode? What is the time of transit if the distance from cathode to anode is 4 mm?

8. In a cathode-ray tube electrons are shot into a field-free space from an "electron gun" having an accelerating potential of 3000 volts. How long will it take an electron to travel from the gun to the fluorescent screen 40 cm distant? (Neglect variation of mass with velocity.)

9. What speed would a doubly-charged mercury atom acquire in being accelerated by a potential difference of 200 volts?

10. What magnetic flux density will bend the path of a 200-eV electron in the arc of a circle of 10 cm radius?

11. An electron and a proton, each of 300 electron volts energy, pass across (at right angles) a uniform magnetic field of 50 gauss (50×10^{-4} weber/m²). Find the radius of the arcs of the circles in which the paths of the particles are bent.

12. Show that if a charged particle passing through a magnetic field is identified as an electron its energy can be determined if the product Br of the flux density B of the field and the radius of curvature r of path is known.

13. An electron having a speed of 10^6 m/sec passes between two grids 1 mm apart. If the difference of potential between the grids is 5 volts and if the field between the grids acts to accelerate the electron positively, with what speed will it emerge?

14. In the previous problem what decelerating field in volts/meter is required between the grids to just prevent the electron from passing through the grids?

15. A 100-eV electron enters a region where there is a uniform electric field having the same direction as the direction of motion of the electron. If the field intensity is 2000 newtons per coulomb, how far will the electron move in the field before it is brought to rest?

16. If electrons of 100-eV energy pass horizontally between the deflecting plates B of the cathode-ray tube of Fig. 2-2, what difference of potential on the plates will produce a deflection of 10 cm on a fluorescent screen at the end of the tube? Take the length of the deflecting plates to be 4 cm, their separation 1 cm, and the distance from the center of the plates to the screen to be 50 cm.

17. If the particles in the previous problem are protons of 10,000-eV energy, what potential difference on the deflecting plates is required to produce a deflection on the screen of 1 cm?

*18. Prove that the direction of an electron beam emerging from the deflecting field of Fig. 2-3 would, if projected backward, intersect the undeflected path between the plates at the mid-point.

19. Two circular metal plates of radius 10 cm form a parallel-plate capacitor. If the separation of the plates is 5 mm and if they are oppositely charged by a potential difference of 100 volts, what is the energy in joules/m³ of the field between the plates? (Assume uniform field.)

20. How much work in joules would be done in separating the plates of the capacitor of the previous problem by an additional 5 mm? Assume field remains uniform.

21. What is the ratio of the mass of an electron, having a speed 0.86 that of light, to its rest mass?

22. What is the relativistic mass, in terms of its rest mass, of an electron having a speed 0.95 that of light?

23. What is the per cent of error in computing the speed of a 60,000-eV electron classically instead of relativistically?

24. What is the speed of an electron with kinetic energy of 1.5 meV? (1 meV = 10^6 eV.)

25. What is the kinetic energy in meV of an electron which has a speed 0.8 times the speed of light?

26. At what fraction of the speed of light would a proton travel if it were given an energy of 10 meV?

27. What is the per cent of error in computing the speed of a 60-meV proton classically instead of relativistically?

28. At what speed v would the mass m_v of an electron equal twice its rest-mass m_0?

29. Find the magnitude and direction of the resultant force (vector sum) acting on an electron moving away from the observer with a speed of 10^5 m/sec when it enters a region where there is a transverse electric field of 10^5 newton/coulomb to the left and superposed on it a magnetic field of 0.5 weber/m² directed toward the right.

30. An electron moving away from the observer with a speed of 10^8 m/sec encounters a transverse electric field $\mathcal{E} = 10^5$ volts/m directed to the right. What must be the direction and flux density B of a magnetic field which will exactly balance the effect of the electric field?

Recommended Reading

Frank, W. H., *Introduction to Electricity and Optics.* New York: McGraw-Hill Book Company, Inc., 1950.

Skilling, H. H., *Fundamentals of Electric Waves*, 2nd ed. New York: John Wiley & Sons, Inc., 1948.

Peaslee, D. C., and H. Mueller, *Elements of Atomic Physics.* Englewood Cliffs, N. J.: Prentice-Hall, Inc., 1955.

Bitter, F., *Current, Fields and Particles.* Cambridge, Mass.: The Technology Press of M. I. T., 1956.

Richtmeyer, F. K., E. H. Kennard, and T. Lauritsen, *Introduction to Modern Physics.* New York: McGraw-Hill Book Company, Inc., 1955.

Zworykin, Morton, Ramberg, Hillier and Vance, *Electron Optics and the Electron Microscope.* New York: John Wiley & Sons, Inc., 1945.

3

Positive Rays and
Mass Spectroscopy

A particularly important application of the deflection of charged particles by magnetic and electric fields has been the separation of particles of different mass and the precision measurement of these masses. This is the field of *positive-ray analysis* and to it we owe most of our knowledge of atomic masses and isotopes.

3-1. Positive Rays

The existence in an ordinary discharge tube of rapidly moving, positively charged particles known as positive rays (originally called "canal rays") was demonstrated in 1886 by Goldstein. These particles (positive

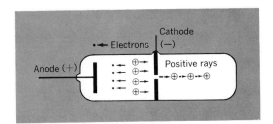

Fig. 3-1. Electric-discharge tube for separating positive rays from cathode rays (electrons) by allowing some positive rays to pass through a hole in the cathode.

ions) move in a direction opposite to that of the cathode rays, that is, from anode to cathode. Goldstein made a small hole or "canal" in the cathode of such a tube and observed a faint glow on the opposite side of the cathode from the anode. This glow is caused by formation of *excited atoms* (§7-4) in the beam of positively charged rays that stream through the hole in the cathode (Fig. 3-1).

If a study is made of the way in which the intensity of the light from the positive ion beam decays with increasing distance behind the cathode and if the speeds of the particles are known, the maximum duration of the process of light emission may be computed and is found to be of the order of a hundred millionth of a second (10^{-8} sec). This quantity is of much interest because of its relation to the question of the nature of light emission which has long been a major problem.

3-2. Positive-Ray Analysis; Isotopes

The nature of positive rays was first studied quantitatively by J. J. Thomson (beginning in 1907) by means of electric and magnetic deflections, and he measured the ratio q/M, of charge to mass, for various positive ions. In his best-known experiment with positive rays, the rays were passed through superposed electric and magnetic fields parallel to one another (Fig. 3-2). Since the fields are parallel the deflection produced by the magnetic field is at right angles to that produced by the electric field and if one deflection is represented by Δx, the other may be represented by Δy. The deflection produced by an electric field may be seen from Eq. 2–12 to be inversely proportional to the square of the velocity of the particle, whereas small deflections produced by a magnetic field can be shown to be inversely proportional to the first power of the velocity.

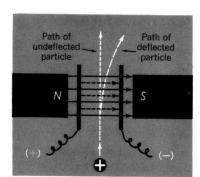

Fig. 3-2. J. J. Thomson's method of deflecting positive rays by superposed and parallel electric and magnetic fields. Path of deflected particle is bent to right and also away from reader.

If the radius of curvature of the deflection produced by the magnetic field is large and if the path through the field is short it may be treated (to a first approximation) like the electrostatic deflection. The electrostatic deflection Δx by a field in the x direction (Eq. 2–13) for a particle of charge q and mass M is

$$\Delta x = \frac{1}{2}\frac{\mathcal{E}q}{M}\left(\frac{l}{v}\right)^2 \qquad [3\text{–}1]$$

where l/v is the time spent in the region of the field, l being the length of the region in which the deflecting field acts and v is the speed of the ion. Consequently the magnetic deflection in the same region, where the force is Bev instead of Ee, will be given approximately by

$$\Delta y = \frac{1}{2}\frac{Bqv}{M}\left(\frac{l}{v}\right)^2 \qquad [3\text{–}2]$$

If we eliminate v from Eq. 3–1 and Eq. 3–2 we have

$$\Delta x = \frac{2\mathcal{E}M}{B^2ql^2}(\Delta y)^2 \qquad [3\text{–}3]$$

This is the equation of a parabola and all ions with the same value of M/q but different speeds will lie at different points on such a curve. If all the ions of a given mass also possessed the same speed they would reveal themselves by a single spot on a photographic plate, but since the ions in a discharge tube are formed at different distances from the cathode they acquire a wide range of velocities from zero to a maximum, and the erstwhile spot is stretched into a section of a parabola (Fig. 3-3).

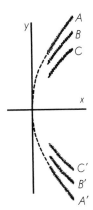

Fig. 3-3. Positive-ray parabolas obtained by method of Fig. 3-2, showing separation of ions of several elements. Ions of the same mass but different speeds form one trace such as **A** or **A'**. Lower halves of curves were obtained by reversing the magnetic field.

Ions of different mass (or different charge) will lie on different parabolas. The fastest ions are deflected the least and since there is an upper limit to the speed of an ion, imposed by the accelerating potential, all parabolas are cut off at the same minimum x deflection as indicated in the figure. Reversal of the magnetic field gives similar parabolas below the x axis. When the rays were allowed to fall on a photographic plate some distance from the region where the deflecting fields were, an enlarged image of the parabolic traces is obtained. Fainter parabolas were frequently found for doubly charged ions of the same atom.

A most important result of this work was that the sharply defined parabolas Thomson obtained gave the first direct evidence that *similar atoms* of any element all have the same mass. This had been a questionable point. However, he found (1913) a distinct trace of a different kind of neon atom having a mass approximately 10 per cent larger than the accepted mass as determined by chemical methods. The new neon atom, which was found to have the same general properties as the more common neon atom except for the difference in mass, was recognized as an *isotope* of neon.

Atoms of any element differing in mass though possessing the same general chemical and optical properties are called *isotopes* of that element. The existence of isotopes of certain heavy atoms resulting from radioactive transformations was first noticed in 1905. With Thomson's important discovery the search was on for isotopes of other elements.

We now know that ordinary neon gas is composed of three different kinds of stable atoms or isotopes with the following mass numbers (approximate masses): neon 20 (Ne^{20}) 90.9 per cent; neon 22 (Ne^{22}) 8.8 per cent; and the rare Ne^{21}, 0.3 per cent. Thomson also made the important observation that the existence of isotopes and their relative abundances could explain a large part of the puzzling question of why fractional atomic weights (or masses) had previously been obtained in measuring the atoms of many elements. For instance it was shown later that ordinary chlorine gas which has an apparent atomic weight of 35.5, is actually a mixture of two isotopes of atomic number 35 and 37 in the approximate ratio of 3 to 1. Now isotopes of all elements are known to exist. Some are stable while others undergo radioactive decay and may not be found in nature.

3-3. The Mass Spectrograph

The first instrument of real precision for determining atomic masses was devised by F. W. Aston in England and is called a *mass spectrograph*. (See Fig. 3-4.)

In the Aston mass spectrograph the ions of different mass are first separated by an electric field after which they are brought to a focus at different points on a photographic plate by a magnetic field. All ions of the same charge and mass were brought to a focus at the same point even though they vary considerably in speed. By putting oxygen into the ion source Aston could use it as a standard of comparison and determine the masses of ions in terms of oxygen. Since what is measured is the mass of an ion it is necessary to add to this the mass of one electron (if the ion is singly charged) to obtain the mass of a neutral atom.

With this device Aston could distinguish particles the masses of which differed by only 1 part in 600, an improvement of 30 times over the original

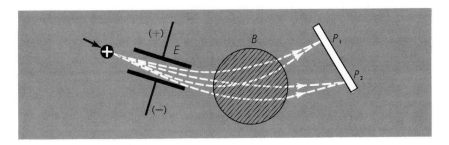

Fig. 3-4. Aston's mass spectrograph. Successive electric and magnetic deflections focus positive rays of the same mass at P_1, and of a different mass at P_2.

method of Thomson. He confirmed Thomson's discovery of the isotopes of neon and went on to make an extensive study of the isotopes of many elements.

Whereas the mass spectrograph focuses ions of different q/M at different points on a photographic film the *mass spectrometer* invented by A. J. Dempster in this country detected only ions of a single q/M at one time. These were focused on a detecting electrode.

In its simplest form the Dempster mass spectrometer is shown in Fig. 3-5. It involves what is called *direction focusing.* Positive ions of the same q/M emerging from the slit S_2 may be traveling in slightly different

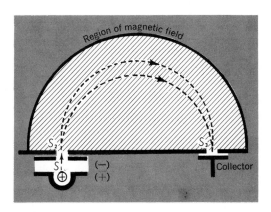

Fig. 3-5. Dempster's first mass spectrometer. Rays are first accelerated by electric field. After passing slit S_2 they are deflected by magnetic field so that rays of only one value of q/M reach collector.

directions. Upon entering the region of a uniform magnetic field (shaded region in diagram) their paths are bent into arcs of circles, and after moving through 180° they are again close together and form an approximate though not perfect focus. The early method of detection was to adjust the accelerating potential between S_1 and S_2 until the rays fell upon a slit S_3, behind which was a collecting electrode connected to a suitable detector.

With this apparatus peaks of electric current were measured, and these peaks indicated reception of beams of positive rays of a given mass. The higher the peak of the curve, the greater is the relative abundance of that particular isotope in any mixture. In Fig. 3-6 the results are shown for magnesium, indicating the existence of isotopes of mass numbers 24,

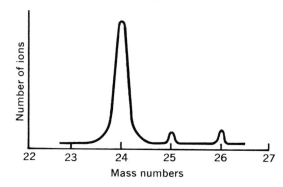

Fig. 3-6. Results of Dempster's spectrometer measurements of magnesium, indicating three isotopes, with that of mass number 24 predominating.

25 and 26. From this it is seen that ordinary magnesium is a mixture of isotopes with that of Mg^{24} strongly predominating. By measuring the abundances it was evident that the fractional atomic mass 24.34 for magnesium, obtained by the chemist, is largely the result of ordinary magnesium being the mixture of these isotopes of different masses.

With an improved instrument in which the ions were first passed through an electric field Dempster obtained both *velocity and direction focusing*. The ions were formed by a spark or arc near the accelerating anode and acquired more nearly the same speed in the accelerating field. With these improvements masses could be measured to 1 part in 4000. With this instrument Dempster measured many of the heavy elements and discovered the relatively rare isotope of uranium 235 (1935) destined to become so important in the field of atomic energy. Later in a similar manner Nier separated enough to show that it was the most important isotope in the fission of uranium.

The race for high precision was now on. Bainbridge, Nier and others joined the race and reached new heights of precision. It is now one of the wonders of science that isotopic masses can readily be determined accurately to a few parts in 100,000 and in some instances to a few parts in 100 million.

Present-day mass spectrographs, in addition to an ion source and some form of detector, for the most part embody two basic parts. An electric field is used as a *velocity selector* (more properly an *energy selector* if the range of speeds is relativistic). Following this a magnetic field acts as a *momentum selector* or *analyzer*. The problems of focusing are dealt with differently in different forms of apparatus. A typical spectrograph is shown in Fig. 3-7.

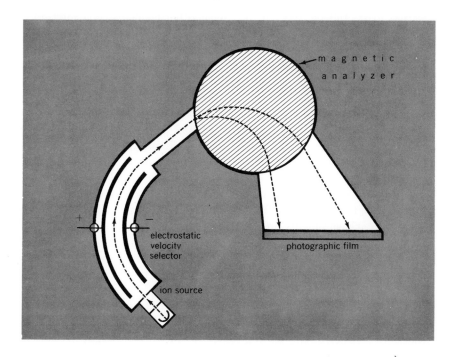

Fig. 3-7. A mass spectrograph of the Bainbridge type.

Since the electrodes that provide the electric field are arcs of circles, the force $\mathcal{E}q$ on the charge may be equated to the centripetal force Mv^2/r_1 if r_1 is the radius of the circular path. If the ions are bent in the arc of a circle of radius r_2 by the magnetic field, the force Bqv on the charge may be equated to Mv^2/r_2 and from this the momentum $Mv = qBr_2$. If the velocity v is eliminated between these two relations the mass M of the ion can be obtained in terms of measurable quantities. Instruments in the form of a *mass spectrometer* which detect ions of only one value of q/M at a time are also in use.

3-4. Isotopic Masses; Physical Scale; Atomic Mass Unit

Before the discovery of isotopes, chemists had been in the habit of measuring *atomic weights* in relation to the *atomic weight* of oxygen which they arbitrarily chose as 16 for reasons of convenience. Accordingly, unit weight was 1/16 the weight of an oxygen atom as then measured. Long after the discovery of isotopes it was found that not all oxygen atoms have the same weight or mass, and it became clear that chemical atomic weights had been measured in terms of a hypothetical average oxygen atom which does not exist. Indeed, oxygen, like most other elements, is a mixture of stable isotopes. Since mass is independent of gravity the use of the concept of *atomic mass* has superseded that of *atomic weight*.

When ordinary oxygen gas was studied, it was found to be a mixture of three isotopes. As luck would have it the chief one of the three turned out to have a mass only slightly less than the hypothetical average, and to this is now assigned the mass 16.0000000. Ordinary oxygen, we now know, is composed of 99.76 per cent O^{16}, 0.2 per cent O^{18}, and 0.04 per cent of the much rarer isotope O^{17}. Such a mixture of the three isotopes gives an average mass of 16.00444. Measurements of mass made with reference to the latter value are said to be made on the *chemical scale*. Measurements made with respect to the one common isotope of oxygen as 16, that is, to O^{16} as 16.0000000, are made on what is called the *physical scale*. Since measurements made on the chemical scale are made with reference to "average oxygen," they are made in terms of a slightly more massive unit, and consequently the number obtained will be slightly smaller. Any atomic mass on the chemical scale must be multiplied by 1.00027 in order to give the correct value on the physical scale of O^{16}.

Although in the earlier days of chemical study of the atoms it was usually considered that the numbers representing atomic weights were only *relative numbers* representing ratios to the atomic weight of oxygen, the numbers representing relative masses are now commonly thought of as actual masses in terms of a new unit of mass, the *atomic mass unit* (amu) which is defined as $\frac{1}{16}$ the mass of 1 atom of O^{16}. In kilograms it has the value

$$1 \text{ amu} = 1.6595 \times 10^{-27} \text{ kg}$$

More recently it has been suggested desirable to be able to refer atomic nuclei to a physical scale based on the common carbon isotope C^{12}. In 1960 and 1961 favorable action was taken on this proposal by international committees, representing both physicists and chemists, but the change will take some time to accomplish. On this scale the atomic mass unit would be $\frac{1}{12}$ of C^{12} and the mass of a carbon C^{12} nucleus would be taken as even 12.0000000. This would make a small difference in the value of an atomic mass unit and in the number of atomic mass units as given in Table 3-1, but of course the actual masses would remain unchanged. For instance oxygen 16 instead of being even 16 would be 15.9949149.

The masses of a number of light atoms are given in Table 3-1 in terms of O^{16}. As previously stated the mass of an electron which is

0.000549 amu must be added to the mass of any singly charged ion to get the mass of the neutral atom.

TABLE 3-1.   SOME PARTICLE AND ISOTOPIC MASSES

(Masses of bare nuclei are less than neutral atoms by the total mass ($0.000549Z$) of the Z extranuclear electrons.)

Particle	Mass (amu)
Electron	0.000549
Proton	1.007593 (± 3)
Neutron	1.008982 (± 3)
Alpha particle	4.002775 (± 15)

Isotope (neutral atom)	
Hydrogen, H^1	1.008145 (± 3)
Hydrogen, H^2	2.014742 (± 4)
Helium, He^4	4.003874 (± 12)
Carbon, C^{12}	12.003815 (± 8)
Oxygen, O^{16}	16.0000000 (standard)
Oxygen, O^{17}	17.004537 (± 15)
Oxygen, O^{18}	18.004885 (± 13)
Neon, Ne^{20}	19.998798 (± 12)
Neon, Ne^{22}	21.998377 (± 19)
Chlorine, Cl^{35}	34.979972 (± 22)
Chlorine, Cl^{37}	36.977657 (± 21)
Silver, Ag^{107}	106.9388
Silver, Ag^{109}	108.9392
Uranium, U^{238}	238.124

Note: See appendix for more complete table.

3-5. Nature of Isotopes; Binding Energy

The question of how isotopes of an element can exist, all having approximately the same general chemical properties yet possessing different masses, was not satisfactorily answered until the discovery of the neutron in 1932. It had been known that the general chemical properties and most of the physical properties of an atom are determined by the number of electrons surrounding the nucleus. All the atoms of any element regardless of mass have the same number of positive charges on the nucleus, and this determines that they must also have the same number of electrons surrounding the nucleus, but the nucleus may also contain neutrons possessing mass without charge. Since an excess or deficit of neutrons does not change the nuclear charge it does not change the number of surrounding electrons or the general properties of the atom, aside from the change in mass. Consequently we may say that the *isotopes of any element are atoms all having the same characteristic nuclear charge but differ-ent numbers of neutrons in the nucleus.* Since each positive charge of electron magnitude in the nucleus is associated with a proton we conclude that the isotopes of any element all have the same number of protons but different numbers of neutrons.

Present-day ideas about the nature of atoms were foreshadowed by Prout, who noticed more than a century ago that the weights of most of the atoms then known were close multiples of that of hydrogen. This led him to suggest a rudimentary theory that perhaps all atoms were in some way built up from hydrogen, the lightest of all. When it was found that some atoms have fractional atomic weights nowhere near integral multi-ples of hydrogen the theory was abandoned. With the discovery of isotopes and the idea that all atomic nuclei are composed of protons and neutrons there was an apparent return to something of the simplicity of Prout's theory but nuclear theory has since become far more complex and the problems have become far more challenging.

BINDING ENERGY

Whereas fractional atomic masses of natural samples of an element could for the most part be readily explained in terms of mixtures of iso-topes, smaller deviations required a different explanation. If the particles of which a nucleus is composed could be brought together with no forces acting between them the resultant mass would be the sum of the separate masses of the particles. However, the forces between nuclear particles require that energy be supplied to separate these particles. The same amount of energy was released when the particles were brought together and this is called the *binding energy*.

According to the Einstein rule (§2-6) that $E = mc^2$ a large loss of energy E represents a small decrease in mass m so that particles held to-gether by binding forces have less mass than the sum of the separate parti-cles. For instance the mass of a helium nucleus is 4.002775 amu whereas the sum of the masses of the two neutrons and two protons of which it is composed is 4.033150 amu. Although the decrease in mass (sometimes called the *mass defect*) is small it represents a total energy of 28×10^6 eV (28 meV), since the energy equivalent per amu is large and

$$1 \text{ amu} = 931 \text{ meV} = 931 \times 10^6 \text{ eV}$$

Without a similar decrease in mass representing binding energy any nucleus would "fall apart." This subject will be discussed more fully in Chapter 14.

Binding energies of nuclear particles are large because of the strong forces acting between these particles when they are in a nucleus. The extranuclear electrons belonging to any atom are more weakly bound and binding energies may vary from a few eV to some thousands of eV. Since the decrease in mass is approximately 10^{-6} amu per 1000 eV (1 keV) this is usually a negligible quantity. When two or more atoms combine chemically the binding energy is in general a few eV and represents for most purposes a negligible loss of mass; nevertheless it is a fundamental requirement for a stable combination of particles.

3-6. Heavy Hydrogen (Deuterium): The Deuteron

Of the more than 1200 different isotopes of all elements now known to exist many are unstable and decay by radioactive emission into atoms of another element. Of the stable isotopes one of the most important is the isotope of hydrogen known as *heavy hydrogen* or *deuterium* represented by the symbol H^2 or D. Although relatively uncommon, the ratio of H^2 to H^1 being about 1 in 6000 in ordinary hydrogen, the large amount of hydrogen in the world means that there is a considerable supply of H^2. A still rarer isotope of hydrogen, called *tritium*, H^3, is unstable and decays rather slowly (half-life = 12.3 years) into a form of helium. The nucleus of the tritium atom is called the *triton*. It was discovered in 1939 by L. Alvarez and R. Cornog at the University of California where they used a cyclotron as a kind of mass spectrometer.

The way deuterium was discovered is a good example of scientific "detective work."

When Aston first measured the atomic mass of hydrogen he found it to be in good agreement with the established value obtained by the chemists of 1.0078. Curiously enough the agreement which first looked so good was actually due to a small, unrecognized error made by Aston. This was before the discovery of the rarer isotopes of oxygen beginning in 1929. When the atomic mass of hydrogen was recomputed on the new physical scale in terms of the oxygen isotope O^{16}, it turned out to be appreciably smaller than the value obtained by the chemists. Here was a puzzle. The difference though small was too large to be assigned to experimental error.

It was suggested by Birge and Menzel in 1931 that the discrepancy might be due to the existence of one or more heavier isotopes of hydrogen, and in 1932 spectroscopic evidence was found of the existence of a rare isotope of hydrogen having a mass almost twice that of ordinary hydrogen. This is the isotope called *heavy hydrogen* or *deuterium*, and its importance has grown rapidly. In combination with oxygen it forms "heavy water," one of the uses of which is as a moderator in nuclear reactors (§16-12).

As mentioned in §1-9 the deuteron is the nucleus of a deuterium (heavy hydrogen) atom. Its mass in amu is

$$M_D = 2.01419 \text{ amu}$$

This is to be compared with the masses of the proton, M_p

$$M_p = 1.007593 \text{ amu}$$

and the mass of the neutron

$$M_n = 1.008982 \text{ amu}$$

Problems

1. A singly-ionized mercury atom of mass number 200 and a similar doubly-ionized mercury atom acquire what speeds in being accelerated by a potential difference of 300 volts?

2. Two particles move through a uniform magnetic field at right angles to it. If one of the particles has 24 times the mass, 6 times the charge, and 10 times the velocity of the other particle, what will be the ratio of the radii of curvature of their paths?

3. A singly-ionized atom moves perpendicularly across a uniform magnetic field of flux density 1045 gauss (0.1045 weber/m²) with a velocity of 10^6 m/sec. Its path is curved in the arc of a circle of 10 cm radius. Compute the mass of the atom.

4. If the protons and deuterons accelerated by a potential difference of 100 volts pass through a small slit and are deflected by a magnetic field of 0.005 weber/m² (50 gauss), what will be the separation of the beams after traversing a semicircle if the particles move at right angles to the field?

5. What is the approximate separation of the lines formed on a photographic film by the two isotopes of neon, of mass number 20 and 22, if the ions emerge from a narrow slit and travel a semicircular path in a magnetic field of flux density 0.01 weber/m² (100 gauss)? (Assume they have been accelerated by a difference of potential of 100 volts, are singly charged, and move at right angles to the field.)

6. It is desired to separate two mercury isotope atoms, one singly-charged atom of mass number 200 and the other of mass number 202. If both cross (perpendicularly) a magnetic field at speeds of 2000 m/sec, what magnetic flux density is required in order that the diameter of their paths differ by 1 cm?

7. Two isotopes of a substance have atomic masses of 44 and 46 respectively. What percentage of each would give an apparent atomic mass of 45.8?

8. The two isotopes of chlorine have masses of approximately 35 amu and 37 amu. Their relative abundances are 75.4 and 24.6 per cent, respectively. Find the chemical atomic weight.

9. Ordinary oxygen has an apparent atomic weight of 16.0044 on the physical scale. If composed chiefly of O^{16} and the rarer O^{18} isotope, what percentage of the atoms are the rare isotope?

10. A proton is accelerated through a difference of potential of 1000 volts. Through what difference of potential must a deuteron be accelerated if both proton and deuteron are to have the same radius of curvature of path if they cross the same magnetic field at the same angle?

11. Find the value of Br in gauss cm for an electron of 10^4 eV energy. (1 gauss = 10^{-4} weber/m²)

*12. Design a velocity selector that will pass oxygen O^{16} atoms having speeds of 10^5 m/sec through a slit 1 mm wide but will reject those having 10 per cent more or less speed. Assume slit is 10 cm from source of atoms.

13. Compute the ratio of 1 amu in the chemical system to 1 amu in the physical system (both based on oxygen) from the following data. The per cents of O^{16}, O^{17} and O^{18} in natural oxygen are respectively 99.757, 0.03920 and 0.2033.

*14. Make an approximate design of a mass spectrograph aimed to separate the isotopes of mercury.

Recommended Reading

Kaplan, I., *Nuclear Physics*, 2nd ed. Reading, Mass.: Addison-Wesley Publishing Company, Inc., 1963.

Aston, F. W., *Mass Spectra and Isotopes*. New York: Longmans, Green and Co., 1933.

Duckworth, H. E., *Mass Spectroscopy*. London: Cambridge University Press, 1958.

Early Work

Thomson, J. J., *Rays of Positive Electricity and Their Application to Chemical Analysis*, 2nd ed. London: Longmans, Green and Co., 1921.

X-rays and Crystal Structure

4-1. Introduction

Many aspects of the intellectual development of man are illustrated by the changing concepts concerning the nature of light, and radiant energy in general. In early Greek times vision was vaguely thought of as an emanation from objects seen or from the eye itself. The emanation was thought of chiefly in terms of invisible particles, and of course there was no adequate concept of wave motion. Centuries later Newton leaned toward a more sophisticated particle theory largely because he thought no waves could possibly be small enough to account for observed effects. Huygens opposed Newton and held to a wave theory, but he supposed the waves to be longitudinal. When in the early nineteenth century polarization and diffraction effects seemed to prove conclusively that light was a form of transverse wave motion, it was conceived to be a mechanical wave in some all-pervasive medium having the character of a solid, yet indetectable. Such irrational properties of this hypothetical medium, called the *ether*, presented one of the great problems in science and will be dealt with in Chap. 6.

When Maxwell put forth his electromagnetic theory in 1864 and concluded that light was a form of electromagnetic wave motion, a revolution was in the making which has continued to this day. Not only visible light but radiation of shorter and longer wavelengths, including thermal radiation and what are called *radio waves*, were found to fall into the same category. The old mechanical ether of space was supplanted by an electromagnetic ether, but many difficulties still remained. However, a generally satisfactory pattern seemed to be forming which would not need further revolutionary changes.

Then came the discovery of x-rays, and a few years later at the turn of the century Planck's idea of the quantization of radiation followed by the Einstein theory of relativity which ignored the existence of any kind of ether. The process of conceptual development was again upset in 1921 when Arthur H. Compton showed that an x-ray quantum has such sharply defined particle-like characteristics as to warrant a new name and the term *photon* was coined. The interpretation and harmonization of the apparently contradictory wave-like and particle-like aspects of radiant energy has been one of the chief concerns of science since that time, and the degree of success has been notable. For this chapter, however, the wave aspect of the x-ray will be found to be most useful. The particle-like aspect of radiation will be dealt with in the next chapter.

Aside from the obvious uses of x-rays in diagnosing broken bones and locating bullets in the body, together with the many more recent industrial applications, the rays have become an increasingly important agent in scientific research leading to advances of extraordinary importance. By their use it was soon possible to determine quickly and accurately the structure of crystalline substances and the spacing of atoms in a crystal. Studies of x-ray spectra next furnished some of the most important information concerning the structure of the atoms themselves and the relations of the elements to one another (Chap. 9).

4-2. Discovery of X-rays; Wave-Like Character

X-rays were discovered by Roentgen in 1895 at the University of Würzburg, and the announcement was made during Christmas week of that year. The rays were so named because of their unknown nature. Roentgen was one of a number of physicists who were carefully studying electric discharges in gases at low pressures. Working in his laboratory with an ordinary electric discharge tube he noticed that a paper screen which had been painted with a fluorescent solution of platinum-barium-cyanide glowed with a greenish light at a distance of as much as two meters from the discharge tube. It glowed even when black cardboard was interposed between the tube and the screen, and Roentgen soon found that the new kind of radiation could penetrate other substances of low density but that denser materials would cast a more or less dark shadow. In a short time the properties listed below were confirmed by Roentgen and others.

1. X-rays make a fluorescent screen glow with visible light.
2. They blacken a photographic plate.

3. In passing through air or any gas they make the gas a conductor by producing ions in the gas.

4. They are strongly absorbed by dense substances such as iron or lead.

5. They cast shadows of dense objects on a fluorescent screen and hence must travel in straight lines.

6. They produce a reddening of the skin which may become a serious (and even fatal) burn.

7. They are not deflected by either electric or magnetic fields.

However, these properties shed little light on the nature of the rays and their nature was at first vigorously debated. Some thought x-rays consisted of particles of extremely small dimensions. Others thought them to be a form of extremely penetrating wave motion. In order to determine whether x-rays showed the common properties of light waves Roentgen himself tried to produce reflection, refraction, polarization, and diffraction. From these experiments he obtained only negative results. However, later experimenters by means of much more refined methods have detected all these effects, and as early as 1902 Brunhes and Blondlot in a series of experiments had shown that x-rays travel at approximately the speed of light. This result was further substantiated by later investigators.

The fact that x-rays could not be deflected by electric or magnetic fields was taken to indicate that they do not consist of charged particles such as the cathode rays or positive rays found in a discharge tube, but there remained the possibility that they might be uncharged particles. In 1905 Barkla in England found that the rays could be polarized like visible light waves.

Barkla's experiment is illustrated in Fig. 4-1. X-rays from the tube T are scattered in all directions from the block A when the rays presumably cause electrons in the carbon to vibrate. The rays scattered in a direction x must be approximately plane-polarized if the incident x-ray is a transverse wave. They can only be formed by electrons vibrating at right angles to the direction x since electrons vibrating in the direction y do not produce waves in that direction. Such waves would have to be longitudinal waves, and longitudinal electromagnetic waves do not exist. To show that the waves in direction x were plane-polarized Barkla scattered them again from another block of carbon at B. A transverse wave could only produce transverse scattered waves along z or z' and not along y or y' since vibrations of electrons in the second carbon block at B could only be along yy', and no radiation in that direction should result. Barkla's experiment demonstrated the existence of scattered waves along z and z' but none along y and y'. Thus it was demonstrated that, whatever the nature of the x-ray was, it could be polarized in the same way as light, and hence behaves like a transverse electromagnetic wave.

It was still conceivable that particles might show some kind of polarization effect, but several inconclusive experiments had seemed to show that when x-rays were passed through a narrow V-shaped slit the point of the image formed was broadened by apparent diffraction more than could be explained if the rays consisted of particles. Up to this time experimenters had no inkling of how short the x-ray wavelengths really were, and their apparatus was entirely too clumsy to give definite results.

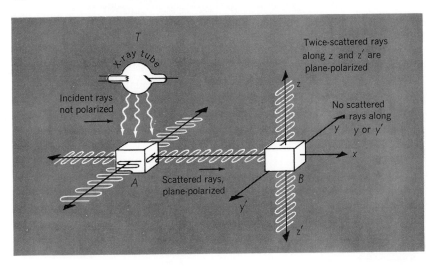

Fig. 4-1. Barkla's experiment to show that x-rays can be polarized. Rays scattered from carbon block *A* are scattered again from second carbon block *B*. Absence of scattered rays along *yy′* and presence along *zz′* indicate that vibrations are transverse and that rays incident on *B* are plane-polarized.

It remained for Max von Laue in Germany in 1911 to show that diffraction effects involving constructive and destructive interference could be obtained. This was the critical experiment which tipped the scales in favor of the wave theory of the ray (§4-8). In 1924 it was found that the rays could, after all, be bent slightly by a glass prism but were bent in the opposite direction from that of ordinary light, the index of refraction being slightly less than 1.0 whereas for visible light the index of refraction is considerably greater than 1. Actual values of the index of refraction vary with the x-ray wavelength selected, but for glass they range from 0.999995 to 0.999990. As this indicates, the bending is found to be extremely small but is sufficient to be measured when the rays strike the prism at a very small glancing angle. These experiments gave generally accepted evidence that the x-ray is a form of electromagnetic wave similar to light waves but with wavelengths a thousandth or less than that of visible light. The particle-like character of the rays was yet to be discovered (§5-6).

4-3. The Production of X-rays; Characteristic X-rays

X-rays are produced whenever high-speed electrons (cathode rays) strike a dense target and are suddenly stopped. The higher the speed of an electron at the moment it is stopped, and the more suddenly it is stopped, the more penetrating is the x-ray produced. The larger the number of electrons per second being stopped, the more intense is the x-ray beam. Tungsten targets are frequently used although less penetrating x-rays can be produced with less dense targets. An x-ray tube contains two electrodes, the cathode which is the source of electrons, and the anode or target upon which they strike. X-rays radiate from the portion of the target being bombarded.

In a modern type of x-ray tube a heated filament is used for the cathode, thereby obtaining a liberal supply of electrons by means of *thermionic emission* (§12-8). Such a tube is represented in Fig. 4-2. Since positive-ion bombardment of the cathode is not required in order to release

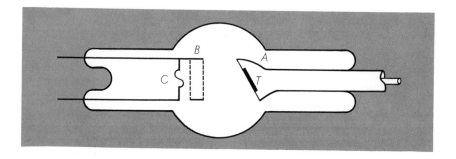

Fig. 4-2.   Hot-cathode or Coolidge-type x-ray tube with anode *A*, focusing electrode *B*, and hot filament cathode *C*. Anode is usually arranged for air or water cooling, and a target *T* of dense metal such as tungsten is set into copper electrode.

electrons, as in the early cold-cathode tubes, the tube may be so highly evacuated that an inappreciable number of gas ions is produced, and it is then possible to apply higher voltages to the tube. Accelerating potentials as high as 100,000 volts are common, and much higher voltages are used for special purposes. The electron current through the tube, and in consequence the intensity of the x-rays, can readily be controlled by adjusting the temperature of the cathode. A subsidiary electrode surrounding the cathode provides an electric field which focuses the electrons at a small spot on the target. The penetration (sometimes called hardness) of the x-rays can easily be changed by varying the potential across the tube since it is this potential that controls the speed with which the electrons strike the target.

Operation of x-ray tubes in the million-volt range has been accomplished by the design of special tubes for the purpose and by making use of Van de Graaff generators (§18-1) to obtain the required high-voltages. By quite different methods of accelerating electrons (Chap. 18) the upper limit of x-ray energies can now be raised to the hundred million and even billion-volt range and a vast new capability for research has opened up.

The x-rays so far mentioned have been produced by a sudden stoppage of electrons upon hitting a dense target. These are known as the *general* or *continuous* *x-rays* and they must be distinguished from what are called the *characteristic x-rays* discovered by Barkla and Sadler in 1908 which are produced by a different process. The general x-rays consist of a continuous range of frequencies up to the maximum possible for a given voltage between cathode and anode. When the intensity of these general x-rays is plotted as a function of the frequency there results a curve like that shown in Fig. 4-3.

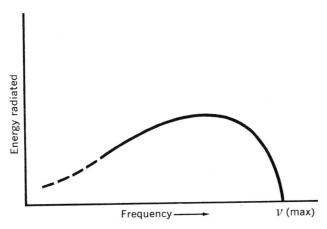

Fig. 4-3. Energy radiated at different frequencies in the continuous radiation from an x-ray tube. For the maximum-energy x-ray quantum the frequency is a maximum and the wavelength is a minimum.

The characteristic x-rays produced in an x-ray tube consist of one or more narrow bands of frequency characteristic of the target material, resulting from disturbances within the atoms of the target produced by the bombarding electrons. They would then appear as peaks of considerable intensity superposed on the continuous background of general radiation (See Fig. 9-9).

Their origin is readily demonstrated. If the accelerating voltage is varied over a considerable range the characteristic x-ray frequencies do not change although the upper frequency limit of the continuous spectrum does change. If the voltage on the tube is held constant while the target material is changed the characteristic x-ray frequencies change but the upper limit of the continuous spectrum does not change.

Characteristic x-rays will be discussed more completely (Chap. 9) after a fuller treatment of atomic theory enables their manner of production to be better understood.

4-4. Classical and Quantum Theories of X-ray Production: Bremsstrahlung

According to classical electromagnetic theory a moving electric charge will radiate energy if it is accelerated. Fig. 4-4 illustrates the ideal case of a moving charge brought suddenly to rest (or at least suddenly decelerated). Classical theory predicts that the inertia of the field will tend to keep it moving forward and during the time it takes to bring it to rest a transverse pulse will be formed and travel outward. Since a moving charge possesses a magnetic as well as an electric field the pulse will be *electromagnetic* although only the electric field is represented.

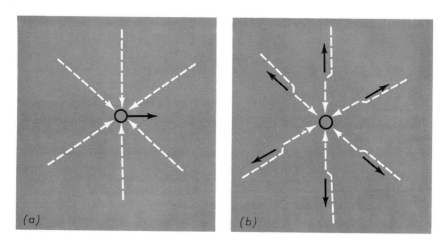

Fig. 4-4. *a,* The electric field of a moving electron is represented by the dotted lines. *b,* If the electron is suddenly stopped, classical theory predicts that the inertia of the field will tend to carry it forward producing an outward moving pulse represented by kinks in the lines of force.

If suitable equations are set up, classical theory predicts that the amount of energy radiated will increase rapidly with increasing speed of the impinging electron and with the suddenness of stoppage. In this fashion classical theory was able to account for some of the broader features of x-ray production but it was helpless to explain such things as the upper frequency limit of the spectrum and the embarrassing fact that a pulse does not represent a sharply defined frequency whereas such frequencies are observed.

For a more satisfactory explanation we must go to the basic ideas of quantum physics. When an electron is accelerated by a difference of potential V, the kinetic energy E_k it gains is given by

$$E_k = eV \qquad [4\text{--}1]$$

If we assume x-rays represent energy radiated discontinuously in the form of quanta, as Planck assumed for thermal radiation, then making use of the Planck quantum relation (§1-3) we find the energy of a quantum is $E_q = h\nu$. For the most favorable collision in which the electron is stopped so completely and suddenly that all of its kinetic energy eV goes into producing a single quantum of radiant energy,

$$eV = h\nu_{\max} \qquad [4\text{--}2]$$

Consequently the maximum frequency of x-rays produced by electrons of energy eV is

$$\nu_{\max} = \frac{eV}{h} \qquad [4\text{--}2a]$$

This is the Duane and Hunt law which is an important approximation. The small amounts of initial energy possessed by an electron when emitted from a hot cathode may usually be neglected as well as the energy lost if it is captured by an atom in the target.

Since any electron may not be stopped by a single collision but may be stopped by a sequence of collisions the energy may be radiated as several successive quanta of lower frequencies. This accounts for the production of a continuous range of frequencies in the general x-rays below a definite limit. Actually the efficiency of production of x-rays is low and 1 per cent or less of the kinetic energy of the electrons striking the target is ordinarily converted into x-ray quanta. The remainder and major part of the energy appears as heat in the target which therefore usually needs to have some kind of a cooling system.

The production of radiation when electrons (or other charges) are decelerated is found not only in an x-ray tube but wherever high-speed charged particles are accelerated. Since the slowing down is somewhat as if a brake had been applied the radiation is sometimes called "braking radiation" or in German "bremsstrahlung." It is a common phenomenon observed when high-speed electrons, found as components of the cosmic rays in our upper atmosphere (Chap. 17), are partially stopped by collisions with air molecules as they plunge toward the earth.

In Fig. 4-5 an electron is represented as being deflected (decelerated) by an atomic nucleus. Classical theory predicts that radiation will occur in the form of an electromagnetic wave and that the electron must lose kinetic energy in the process. Quantum theory requires that the radiation occur in the form of one or more definite quanta and the frequency of a quantum is determined by the Planck quantum relation. Since the mass

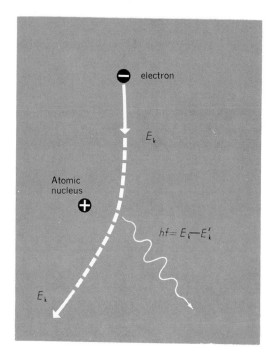

Fig. 4-5. Radiative "collision" of electron and atomic nucleus. Electron of energy E_k is decelerated, losing energy in the form of quantized radiation (bremsstrahlung).

of the atomic nucleus is relatively very large, the energy of recoil of the nucleus may usually be neglected. Since the frequency of a wave is the velocity divided by the wavelength λ, the quantity c/λ may be substituted in Eq. 4–2, giving

$$eV = \frac{hc}{\lambda} \qquad [4\text{--}3]$$

where c is the velocity of light.

From Eq. 4-3 the minimum wavelength of the x-ray (corresponding to the maximum frequency, Fig. 4-3) for a given voltage V on an x-ray tube is

$$\lambda_{\text{min}} = \frac{hc}{eV} \qquad [4\text{--}4]$$

Putting into Eq. 4–4 the numerical values of the Planck constant, the velocity of light, and the charge of the electron, there results

$$\lambda_{min} = \frac{12395}{V \text{ (volts)}} \times 10^{-8} \text{ cm} \qquad [4\text{–}5]$$

or

$$= \frac{12395}{V \text{ (volts)}} \text{ angstrom units} \qquad [4\text{–}5a]$$

(As a memory device the numerical constant in the latter equation may be remembered with an error of less than 1 per cent as 12345.) The angstrom unit, Å, is the common unit in which to measure small lengths such as the wavelengths of light or x-rays.

$$1 \text{ Å} = 10^{-10} \text{ m} = 10^{-8} \text{ cm}$$

For very short x-ray wavelengths a still smaller unit is sometimes employed, called the X unit. For practical purposes it may be defined as a thousandth of an angstrom unit.

$$1 \ X \text{ unit} = \frac{1}{1000} \text{ Å}$$

The exact definition is given in §4-11.

Example   What is the minimum wavelength in meters and angstroms of the x-rays produced by electrons accelerated by a potential difference of 50,000 volts?

$$\lambda = \frac{12395}{V(\text{volts})} = \frac{12395}{50000} = 0.248 \text{ Å}$$

$$= 0.248 \times 10^{-10} \text{ m}$$

4-5. Absorption of X-rays; Absorption Coefficients

All substances absorb x-rays to a greater or lesser degree. The more dense the substance and the thicker the absorbing layer, the greater will be the absorption for a given wavelength. Even in a gas there is some absorption of x-rays caused by energy losses in ionizing some of the gas molecules, but because of the low density of matter in a gas the absorption is slight.

The decrease in intensity of a monochromatic x-ray beam when it passes through an absorbing medium is very closely represented by a logarithmic decay curve, Fig. 4-6, and the formula for the intensity at any distance x is given by

$$I = I_0 \, \epsilon^{-\mu x} \qquad [4\text{–}6]$$

where I_0 is the intensity of the incident beam, ϵ is the base of the natural system of logarithms, and μ is a coefficient characteristic of the absorber.

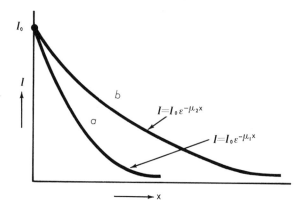

Fig. 4-6. Logarithmic decay curves representing the reduction of intensity of an x-ray beam of initial intensity I_0 after passing through different thicknesses x of an absorbing medium. *a*, Less penetrating rays; *b*, more penetrating rays.

The rate of absorption varies with the wavelength of the rays, being greatest for the longer wavelengths. Fig. 4-7 shows how (*a*) "soft" or less penetrating x-rays and (*b*) "hard" or more penetrating x-rays are absorbed in a dense medium such as lead. The absorption coefficient μ_1 for the "soft" x-ray is larger than the absorption coefficient μ_2 for the "hard" x-ray (Fig. 4-6).

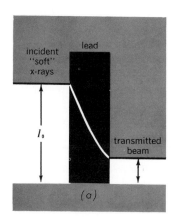
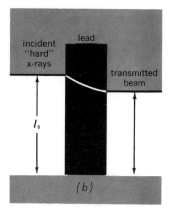

Fig. 4-7. Reduction of intensity of x-ray beam of initial intensity I_0. *a*, Absorption of soft x-rays (long wavelength) in thick lead plate; *b*, absorption of more penetrating (hard) x-rays (short wavelength) in similar plate.

The type of equation [4–6] involving exponential decrease of a variable is of great importance in physics and is of similar form to the one to be encountered later for decay of a radioactive substance. In its application to x-rays it may be readily obtained by the following method, which involves the integration of a simple equation.

Let ΔI be the decrease in intensity of the beam when passing through a thin layer of absorbing material the thickness of which is Δx. The decrease in intensity is represented by a negative sign, and it may be assumed to be proportional to the thickness Δx, to the intensity of the beam I, and to a constant μ, representing the absorbing ability of the material. Then

$$-\Delta I = \mu I \, \Delta x$$

In the limit this becomes

$$-dI = \mu I \, dx$$

or

$$\frac{dI}{I} = -\mu x \qquad [4\text{--}7]$$

which, being integrated readily, gives the previous equation (4–6), the constant of integration being the value of the intensity at $x = 0$ or I_0. (The method of solving Eq. 4–7 is given for the mathematically similar equation for radioactive decay in §13-5 and may be referred to now.)

If I is taken to represent the intensity of the x-ray beam in terms of energy per second per unit area falling on the absorber, μ is called the linear coefficient of absorption. If this is divided by the density ρ of the absorbing material the quantity μ_m is obtained where $\mu = \mu_m \rho$, and μ_m is known as the mass absorption coefficient of the substance. Equation 4–6 may now be written

$$I = I_0 \, \epsilon^{-\mu_m \rho x} \qquad [4\text{--}8]$$

The mass absorption coefficient makes it simpler to compare the absorption of samples of different substances regardless of thickness.

When two absorbers of different material and thickness are found to give the same absorption the exponential terms for each must be equal, and

$$\mu_{m1} \rho_1 x_1 = \mu_{m2} \rho_2 x_2 \qquad [4\text{--}9]$$

from which

$$\mu_{m1} = \mu_{m2} \frac{\rho_2 x_2}{\rho_1 x_1} \qquad [4\text{--}10]$$

and an unknown mass absorption coefficient μ_{m1} can be computed from the known value of a standard μ_{m2} when the relative densities and thicknesses are known. Carbon is usually taken as the standard reference material because its absorption is more nearly constant for different wavelengths than that of most substances.

If we divide both sides of Eq. 4–7 by x it becomes evident that the absorption coefficient μ represents the fractional decrease in intensity of the x-ray beam per unit thickness of absorber.

EXAMPLE   To what fraction of its original intensity will an x-ray be reduced by a lead shield of 2-mm thickness if the mass absorption coefficient of the lead for the particular wavelength of x-ray used is $\mu_m = 3$. The density ρ of the lead is 11.3 gm/cm³.

$$\frac{I}{I_0} = \epsilon^{-\mu_m \rho x} = \epsilon^{-3(11.3)0.2}$$

$$= \epsilon^{-6.78} = \frac{1}{880}$$

and the intensity has been reduced to $I = 0.00114\, I_0$.

4-6. Means of Detecting X-rays

The most common methods of detecting x-rays are by means of a fluorescent screen, photographic film, an ionization chamber, or an electroscope. The fluorescent screen is the oldest method and is the simplest and most direct. A number of fluorescent materials such as, for instance, calcium tungstate, will emit visible light when subjected to sufficient intensity of x-rays and such materials can therefore be used to coat a screen. Photographic emulsions in general are sensitive to x-rays and special emulsions are made for the purpose. One advantage is that radiation intensities too low to visibly affect a fluorescent screen may be detected by making long exposures.

An ionization chamber (§13-18) and also an electroscope are often used to measure the number of ions formed in an enclosed volume of gas by x-rays or other high-energy rays. In the ionization chamber the number of ions collected by an electrode can be measured by extremely sensitive electrical methods. One advantage is that the number collected per second is directly proportional to the intensity of the radiation whereas with photographic film the blackening is not necessarily so. The loss of charge from the leaves of an electroscope may similarly measure radiation intensities. Sometimes scintillation detectors and Geiger-Müller tubes are used, as in measuring the low intensities encountered in x-ray spectroscopy. These devices are common in cosmic-ray and nuclear studies and are discussed in Chap. 13.

4-7. Radiation Hazards: the Roentgen

All workers with x-rays must take proper precautions to avoid burns or overexposure. X-ray equipment must be properly shielded with some good absorber. Lead is commonly used and is easy to manipulate. The safety of any shielding system may be tested by photographic test film exposed for considerable periods of time or worn by workers in the form of "film badges." Radiation meters are also effective. Any unnecessary exposure to x-rays should be scrupulously avoided. Similar hazards occur with various radiations from radioactive substances and from nuclear reactors.

A common unit for measuring the possible physiological effects of x-rays is the *roentgen*. It is defined as the amount of x-radiation (or the amount of gamma radiation from a radioactive source) that will produce 2.08×10^9 ion pairs or 1 statcoulomb of electricity of each sign by ionization in 1 cm³ of air at standard conditions. Exposures of less than 0.3 roentgen per week are considered fairly safe for most people as far as short-range ill effects are concerned.

4-8. X-ray Crystal Diffraction—von Laue's Method

When Newton years ago was concerned with the problem of the nature of visible light he leaned toward the corpuscular theory, as previously mentioned, because he felt that to describe light in terms of wave motion required unbelievably short wavelengths. A similar difficulty arose in the study of the nature of x-rays, where wavelengths are so very much smaller even than those we now recognize as belonging to visible light. However, by 1911, increased evidence had begun to indicate that x-ray wavelengths might be as short as a few hundred millionths of a centimeter or a few angstrom units. This led Max von Laue in Germany to the brilliant idea that, since atomic layers in a crystal usually have spacings of a few angstrom units, they might act to give an effect somewhat similar to crossed diffraction gratings closely ruled with very fine lines and thus afford the means for a critical test.

Von Laue predicted that if x-rays were passed through such a crystal a diffraction pattern of spots would be found, the geometrical arrangement of which would depend on the arrangement and spacing of the atoms in the crystal. The spots would be found where the waves reach the point in the same phase and constructive interference (reinforcement) would occur. The prediction was complicated by the fact that a crystal could not act as a two-dimensional grating, but would constitute a kind of three-dimensional grating and furthermore that atomic layers could be thought of as existing in many planes. However, at von Laue's suggestion the experiment was tried by two of his students, Friedrich and Knipping, and it was a notable success.

A typical photograph of von Laue spots is shown in Fig. 4-8. The large central spot is merely the result of the direct beam of x-rays from which only a relatively small fraction of the rays are diffracted by the

Fig. 4-8. X-ray diffraction. Von Laue spot pattern obtained by passing narrow beam of x-rays through crystal of rock salt.

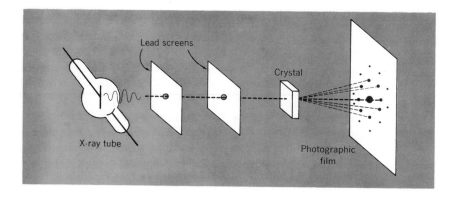

Fig. 4-9. Schematic diagram of apparatus for producing von Laue spots.

crystal. The positions of the spots were close to where von Laue had calculated they would be. Here was direct evidence of the wave character of x-rays.

The experimental arrangement to secure a spot pattern is shown in Fig. 4-9. X-rays are confined to a narrow beam by means of blocks of lead through which a small hole is drilled. This pencil of x-rays is allowed to pass through a crystal of some substance such as potassium chloride. The spots are obtained on a photographic film, in the position shown, after an exposure of as much as 30 minutes or more.

4-9. X-ray Crystal Diffraction—Bragg's Method

The way in which the diffraction of x-rays depends upon the wavelength and the crystal spacing is more simply seen from the work of W. H. Bragg in England, in which his son, W. L. Bragg, took part. Whereas von Laue passed the x-rays through a crystal to obtain diffraction, the Braggs reflected the x-rays from the successive planes parallel to the face of a crystal and also obtained a diffraction pattern. Such a pattern is much simpler to analyze than the one obtained by von Laue. For one thing, in von Laue's method a large number of directions may be chosen to represent the crystal planes. For another he did not use x-rays of a single wavelength, since the radiation from an x-ray tube has a distribution of wavelengths, as previously shown in Fig. 4-4.

The geometrical arrangement of atoms in a crystal is represented by a pattern of lines called a *crystal lattice*, the intersections of the lines representing the locations of the atoms. In Fig. 4-10 a two-dimensional repre-

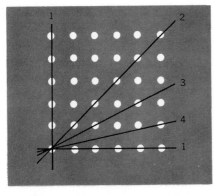

Fig. 4-10. One face of a cubic crystal lattice. The lines represent traces of planes through lattice points. Line I represents the greatest population density of points and line 4 one of the least.

sentation of atoms arranged on a cubic lattice is shown. Lines are drawn to indicate the traces of planes in different directions, any one of which may be considered a crystal plane. Note that the rectangular axes represent planes with the greatest population of atoms. The main diagonal axis represents the direction of planes with almost as much population, but other directions may be taken in which the populations are less and less. These account for the weak "reflections" which produce the fainter spots in a von Laue photograph.

In order to simplify the description of various crystal planes, certain numbers known as *Miller indices* are used. If a rectangular crystal is set with its axes parallel to the x, y, and z axes of Fig. 4-11, the direction of the perpendicular line from the origin to any plane in the crystal serves to specify that plane. The term *plane* is taken to mean not an individual plane but any plane parallel to a given plane. The direction of the perpendicular to a given plane could be specified by directional cosines, but it is simpler to specify the plane in terms of its intercepts on the x, y, and z axes. This is particularly true since the spacing of planes may be different in the three directions, and furthermore the crystal axes may not even be at right angles to one another.

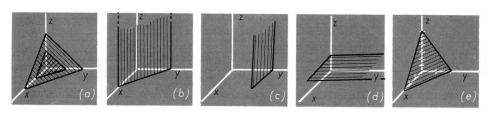

Fig. 4-11.   Representation of some planes of a crystal by Miller indices: a, 111; b, 110; c, 010; d, 001; e, 231.

Referring to Fig. 4-11e, let a be the lattice spacing in the x direction, and b and c be the spacings in the y and z directions. For example, let the plane for which it is now desired to obtain the Miller indices cut the x axis at $3a$, the y axis at $2b$, and the z axis at $6c$. Write the reciprocals of the numerical values as

$$\frac{1}{3}, \frac{1}{2}, \frac{1}{6}$$

Reducing these to a least common denominator we have

$$\frac{2}{6}, \frac{3}{6}, \frac{1}{6}$$

The numerators 2, 3, 1 are the Miller indices. For the plane in Fig. 4-11a intersecting the axes at equal numbers of units the Miller indices are 111. When a plane is parallel to an axis the intercept is at infinity, and the index is $1/\infty = 0$. The indices 110 for the plane at b indicate that the plane is parallel to the z axis. At c it is parallel to both x and z axes, and at d it is parallel to the x and y axes.

Let us consider how x-rays would be reflected from the planes of such a crystal lattice according to Bragg's method. Figure 4-12 represents an x-ray beam incident upon the crystal plane at an angle θ, called the grazing angle. Rays reflected at the same angle θ are also indicated. The term *reflection* in a general sense embodies the idea that each atom with its electrons acts as a center of scattering of x-rays from which wavelets spread out in all directions. These wavelets add to form a clearly defined wave front in the direction of ordinary reflection so that the angle of incidence equals the angle of reflection and the complementary or grazing angles are also equal.

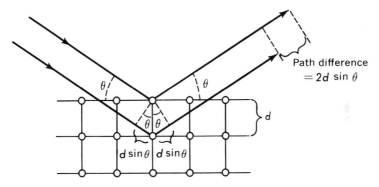

Fig. 4-12. Diagram for derivation of the Bragg equation for x-ray diffraction by reflection of x-rays from face of a crystal. For constructive interference, path difference *2d sin θ* must equal an integral number *n* of whole wavelengths λ.

From the diagram it is seen that the difference in path between rays from successive planes is $2d \sin \theta$, where d is the spacing between the crystal planes. Constructive interference occurs for the emerging beam if the waves are in phase. This occurs only at those angles for which the path difference is a whole wavelength or an integral number of wavelengths and if the angles of incidence and reflection are equal. A reinforcement spot (or line) then occurs when

$$n\lambda = 2d \sin \theta \qquad [4\text{--}11]$$

where n may have integral values 1, 2, 3, ... At other angles the waves are out of phase and destructive interference occurs. For the most precise work a small correction has to be made for refraction of the ray entering or leaving the crystal.

The smallest angle θ for a spot would be given when n has the value 1, called *first-order* interference. At a larger angle constructive interference would occur again for $n = 2$, called a *second-order* spot, and so on. It is now possible to set up a *crystal x-ray spectrometer* in such a way that angles for constructive interference positions can be measured with suitable detectors such as an ionization chamber or photographic film. The experimental arrangement is shown in Fig. 4-13. With such a crystal x-ray spectrometer the wavelength of x-rays can be computed if the spacing of the crystal planes is known and if the angle to the observed spot is measured.

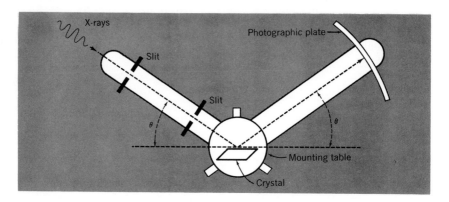

Fig. 4-13.   Essential elements of a Bragg x-ray crystal spectrometer (top view).

Instead of its serving to determine wavelengths when the crystal spacing is known, the x-ray spectrometer may be used to determine the crystal spacing if the wavelength of the x-ray is known. W. H. Bragg and his son, now Sir Lawrence Bragg, made many such measurements, and the crystal spacings have now been accurately measured for many crystals. This is one of the great achievements in the field of x-rays. Whereas by older methods crystallographers could only estimate approximate positions and spacings of atoms in the crystal, precise information can now be obtained in a relatively short space of time.

Since, however, it is required to know either the wavelength of the x-rays or the spacing of the atomic planes in the crystal in order to compute the other by the Bragg formula, the question arises as to how either one can ever be obtained. The answer is that a start was made by computing the atomic spacing as nearly as possible by means of data obtained from other experimental sources, and in particular by the accurate value of Avogadro's number, as in the following example.

EXAMPLE   To find the distance between adjacent atoms in a sodium chloride (NaCl) crystal.

Atomic weight of Na	= 23.00
Atomic weight of Cl	= 35.46

Molecular-formula weight of NaCl = 58.46

One gram-formula weight of NaCl = 58.46 gm

The number of "molecules" or ion-pairs in 1 gram-formula weight of an ionic crystal such as NaCl would be

$$N_0 = \text{Avogadro's number} = 6.025 \times 10^{23}$$

Since there are equal numbers of atoms of each kind

$2N_0 = $ number of atoms of both kinds in 58.46 gm NaCl
Mass per unit volume = density
Density of NaCl = 2.163 gm/cm³

Hence the number of atoms in 1 cm³ is

$$2(6.025 \times 10^{23}) \frac{2.163}{58.46} = 2 \times 22.3 \times 10^{21}$$

If the number of atoms along 1 centimeter of edge of a cubic crystal is n, then

$$n^3 = 44.6 \times 10^{21}$$

from which

$$n = 3.55 \times 10^7$$

The spacing between atoms d is consequently $1/n$, and

$$d = \frac{1}{n} = 2.82 \times 10^{-8} \text{ cm} = 2.82 \text{ Å}$$

From such values as those of the preceding example put into the Bragg formula it was possible to compute x-ray wavelengths from experimental measurements of the angle θ. However, an independent method of measuring such wavelengths was greatly desired. Independent measurements were finally obtained with great accuracy by means of ruled gratings (§4-11).

4-10. X-ray Crystal Diffraction—the Powder Method

Later, a diffraction method of analyzing crystals was developed by Hull and by Debye and Scherrer, in which it is not necessary to use a large single crystal, as in the original Bragg method. Crystal fragments such as those of which a metal wire is composed, or fragments in the form of a powder, are effective since they are actually large compared to the x-ray wavelengths. These fragments present relatively large crystal planes to the incident rays, just as the single crystal does in the Bragg method, but they are oriented in nearly all possible directions.

Instead of lines or spots being produced on a photographic film, circles are obtained. The random orientation of crystal fragments causes the spots from a given set of crystal planes (that is, for a given grazing angle) to fall on the arc of a circle about the central spot formed by the

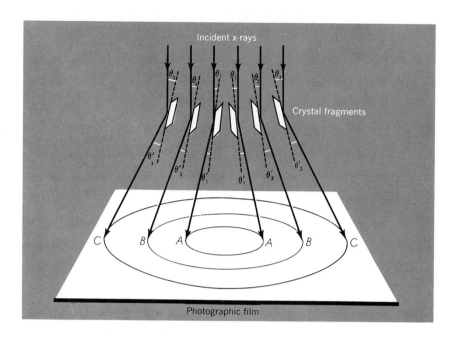

Fig. 4-14. X-ray powder diffraction. Constructive interference occurs at points such as A, B, C only when $\theta = \theta'$ and if $n\lambda = 2d \sin \theta$. Some crystal fragments will always be found at the proper angle. Since rotation of a crystal about an axis parallel to the incident rays does not affect the relations, these points will fall on a circle.

original beam (Fig. 4-14). For different grazing angles and for different sets of atomic planes there would be other circles concentric with the first. If a strip of photographic film is not wide enough to show the complete circles, it will show the regions as arcs of circles, as in Fig. 4-15. From the radii of the circles and the angles at which they are formed the crystal spacings can be readily determined. The convenience of this method

Fig. 4-15. Powder-diffraction x-ray photograph of crystals of lead oxide. The lines would form complete circles, but for convenience only a strip is usually taken with central dark spot blocked off. (Courtesy, General Electric Co.)

has led to its widespread scientific and industrial adoption in the study of metals and alloys.

4-11. X-ray Wavelengths Determined with Ruled Gratings

X-rays are so penetrating that no appreciable reflection is observed from an ordinary mirror surface, and early attempts to detect such reflections were unsuccessful. In 1922 A. H. Compton found that there was considerable reflection for an x-ray beam falling on a surface at a very small glancing angle, that is, almost parallel to the surface. The reflection occurs at angles less than the critical angle for total reflection. Applying this to a high-grade, ruled diffraction grating such as that used for visible light, Compton and Doan found in 1925 that it was possible to obtain diffraction of x-rays with this grating and thus independently to determine the wavelength of x-rays with precision.

It is evident that the grating, if observed at a very small glancing angle, appears to have lines ruled far more closely together than could actually be accomplished by direct ruling. This apparent close spacing for any such angle can be readily computed. X-rays reflected from the flat spaces between the rulings were found to form a diffraction pattern of reinforcement and interference regions, just as with visible light. By this method the wavelength of incident x-rays could then be determined. This was exactly what was needed to make certain of the accuracy of previous values of atomic spacings in crystals.

With the Bragg method of crystal analysis, and x-ray wavelengths determined by means of a ruled grating, Bearden was able to obtain precise values for the atomic spacing of calcite ($CaCO_3$), sodium chloride, and other crystals. These values in turn could now be applied in the Bragg formula when it was desired to measure unknown x-ray wavelengths. The *X unit* is then defined in such a way as to make the atomic spacing of sodium chloride exactly 2814.00 *X* units. It was this work by Bearden which also led to a precise determination of Avogadro's number which in turn led to a revision of the accepted value of the electronic charge (§1-10).

4-12. Complete Spectrum of Electromagnetic Radiation

The recognition that the x-ray is fundamentally an electromagnetic wave of very short wavelength filled another gap in the extensive range of known electromagnetic waves (Fig. 4-16). From the longest radio waves to the shortest waves produced by electrical methods there is now a con-

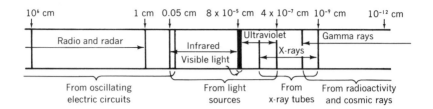

Fig. 4-16.   A complete spectrum of electromagnetic radiations.

tinuous stretch from 20,000 meters to less than 1 millimeter. From the shortest of these up through those waves classed as thermal radiation and infrared to the visible red, a little less than a ten-thousandth of a centimeter in wavelength, there is no gap. Beyond the visible violet, in the ultraviolet, the wavelengths become still shorter and shorter, merging with the longer and less penetrating x-rays known as soft x-rays of a few angstroms in length. Then on they continue to the more penetrating (hard) x-rays and to the realm of gamma rays from radioactive substances and finally to the similar but even shorter gamma-ray component of cosmic rays, with wavelengths as short as a millionth of an angstrom or even less.

The tremendous range of wavelengths (of the order of 10^{20}) is most impressive; the chart (Fig. 4-16) is worth careful study and provides a striking illustration of how science has brought relatedness and uniformity out of what at first appeared to be quite separate phenomena.

4-13. Structure of Metals

One characteristic that metals have in common is that all are crystal-line in the solid state. A substance such as paraffin or glass is noncrystalline. The atoms or molecules of a noncrystalline substance are not fixed in a regular geometrical order. They often more closely resemble the relation between molecules of a substance dissolved in a liquid, and for this reason glass is sometimes spoken of as a *solid solution*. On the other hand, the atoms of a metal preserve the characteristic geometrical order described as a crystal lattice. Crystal x-ray analysis of the metals has led to interest-ing results. Of the 32 known geometrical forms of crystal structure, the great majority of metals crystallize in one of three forms.

The simplest geometrical arrangement of atoms would be a cubic arrangement, the atoms being related to each other as the eight corners of a cube. This simple cubic structure does not quite exist in nature, but two modifications of the cubic structure are common. These are known as the *body-centered cubic* and the *face-centered cubic*. In Fig. 4-17*a* a simple cubic structure is shown; at *b* a body-centered cubic is indicated; and *c* represents a face-centered cubic. The body-centered cubic is one in which,

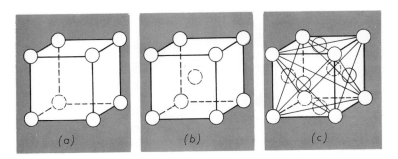

Fig. 4-17.   The three types of cubic crystal lattice structure: a, simple cubic; b, body-centered cubic; c, face-centered cubic.

in addition to eight atoms at the corners of each cube, there is one atom at the center of each cube. In the face-centered cubic arrangement, in addition to the eight atoms at the corners of each cube, there is one atom at the center of each of the six faces of the cube.

Potassium chloride and sodium chloride (table salt) crystallize on a cubic lattice in what is the nearest to simple cubic to be found in nature. Potassium and chlorine atoms (or sodium and chlorine) are found alternately at the corners of the cubes, but the arrangement is not quite pure cubic, because the atoms are not quite the same size and the cubes are thus not perfectly symmetrical.

Examples of metals that crystallize on a body-centered cubic lattice are iron, tungsten, vanadium, sodium, potassium, and molybdenum. In Fig. 4-18 a body-centered cubic lattice is shown to be the equivalent of two interpenetrating cubic lattices. This interlocking arrangement is thought to explain in part the fact that the metals, iron and tungsten and others of this type, are very tough and not very ductile. Examples of metals that crystallize on a face-centered cubic lattice are copper, gold, nickel, silver, aluminum, and lead. For the most part these are ductile metals, and they are not particularly tough.

The third common type of metal structure is known as *hexagonal close-packed*. The arrangement is indicated in Fig. 4-19 and is recognized as the manner in which oranges are often packed in a crate. Examples of metals that crystallize in this fashion are beryllium, cobalt, cadmium, zinc, titanium, and zirconium.

The study of the alloys formed by combining various metals is of great importance but represents further complications, and many alloys are found to have properties quite different from their constituent metals.

One of the most interesting of all metals because of its great industrial use is iron. At ordinary temperatures iron forms a body-centered structure known as *alpha iron*. At higher temperatures (around 900°C) the iron

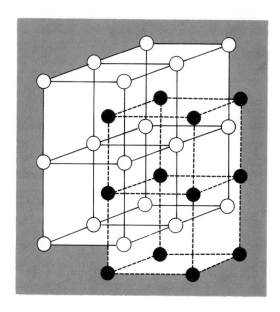

Fig. 4-18. A body-centered crystal lattice is equivalent to two interpenetrating simple cubics. The atoms at the centers of the cubes are shaded for easy identification.

changes to the face-centered state in which it is called *gamma iron*. Alpha iron is strongly magnetic. Gamma iron has lost this magnetic property. The temperature at which it loses its characteristic magnetic properties is called the *Curie point*.

Steel is an alloy of iron with carbon and frequently with other components. These elements modify the crystal structure. The iron may form different arrangements with the carbon, some of which are analogous to chemical combinations, whereas in other circumstances the carbon atoms may displace iron atoms on the crystal lattice. The size and character of the crystal grains formed when steel cools determine the hardness and other properties.

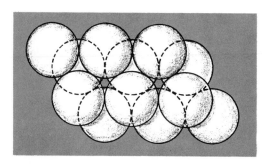

Fig. 4-19. Hexagonal close-packed ("orange-crate") pattern of a crystal lattice, showing two layers superposed.

Problems

1. What difference of potential across an x-ray tube will produce x-rays having a minimum wavelength of 1 Å? Of 0.01 Å? (1 Å = 1 angstrom = 10^{-10} m = 10^{-8} cm.)

2. What is the maximum frequency of the x-rays produced by electrons accelerated by a uniform field resulting from a potential difference of 50,000 volts?

3. If the electrons arriving at the anode of an x-ray tube have fallen through a potential difference of 100,000 volts, and if they represent a current of 10 ma, how much power in the form of heat must be dissipated at the anode, assuming that 0.3 per cent of the electrons are effective in producing x-rays? How can this much power be dissipated?

4. The cooling system of an x-ray tube can dissipate heat at the cathode at a rate of 2000 watts. What is the maximum safe electron current to the anode for continuous operation if the cathode-anode voltage is 200,000 volts?

5. A beam of electrons strikes a tungsten target at a rate of 10^{16} electrons per sec. If the electrons have an average speed of 0.9 c and if the production efficiency of x-rays is 0.8 per cent, what is the x-ray power output of the tube in watts? (Hint: Find relativistic electron energy.)

6. The mass absorption coefficient of iron per cm per unit density for x-rays of wavelength 0.2 Å is 1. If the density of iron is 7.8 gm/cm³, to what value will the intensity I_0 of such an x-ray beam be reduced by 1 cm of thickness of iron?

7. How much lead shielding is required to reduce the intensity of a penetrating x-ray beam to 1/1000 of its value if the mass absorption coefficient of lead per cm per unit density for the wavelength in question is 6? (Density of lead = 11.3 gm/cm³.)

8. An x-ray beam having an intensity of 10^9 photons per sec is incident upon a plate of lead 1 mm thick. It then passes through an iron plate 2 mm thick in contact with the lead plate. If the linear absorption coefficients of the lead and iron for the particular wavelengths are $\mu = 50$ and $\mu = 12$ respectively per cm, how many photons per sec emerge?

9. What thickness of aluminum will give the same amount of absorption as 1 mm of lead if the linear absorption coefficients of the lead and aluminum are 50 cm⁻¹ and 0.4 cm⁻¹?

10. A ruled diffraction grating has 20,000 lines/cm. What is the effective number of lines per cm if the grating is viewed at a glancing angle of 4°? Of 1°? Why would smaller angles be needed for x-ray reflection?

11. Bearden made a precise measurement of the $K_{\alpha 1}$ line in the characteristic x-rays (§9-12) of copper by reflection from a ruled grating and found it to have a wavelength of 1.5406 Å. The grating which was ruled on glass sputtered with gold had 3000 lines/cm. Such reflection occurs at grazing angles less than the critical angle of approximately 0.25 degree. What would be the effective lines per cm at right angles to the beam at that angle?

12. A plane cuts across a crystal so as to intersect the x axis at $5a$, the y axis at $3b$, and the z axis at $1c$, where a, b, and c are the spacings of the lattice planes along the respective axes. What are the Miller indices?

13. A plane intersects the axes of a crystal at $2a$, $5b$, and ∞, where a and b are the intervals between planes along the x and y axes. What are the Miller indices?

14. For a simple cubic crystal find the ratios of the spacings of the 111, 110 and 100 planes.

15. The spacing of the 111 planes of a simple cubic crystal is found to be 1.80 Å. What is the spacing of the 100 planes?

16. The distance between planes of a crystal is 3 Å. Compute the smallest angle for which a diffraction line maximum will be formed if the wavelength of the x-ray is 0.7 Å.

17. If the spacing of certain planes in calcite is 3.14 Å, find the angles at which the first- and third-order diffraction maxima are found for x-rays of wavelength 0.8 Å.

18. What is the theoretical minimum frequency of x-rays that could be measured with second-order diffraction with a Bragg spectrometer if the separation of the crystal planes is 2.2×10^{-8} cm?

19. What is the theoretical maximum wavelength of x-rays that could be measured with a Bragg spectrometer if the spacing of the crystal planes is 2.4 Å?

*20. An electron traveling with a speed of 0.9c is suddenly decelerated to a speed of 0.5c. If energy loss is radiated in the form of a single photon (quantum), what will be the wavelength? Use relativistic methods.

*21. An electron having a speed of 2×10^8 m/sec makes a near collision with an atom and is deflected in such a way that its speed is reduced to 1×10^8 m/sec. If the energy is radiated in the form of a single quantum, what will its wavelength be? Use relativistic methods.

22. A beam of x-rays from an x-ray tube is reflected from a crystal having a spacing between planes of 7.6 Å. If the smallest angle between the beam and the face of the crystal (grazing angle) for reflection is 30°, with what minimum energy in eV do the electrons strike the target in the x-ray tube?

23. The sodium (Na) and chlorine (Cl) atoms of a sodium chloride crystal occupy alternate positions on a simple cubic lattice. Measurements with a monochromatic beam of x-rays by the Bragg method show that the distance between adjacent crystal planes is 2.82×10^{-8} cm. If the density of the NaCl crystal is 2165 kg/m³, compute Avogadro's number.

24. A crystal of KCl consists of alternate potassium (K) and chlorine (Cl) atoms on a simple cubic lattice. When x-rays of wavelength 0.710 Å (measured accurately by means of a ruled grating) are reflected from the crystal, the angle of reflection for first-order constructive interference is 6.475°. From this information compute Avogadro's number if the density of KCl is 1990 kg/m³.

25. In the powder diffraction method of x-ray crystal analysis a narrow monochromatic pencil of x-rays of 0.66 Å wavelength is incident upon randomly oriented crystals (Fig. 4–14). If the crystal lattice spacing of the 100 planes is 2.4 Å and if diffracted rays are detected by a flat photographic plate 10 cm from the crystals, what is the radius of the first-order diffraction ring? What is the effect of diffraction from other planes in the crystals?

26. Taking the data of the former problem, find the radius of the first-order diffraction circle for reflection from the 111 planes assuming the crystals to be simple cubic.

27. In the ideal case the anode of an x-ray tube is held at a positive potential with respect to the cathode. Explain how it is possible (and indeed common practice) to use alternating voltage on such a tube. Consider the "self-rectifying" property of a tube with a hot cathode and thermionic emission of electrons (§12-8).

Recommended Reading

Compton, A. H., and S. K. Allison, *X-Rays In Theory and Experiment*, 2nd ed. Princeton, N. J.: D. Van Nostrand Co., 1935.

Clark, G. L., *Applied X-Rays*. New York: McGraw-Hill Book Company, Inc., 1955.

Richtmeyer, F. K., E. H. Kennard and T. Lauritsen, *Introduction to Modern Physics*. New York: McGraw-Hill Book Company, Inc., 1955.

Early Work

Bragg, W. H., and W. L. Bragg, *X-Rays and Crystal Structure*. London: G. Bell, 1915.

Quantum Properties of Waves and Particles

5-1. Photoelectric Emission

The ejection of electrons from a surface by the direct action of electromagnetic radiation is called the *photoelectric effect*. In the same year (1887) that Hertz produced electromagnetic waves experimentally and confirmed the predictions of Maxwell he observed another effect. Light from an electric spark falling on the electrodes of another spark gap produced a lower breakdown voltage of that gap. This observation was quickly followed in 1888 by Hallwach's discovery that ultraviolet light falling on a clean or freshly polished zinc plate causes a loss of negative charge from the zinc plate connected to an electroscope.

This was the beginning of a long series of experiments confirming the idea that electrons may be liberated from a metal by the direct action of light of sufficiently high frequency. Aluminum shows an effect similar to that of zinc but less intense. Certain metals, such as the alkali metals, possess this property to a marked degree although all substances show some effect. It was found that with aluminum light of higher frequency was required to produce emission than for zinc. These and other observations led to the formulation of certain general conditions of photoelectric emission.

The conditions listed below are sometimes called the "laws" of photoelectric emission. They are uniformities derived from many experimental observations. Foremost among those who established their validity was R. A. Millikan.

1. The number of photoelectrons emitted per second varies directly as the intensity of the incident light.

2. Emission from a given surface does not occur unless the frequency of the incident light is equal to, or greater than, a particular minimum value, known as the threshold value.

3. The maximum energy of the photoelectrons after emission from a surface does not depend upon the intensity of the light.

4. The maximum energy of the photoelectrons after emission increases with increase in frequency of the light.

5. Emission of photoelectrons occurs at once, regardless of the intensity of the light.

Certain questions presented by these observations cannot be explained on the basis of the classical electromagnetic theory of light but require the radically different concepts of quantum theory.

5-2. The Einstein Photoelectric Equation

For one thing it was impossible to explain on any classical basis how photoelectric emission occurs almost instantly in light so weak in intensity that according to classical theory it would be impossible for an electron to absorb sufficient energy to cause its emission. Another difficulty was how to explain, on the basis of classical theory, why emission only occurs for frequencies of incident light larger than a certain minimum, the minimum being different for different metals.

TABLE 5-1.   SOME WORK FUNCTIONS
(in electron volts)

Element	Thermionic Work Functions	Photoelectric Work Functions
Cesium	1.81	1.9
Sodium	——	2.28
Nickel	5.03	5.01
Mercury	——	4.53
Platinum	6.27	6.30
Tantalum	4.07	4.12
Tungsten	4.52	4.54
Zinc	——	4.3

No satisfactory explanation of the photoelectric effect was evident until 1905 when Einstein, with great insight, applied the basic principle of quantization of radiation originally proposed by Planck in 1900. Good experimental confirmation of Einstein's ideas did not come for seven years, but in 1921 he was awarded the Nobel Prize for this work.

Einstein assumed that a photoelectron first absorbs a definite quantum of energy E_q of the incident light where $E_q = h\nu$. In the equation h is the Planck constant, the accepted value of which is

$$h = 6.626 \times 10^{-34} \text{ joule sec}$$

or

$$= 6.626 \times 10^{-27} \text{ erg sec}$$

Photoelectrons then are emitted if they have absorbed a quantum of energy large enough to enable them to pass through the *potential barrier* at the surface of the emitter. But in going through this surface the photoelectron loses on the average an energy w_0, and the kinetic energy, $\frac{1}{2}mv^2$, that it retains on leaving the surface then equals the energy $h\nu$ of the absorbed quantum minus w_0 or

$$\frac{1}{2} mv^2 = h\nu - w_0 \qquad\qquad [5\text{--}1]$$

where w_0 is called the *photoelectric work function* of the substance. This is the *Einstein photoelectric equation*. Although all three terms in Eq. 5–1 must be measured in the same units, the work function w_0 is commonly measured in electron volts and some typical values are given in Table 5-1. These are seen to agree within the limits of experimental error with the thermionic work functions to be discussed in Chap. 12 (§12-8).

The Einstein photoelectric equation agrees with the experimental observation that emission can only occur at frequencies equal to or above a certain minimum called the threshold frequency. Also it predicts that the maximum energy of emitted electrons increases linearly with the frequency of the light and is directly proportional to the energy excess of the quantum over that required to pass the surface barrier. Since a quantum of light is indivisible an electron either absorbs a quantum or none at all, and hence if absorption occurs the electron may escape almost instantly.

Thus the quantum theory served to explain photoelectric emission, and also the phenomenon of photoemission is now seen to be one of the important experimental confirmations of the quantum theory and makes possible an experimental determination of the Planck constant (§5-5).

EXAMPLE   Find the lowest frequency of light (threshold frequency) which will just release electrons from a surface for which the photoelectric work function is 3.3 electron volts.

Required energy of quantum absorbed is

$$E_q = 3.3 \text{ eV} = 3.3 \times 1.6 \times 10^{-19} \text{ joule}$$
$$= 5.28 \times 10^{-19} \text{ joule}$$

but
$$E_q = h\nu$$
$$h = 6.62 \times 10^{-34} \text{ joule sec}$$
$$\nu = \frac{5.28 \times 10^{-19}}{6.62 \times 10^{-34}}$$
$$= 7.98 \times 10^{14} \text{ sec}^{-1}$$

For this example the frequency is just beyond the usual visual limit at the violet end of the visible spectrum. For some substances the threshold frequency is in the visible region or even in the infrared.

5-3. X-ray Production as Inverse Photoelectric Effect

In §4-3 the production of x-rays was described as the transformation of part or all of the kinetic energy of a moving electron into one (or more) x-ray quanta. It is worth noting that this process is almost the exact inverse of the photoelectric effect in which the quantum of absorbed radiant energy is transformed into kinetic energy of the photoelectron.

For instance, according to Eq. 4–2, the kinetic energy $\frac{1}{2}mv^2 = eV$ of an electron may be converted into an equal amount of energy $h\nu$ of a single quantum of radiant energy in an x-ray tube. On the other hand the energy $h\nu$ of a quantum of radiation may eject a photoelectron with a kinetic energy $\frac{1}{2}mv^2 = eV$ where V is the "stopping potential" (next section). When the energy w_0, lost by the photoelectron in crossing the surface of the emitter, is taken into consideration, the maximum energy of the photoelectron is equal to that of the absorbed quantum $h\nu$. In the first case the frequency of emitted radiation increases with the accelerating voltage. In the latter case the required stopping voltage increases with the frequency of absorbed radiation.

5-4. Measuring Energies of Photoelectrons

Since it has been observed that the maximum energies of emitted photoelectrons increase with increasing frequency of the incident light, it may be asked how these energies can be measured. In the simplest form of such an experiment a stopping electrode (Fig. 5-1) is placed near a photosensitive surface and is connected with a variable source of potential so that the electrode potential may be made increasingly negative with respect to the photosensitive surface. All electrodes should be of the same material to avoid *contact potentials*. The speeds that the electrons possess after emission enable them to travel to this electrode unless they are sufficiently repelled by the retarding field. If the electrode is made negative enough,

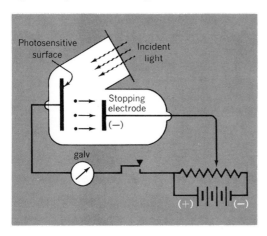

Fig. 5-1. Photoelectric tube with stopping electrode to measure energies of photoelectrons emitted by photosensitive surface.

photoelectrons of maximum speed will just fail to reach this electrode. Under this condition the opposing field has done an amount of work eV on the electron exactly equal to the kinetic energy of the electron and has brought it to rest just before reaching the stopping electrode. By the Einstein photoelectric equation

$$eV = \frac{1}{2} mv^2 = h\nu - w_0 \qquad [5\text{--}2]$$

5-5. Determination of the Planck Constant

If the maximum energies of photoelectrons from a given photosensitive surface are measured for different frequencies of light a graph such as that shown in Fig. 5-2 may be obtained in which stopping potentials are plotted against frequency. Setting the right-hand side of Eq. 5–2 equal to the energy eV and dividing both sides by e gives the result

$$V = \left(\frac{h}{e}\right)\nu - \frac{w_0}{e} \qquad [5\text{--}3]$$

This is the equation of a straight line in terms of V and ν, with h/e as the slope of the line and $-w_0/e$ as the intercept on the y axis in the figure.

From the slope of the experimental graph and the known charge e of the electron the value of h is readily obtained. The experiment, however, is by no means as simple as this description makes it seem. To secure correct values for h and w_0 and also for the threshold frequency of a given

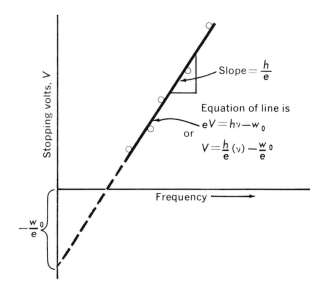

Fig. 5-2. A graph of experimental values obtained by an apparatus similar to that of Fig. 5-1 enables one to determine the Planck constant h.

metal, the surface of the metal should be perfectly clean. Such a clean surface may be approached but can hardly be attained. The very slightest contamination has been found to affect the results considerably. Millikan performed a noteworthy experiment in which he arranged to scrape the surface of the emitter inside a tube in which a very high vacuum was maintained. By this means he was able to make the first precise experimental determination of the value of the Planck constant h. Various experimenters by means of the best techniques have obtained good agreement for the value of h, but threshold frequencies are more difficult to achieve. Work functions for a pure metal are equally difficult to get with precision.

5-6. The Compton Effect; Photons

When A. H. Compton studied the scattering of x-rays by matter in 1921 he found that observed effects could be satisfactorily described only if the radiation was assumed to consist of individual quanta, each quantum possessing a definite amount of momentum just as a moving mechanical object does. He then found that when a quantum collides with a particle of matter the quantum itself behaves like a particle and transfers momentum to the particle hit, according to the fundamental laws of mechanics. To emphasize this particle-like character a quantum of radiation is called a *photon*.

Compton was studying the ways in which x-rays are scattered in various directions when a beam of x-rays falls upon a slab of some material such as carbon. It was well known that ordinary light is scattered in all directions by dust particles and small water droplets without appreciable change in wavelength. According to classical theory any loss of energy in the scattering process is at the expense of the amplitude of the incident wave. From this it might be expected that scattered x-rays would have the same wavelength (or frequency) as the rays of the incident beam. Compton did find such scattering, but he also detected a new and different kind of scattering in which the scattered x-rays were found to have a longer wavelength (lower frequency) than that possessed by the rays of the original beam.

This shift in wavelength, sometimes called the *Compton shift*, presented an obstacle to any simple explanation of the scattering on the basis of the classical wave theory of radiation. According to the classical theory any radiation absorbed by an electron in an atom would be reradiated with varying amplitudes in all directions without change in frequency. However, the possibility of a shift in frequency is implicit in the definition of the energy $E_q = h\nu$ of the quantum. Since h is constant any loss of energy can only be at the expense of the frequency ν. To compute the energy loss in the collision, Compton applied the familiar laws of collision of ordinary objects, and thus with the aid of the quantum concept he was able to obtain a simple explanation of the observed effect. Some of the electrons in a block of carbon are so loosely bound as to be considered free electrons. An x-ray quantum or photon striking one of these electrons bounces back from the collision much as if the collision had occurred between two perfectly elastic spheres. Although billiard balls are by no means perfectly elastic, collisions of billiard balls are familiar and well understood, and they represent many aspects of the collision between an x-ray quantum and an electron.

According to familiar mechanical principles, when two perfectly elastic smooth spheres, such as ideal billiard balls collide on a perfectly smooth surface both momentum and translational kinetic energy are conserved. Momentum and kinetic energy may be transferred from one billiard ball to the other, but the total momentum of the two balls after collision will be the same as the total momentum of the two balls before the collision. In the ideal case no energy will be lost in the form of heat, and the total kinetic energy of the balls after collision will be the same as the total kinetic energy before (Fig. 5-3). Compton suggested that exactly such a transfer of energy and momentum occurs in the collision between a photon and an electron. This suggestion violated classical wave theory and seemed radical at the time, but its experimental confirmation has now become one of the cornerstones of the modern quantum theory. Assuming that an x-ray photon of energy $h\nu$ loses energy in a collision, just as a particle would, it is evident that it must suffer a decrease in frequency (increase in wavelength) as in Fig. 5-3. Since the speed of the photon must remain constant Compton found that, with the aid of this assumption plus the laws of conservation of energy and momentum, he could describe exactly the observed wavelength shift of the scattered x-rays no matter at what angle the collision took place.

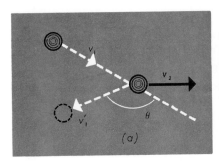 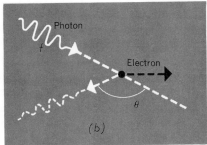

Fig. 5-3.   a, Ideal billiard ball recoils from collision with change in velocity; b, photon recoils from collision with electron with change in frequency. θ is the angle of scattering.

Consider the simplest possible collision, a head-on collision in which the photon bounces directly back from the electron, exactly reversing its path. In addition to the classical laws of conservation of energy and momentum two other basic relations are involved.

1. By the Planck hypothesis the energy E_q of a quantum is

$$E_q = h\nu \qquad [5\text{--}4]$$

2. From classical electromagnetic theory it had been known that radiation could exert a pressure and could be thought of as possessing momentum p represented by

$$p = \frac{E}{c} \qquad [5\text{--}5]$$

where E is the energy of the radiation and c is the velocity of light. This equation implies that if the energy of a photon is $h\nu$ it should possess momentum p where

$$p = \frac{h\nu}{c} = \frac{h}{\lambda} \qquad [5\text{--}6]$$

and where λ is c/ν. Applying the law of conservation of energy

$$\begin{pmatrix} \text{Energy of} \\ \text{incident photon} \end{pmatrix} = \begin{pmatrix} \text{Energy of} \\ \text{scattered photon} \end{pmatrix} + \begin{pmatrix} \text{Energy given} \\ \text{to electron} \end{pmatrix}$$

$$h\nu = h\nu' + \frac{1}{2}mv^2 \qquad [5\text{--}7]$$

where ν' is the new and lower frequency of the scattered photon. Applying the law of conservation of momentum

$$\left(\begin{array}{c}\text{Momentum of} \\ \text{incident photon}\end{array}\right) = \left(\begin{array}{c}\text{Momentum of} \\ \text{scattered photon}\end{array}\right) + \left(\begin{array}{c}\text{Momentum given} \\ \text{to electron}\end{array}\right)$$

$$\frac{h}{\lambda} = \frac{-h}{\lambda'} + mv \qquad\qquad [5\text{--}8]$$

where λ' is the wavelength of the scattered photon corresponding to its frequency ν' and the sign of the momentum associated with the momentum of the scattered photon is negative because the direction is reversed. Equation 5–7 expresses the fact that when, at the time of collision, the incident photon of energy $h\nu$ transfers kinetic energy $\frac{1}{2}mv^2$ to the electron, the resulting energy of the photon becomes $h\nu'$ where $h\nu' = h\nu - \frac{1}{2}mv^2$. Equation 5–8 represents a similar transfer of momentum and may be written

$$\frac{h}{\lambda} + \frac{h}{\lambda'} = mv = \frac{2h}{\lambda} \text{ (approximately)} \qquad\qquad [5\text{--}9]$$

since for a small change in wavelength the product $\lambda\lambda'$ is approximately equal to λ^2 and $\lambda + \lambda'$ is approximately 2λ. Now by squaring Eq. 5–9 and eliminating mv^2 between it and Eq. 5–7 there results

$$\nu - \nu' = \frac{2h}{m\lambda^2} \qquad\qquad [5\text{--}10]$$

This gives the frequency shift or difference in frequency between the incident and scattered photons. To convert this to a change in wavelength, divide both sides of the equation by c, the velocity of light, and substitute $1/\lambda$ for ν/c. This gives

$$\lambda' - \lambda = \frac{2h}{mc} = 0.048 \times 10^{-8} \text{ cm} = 0.048 \text{ Å} \qquad\qquad [5\text{--}11]$$

This is the change in wavelength (Compton shift) for direct rebound of the photon. It can be shown (see end of section) that for Compton scattering at any angle θ (Fig. 5–3b), with respect to the direction of the incident photon,

$$\lambda' - \lambda = \frac{h}{mc}(1 - \cos\theta) \qquad\qquad [5\text{--}12]$$

$$= 0.024\,(1 - \cos\theta) \text{ Å} \qquad\qquad [5\text{--}12a]$$

The quantity h/mc in Eq. 5–12 has the dimensions of a length and when written h/m_0c where m_0 is the rest mass it is called the *Compton wavelength*. It is the wavelength of a gamma ray having the same energy as the rest-mass energy of the particle, in this case an electron.

With ordinary light these shifts would be too small to be detectable, but with x-rays the frequency is so high that each photon possesses sufficient energy and momentum to produce a shift which can be measured with a good x-ray crystal spectrometer. At very high energies, however, the simple mathematical treatment must be modified by relativistic corrections.

When the experiment is performed, scattered photons that have not undergone change in frequency and wavelength are also detected and present a problem. It is well known that a small object in elastic collision with a more massive object or with an object that is held in position does not lose appreciable energy by transfer to the second object. Since many electrons in a block of carbon are more firmly bound to the parent atom, photons in collision with them lose little energy, and thus the scattering occurs with no appreciable shift in wavelength.

That an electron in free space cannot absorb all the energy of a quantum is evident from consideration of the conservation of energy and momentum. A photon has an energy $h\nu$ and this would give the electron an energy $\frac{1}{2}mv^2$

$$h\nu = \frac{1}{2}mv^2 \qquad [5\text{--}13]$$

But the photon has momentum $h/\lambda = h\nu/c$ and this would give the electron momentum

$$\frac{h\nu}{c} = mv \qquad [5\text{--}14]$$

Eliminating $h\nu$ between these two equations we find the velocity of the electron comes out to be

$$v = 2c$$

which is impossible according to relativity (next chapter).

Compton's measurements confirmed his hypothesis completely. Nevertheless, with characteristic scientific thoroughness he made additional measurements with a cloud chamber in which the directions of the recoil electrons were observed and measured directly.

For a more general description of the Compton effect, assume that a photon hits an electron in a glancing collision (Fig. 5-4) such that the photon is scattered at an angle θ from its original direction and the electron e rebounds at an angle φ. As before by the law of conservation of energy, and writing hc/λ for $h\nu$ in Eq. 5–7, we have

$$\frac{hc}{\lambda} - \frac{hc}{\lambda'} = \frac{1}{2}mv^2 \qquad [5\text{--}15]$$

Momentum will now be conserved not only in the initial direction of motion of the photon but also at right angles to this direction in the plane of the three vectors.

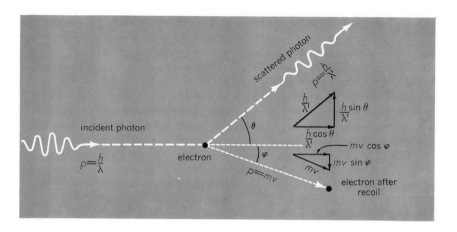

Fig. 5-4. Diagram for more general theory of Compton scattering at any angle θ.

From the figure it is evident that for conservation of momentum in the initial direction of the photon

$$\frac{h}{\lambda} - \frac{h}{\lambda'} \cos \theta = mv \cos \varphi \qquad [5\text{-}16]$$

and in a direction at right angles to this

$$\frac{h}{\lambda'} \sin \theta = mv \sin \varphi \qquad [5\text{-}17]$$

We now need to eliminate φ and v from the three equations 5–15, 5–16 and 5–17. One way of doing this is by squaring Eqs. 5–16 and 5–17 and adding them. This gives

$$\frac{h^2}{\lambda^2} - \frac{2h^2}{\lambda\lambda'} \cos \theta + \frac{h^2}{(\lambda')^2} = m^2v^2 \qquad [5\text{-}18]$$

If we square Eq. 5–15

$$\frac{h^2c^2}{\lambda^2} - \frac{2h^2c^2}{\lambda\lambda'} + \frac{h^2c^2}{(\lambda')^2} = \frac{1}{4} m^2v^4$$

which may be rearranged to give

$$\frac{h^2}{\lambda^2} - \frac{2h^2}{\lambda\lambda'} + \frac{h^2}{(\lambda')^2} = m^2v^2 \left(\frac{v^2}{4c^2}\right) \qquad [5\text{-}19]$$

Subtracting Eq. 5–18 from Eq. 5–19

$$\frac{h^2}{\lambda\lambda'} (1 - \cos \theta) = \frac{1}{2} m^2v^2 \left(1 - \frac{v^2}{4c^2}\right)$$

Substituting the value of $\frac{1}{2}mv^2$ from Eq. 5–15, the right-hand side becomes

$$= hc\left(\frac{1}{\lambda} - \frac{1}{\lambda'}\right)\left(1 - \frac{v^2}{4c^2}\right) \qquad [5\text{–}20]$$

This is readily solved for the shift in wavelength $\Delta\lambda = \lambda' - \lambda$. In the non-relativistic case where v/c is small enough to be neglected

$$\Delta\lambda = \lambda' - \lambda = \frac{h}{mc}(1 - \cos\theta)$$

which is Eq. 5–12.

5-7. The de Broglie Hypothesis

The particle-like behavior of radiant energy under such conditions as given in the preceding section raised a question in the mind of Louis de Broglie in France. If waves might sometimes act as particles, perhaps particles might sometimes act as waves. This thought did not come entirely from a clear sky. De Broglie derived it in 1922 from an analysis of the requirements of the theory of relativity, combined with Planck's idea of the quantum of energy $h\nu$. In Eq. 5–6, where p, the momentum of the photon, is found to be h/λ, a possible duality of particles and waves appears. If for the momentum p of the photon there is substituted the momentum mv of a particle of mass m and velocity v

$$p = mv = \frac{h}{\lambda} \qquad [5\text{–}21]$$

and

$$\lambda = \frac{h}{mv} = \frac{h}{p} \qquad [5\text{–}21a]$$

The wavelength λ may then be considered the equivalent wavelength of a particle of momentum mv.

This is the now famous de Broglie wavelength equation, which not only implies that a particle may exhibit a wave-like character but that the equivalent wavelength is dependent upon h, the basic constant of the quantum theory, and that it is inversely proportional to the momentum p of the particle.

5-8. Electron Diffraction

Three years after the suggestion by de Broglie that electrons might sometimes act as waves, experimental confirmation was obtained first by Davisson and Germer in this country (1925), and shortly after by G. P. Thomson in England, son of J. J. Thomson. Davisson and Germer used electrons accelerated by only a few volts, since according to the de Broglie formula they would then have wavelengths approximating those of ordinary x-rays. The electron beam was directed toward the face of a single crystal of pure nickel. The experimenters found that electrons were most strongly reflected at a certain favored angle (Fig. 5-5). This angle corresponded almost exactly to the angle which would have been observed for reinforcement of x-rays of the same wavelength as that of the electrons given by the de Broglie formula.

The observed peak of the curve was superposed upon a background of electrons found at different angles which were largely identified as *secondary electrons* knocked out of the nickel by the primary beam. Also some of the broadening of the observed peak was explained by change of wavelength (refraction) of electron waves inside the crystal.

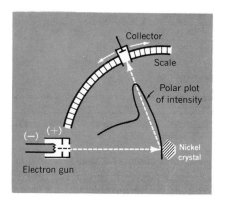

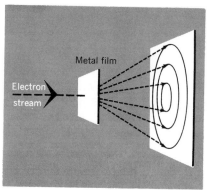

Fig. 5-5　In the Davisson and Germer experiment electrons of a particular speed were reflected from a certain plane in a nickel crystal, giving a maximum at that angle for which the de Broglie wavelength would give reinforcement.

Fig. 5-6.　Method by which G. P. Thomson obtained electron diffraction. Owing to the random orientation of the small crystals, or fragments, of which the metal film is composed the regions of reinforcement become circles.

G. P. Thomson applied electrons of higher speed in an experiment similar to the x-ray experiment of von Laue. Instead of passing a narrow beam of x-rays through a crystal as von Laue did, Thomson passed a narrow beam of electrons through a metal film (Fig. 5-6), but in order to get penetration he had to use a quite thin film. Since even the thin film of metal contains many small broken crystals in all possible orientations the pattern obtained consists of circles instead of spots. These circles are similar to those obtained by the x-ray powder diffraction process. Indeed, the diffraction pattern produced by electrons passing through a thin metal film may be so similar to the diffraction of a beam of x-rays as to appear indistinguishable (Fig. 5-7). Actually the patterns can be distinguished experimentally in a simple manner. The application of an electric or magnetic field to the rays will shift the electron diffraction pattern but not the x-ray pattern.

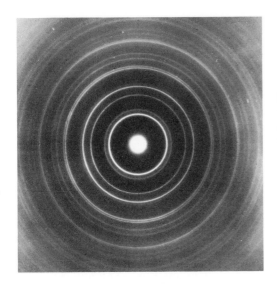

Fig. 5-7. Diffraction rings formed by passing narrow beam of electrons through thin silver foil, following the method of G. P. Thomson. (Courtesy, L. H. Germer, Bell Telephone Laboratories.)

The preceding experiments afford striking confirmation of de Broglie's suggestion; indeed, further experiments have revealed the wave-like properties of protons, neutrons (§16-4) and other atomic or subatomic particles. Because de Broglie waves now represent a fundamental mode of description of finely divided matter they are often called by the somewhat contradictory name *matter waves*.

5-9. The Correspondence Principle

That the de Broglie equation would lose its customary significance if applied to large objects such as those of everyday life is fairly evident. Since the objects would be relatively enormous and the wavelengths would be almost vanishingly small, diffraction experiments would be impossible. In the quantum mechanical treatment of large-scale phenomena quantum effects become "smoothed out" and gradually merge into those of classical mechanics. This is an expression of the Bohr *correspondence principle*.

In the early days of these theories it appeared that whereas the realm of everyday phenomena was governed by classical laws the realm of atomic phenomena was governed by an entirely different set of laws deriving from the wave character of particles and commonly represented by what is called *wave mechanics* which is one form of *quantum mechanics*. In proposing the correspondence principle Bohr concluded that where these realms overlap the theories if correct should gradually merge into each other. For instance in the case of the Compton effect, if the incident radiation were to have a very long wavelength the fractional change in wavelength $\Delta\lambda/\lambda$ would be so very small as to be indetectable. Consequently as far as measurements would indicate, the wavelengths of Compton scattered radiation and the wavelength for classical scattering would be indistinguishable and either theory would give the right answer as nearly as can be told.

Another important example of the principle of correspondence will be given when we study the radiation of light by a hydrogen atom (§7-8). Still others will suggest themselves. At present quantum-mechanical theory is required in the atomic realm and according to the correspondence principle it should lead to classical results for large-scale events. This makes it appear to be more fundamental and more inclusive than classical theory, however, the application of classical theory is far simpler and more direct in the everyday world.

5-10. Waves and Particles; Complementarity

The Compton effect and the nature of photoelectric emission clearly indicate the particle-like behavior of light quanta (photons). Similarly the experiments of Davisson and Germer and of G. P. Thomson clearly indicate the wave-like behavior of electrons. If wave and particle concepts are both used in the description of photons and electrons it might at first seem that all sharpness of distinction between waves and particles had been lost. This is by no means true. Photons travel through empty space at the speed of light and the speed is not known to be affected by collisions with other photons. Particles, on the other hand, such as electrons, can never travel as fast as the speed of light in empty space and can only approach that speed. Moreover, the velocity of such particles is affected by collisions with other particles.

It is further true that, as far as any detecting device is concerned, electrons do not act as both particles and waves at the same time. Neither do photons act simultaneously as waves and particles. Under one set of circumstances the experimental arrangement may reveal the particle-like character of radiation, but a different experimental arrangement may reveal the wave-like character. The same is true of electrons. We must remember these fundamental distinctions between radiant energy and matter, and we may help preserve these distinctions by being careful to say that radiant energy *may* exhibit particle-like characteristics and that electrons and other particles *may* exhibit wave-like characteristics. Thus we avoid the logical contradiction of saying that an electron is both a particle and a wave and that a photon is also both a wave and a particle.

Resolution of the apparent particle-wave difficulty has been carried further by a statement of Niels Bohr, called the *principle of complementarity*. This statement asserts that wave and particle aspects in the atomic world are not so much contradictory as they are complementary. This implies that we have reached a limit in attempting to give a complete description of the elements of either matter or radiation by means of a single word. The terms *wave* and *particle*, borrowed from everyday life, cannot be applied in the atomic realm with such assurance and mutual exclusion as in the realm of everyday affairs. To adequately describe phenomena involving photons and electrons and other elementary particles we must resort to both concepts of wave and particle in a complementary manner, not in a contradictory manner, and each mode of description has its sphere of usefulness. This indicates that atomic phenomena are not simple but complex. However, as we probe deeper into the atomic and subatomic realms we come to recognize the limitations of the particle concept and the greater generality and applicability of the wave concept, and we are thus forced to give up deterministic physics for statistical methods.

Complementary descriptions of phenomena are not unknown in classical physics. In optics, for instance, we may solve problems by using the wave concept as in applications of Huygens' principle. On the other hand we may treat light as if it travels in straight lines called *rays* implying that it travels in much the same manner that a stream of free particles would. The basic phenomena of reflection and refraction may be solved by either method but we do not combine the two methods at any one time. After the experiments of Young and Fresnel on the diffraction of light the wave theory was found to be capable of describing a wider range of phenomena and so was accepted as the more general theory. Indeed the particle description apparently failed completely to explain diffraction. Even Newton who had tried with some difficulty to formulate a crude particle theory of light admitted that if such phenomena as diffraction were ever observed his particle theory must be given up in favor of the wave theory which had already been suggested by Huygens.

For instance, suppose monochromatic light is allowed to pass through a slit and fall upon a screen as in Fig. 5-8. In the figure at a the slit is very wide compared to λ the wavelength. The pattern of light on the screen shows no easily observable diffraction effects and can be adequately described by ray optics (particle optics) which implies that light travels in straight lines just as a stream of free particles would. As a matter of fact, wave optics though more complicated would lead to the same result. In Fig. 5-8b where the slit is much narrower but larger than λ, ray optics would give an approximate result whereas wave theory could explain why there is seen to be a slight spreading of light into the shadow and why very faint dark bands occur near the edge of the illuminated region. However at c where the slit width is nearly equal to λ the simple deterministic ray method fails completely to describe the light pattern and only the wave method can determine with precision the central bright band with the fainter alternately dark and light bands on either side extending far into the region of shadow.

We now ask if it is possible to describe any aspect of the phenomena of diffraction by means of the particle or photon picture of radiation and quantum-mechanical methods? The answer is *yes*, if we are willing to make additional assumptions and give up the direct relations of cause and effect to which we have long been accustomed. We must then substitute the concept of probability for rigid deterministic law as was first done in kinetic

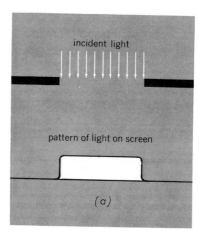

Fig. 5-8. The diffraction effects obtained when light passes through a slit depend on the width of the slit. With a wide slit as at a, the diffraction effects are in general not readily observed. At b the slit is much narrower and at c is of the order of the wavelength of light.

theory in the last century in the study of gases (§11-3). Let us now see how we may apply probability methods to the interpretation of diffraction experiments in optics assuming that a beam of light consists of a stream of photons.

In the early wave theory of light the intensity of light in the light and dark bands of an interference pattern was given by the square of the amplitude of the wave motion assumed to exist in an unknown mechanical medium called the *ether*. After light was shown to be electromagnetic the wave was assumed to occur in a new medium the *electromagnetic ether* but the exact action was still unknown. Today we speak of electromagnetic waves being transmitted by *empty space* and we do not know quite what we mean by "empty space." But we do know that we can compute the energy of the light received at any point on a screen in terms of the square of the intensity of the electric field (or of the magnetic field).

If we define the intensity of the radiation as the energy received per unit area per unit time, then the intensity I in joules per second per square meter is

$$I = \epsilon_0 \mathcal{E}^2 c \qquad [5\text{–}22]$$

where $\mathcal{E}$ is the electric field intensity in volts per meter, c is the velocity of light and $\epsilon_0 = 8.85 \times 10^{-12}$ is the required constant in the mks system (the *permittivity of free space*, §2-1).

We may also, however, equally well describe the overall intensity of the light in terms of photons. If N photons fall on unit area per unit time and if the quantized energy per photon is $h\nu$, then the intensity I of the light is

$$I = (h\nu)N \qquad [5\text{--}23]$$

In mks units this would be in joules per sec per square meter.

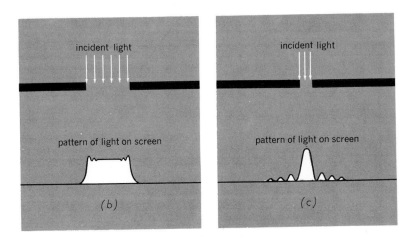

Setting Eqs. 5–22 and 5–23 equal to each other we have

$$(h\nu)N = \epsilon_0 \mathcal{E}^2 c$$

or

$$N = \frac{\epsilon_0 \mathcal{E}^2 c}{h\nu} = \frac{\epsilon_0 \mathcal{E}^2}{h} \lambda \qquad [5\text{--}24]$$

From this we conclude that the intensity of the photon stream is proportional to the square of the intensity of the electric field. But since the equation does not give us the slightest information as to where any particular photon will strike the screen we conclude that $\mathcal{E}^2$ measures only the *probability* that N photons per second per unit area will strike a given area in a given time and there is no deterministic method by which a single photon can be precisely located.

We now wish to show that modern wave mechanics pursues a similar method in locating the position of an electron in terms of de Broglie waves. If we forget the origin of the concept of electric field intensity $\mathcal{E}$ we can define $\mathcal{E}$ in the example of diffraction just given as *the wave amplitude the square of which gives the probability of locating one or more photons in a particular region*. Since the de Broglie wave equation, $\lambda = h/p$, gives only the wavelength of a particle in terms of its momentum and the Planck constant, it says nothing about the location of the particle. Indeed it says nothing about the amplitude of the wave representing the particle. It therefore became desirable to assign an amplitude ψ to the wave and it is this amplitude which if squared measures the probability of locating the particle in a given region. Thus we find that in the atomic realm strictly causal (deterministic) methods cannot be applied and statistical or probability methods must be resorted to. This is the basis of modern wave mechanics more about which will be given in the next section.

It should be remarked that there is a fundamental difference between the statistical treatment of gas molecules in kinetic theory and the statistical treatment of electrons by wave-mechanical methods. The obstacle of large numbers alone does not preclude the possibility in theory at least of treating gas molecules by deterministic methods, but in quantum mechanics a similar treatment of the electron is impossible in theory as will be shown in what follows.

5-11. Wave Mechanics

The wave description of the electron had its first successes, as previously mentioned, in predicting the observed distributions of electrons reflected from a crystal (or scattered by passing through thin films). Today the concept forms the basis of the far more general and complete quantum mechanical theory the common form of which is known as *wave mechanics*.

The fundamental relations of quantum mechanics were established by Heisenberg (1925) (using the methods of matrix algebra) and by Schrödinger (1926) who gave them in the form known as the *Schrödinger wave equation*. This is a differential equation and, in its simplest form for a particle in one dimensional space with no time dependent term, is

$$\frac{d^2\psi}{dx^2} + \frac{8\pi^2 m}{h^2}(E - V)\psi = 0 \qquad [5\text{–}25]$$

where E is the total energy of a particle of mass m such as an electron, V is its potential energy, and h is the Planck constant. The quantity ψ is the amplitude function the variation of which constitutes the wave.

Just as the amplitude function in the development of the wave theory of light went through various interpretations from the elastic solid theory to the electromagnetic and quantum theories so has the quantity ψ, which we now call simply the *wave function*, taken on new significance. The crowning achievement in its interpretation was the recognition by Born in 1926 that ψ^2 like $\mathcal{E}^2$ in Eq. 5–22 could represent a probability function. Whereas $\mathcal{E}^2$ could be interpreted to give the probabilities of the photon distribution in diffraction, so also could ψ^2 be interpreted to give the probabilities of an electron distribution in a variety of problems. The way this can be done and the more complete interpretation of ψ and ψ^2 will form the subject of Chapter 8.

A note of caution may be sounded here. Analogies must never be pushed too far. Although $\mathscr{E}$ represents a force field that can often be measured directly, ψ does not represent such a field. On the other hand although ψ does not represent anything observable or measurable and actually drops out of the final results, it does provide the only means we have of obtaining information concerning such "observables" as energies and momenta in an assemblage of particles. Furthermore classical field theory is helpless in dealing with strictly quantum effects.

If the student's mathematical background has not prepared him to deal with the Schrödinger equation, some or all of Chap. 8 may be omitted but he can at least become familiar with the equation and there is much that he can understand of its physical significance.

5-12. The Heisenberg Principle of Indeterminacy

The duality of the wave and particle concepts has been given a more quantitative meaning by Heisenberg in what is called the principle of indeterminacy. Heisenberg, formulating it, called it the principle of "Unbestimmtheit." This word has also been translated as "indefiniteness" and "uncertainty." Neither name expresses the complementary nature of the quantities involved, and although the word *uncertainty* is commonly used it has objectionable connotations. The principle expresses a fundamental limitation inherent in the nature of things. In dealing with ordinary mechanical phenomena we can determine both the velocity (or momentum) of an object and its position at any instant by making two successive measurements of time at different positions. Any disturbance of an ordinary object by the act of measuring it is inappreciable, but in the atomic realm the very act of measuring the momentum of an electron disturbs the position, and vice versa.

Heisenberg's principle states that in the atomic realm it is impossible to simultaneously measure both position and momentum with equally high precision. There is no "uncertainty" about individual measurements. It is possible to measure either momentum or position with any desired degree of precision within the limits of experimental equipment, but in general an attempt at exact measurement of one quantity destroys the possibility of an exact measure of the other. The more precisely the momentum is measured the less precisely can the position be measured, and, conversely, the more precisely the position is measured the less precisely can the momentum be measured.

Heisenberg determined from basic theory that the product of the indeterminacy Δx of the position of a particle by the indeterminacy Δp in the measurement of its momentum will be of the order of magnitude of $h/2\pi$ where h is the Planck constant.

$$\Delta x\, \Delta p \geq \frac{h}{2\pi} = \hbar \qquad [5\text{--}26]$$

Since the product is equal to a constant, increase in determinateness of one of the factors means decrease in the determinateness of the other.

Interesting examples of the necessity for accepting Heisenberg's principle in the atomic realm were given by Heisenberg himself. With very sensitive apparatus we could perform the following experiment and measure the velocity (or momentum) of an electron by timing its flight between two points. The electron could presumably be located at these points by two extremely sensitive microscopes (Fig. 5-9). The minimum amount of light that could be reflected from an electron would, of course, be one photon. From the small quantities involved it may be seen that this is an idealized experiment, not one which could actually be realized. By referring to the figure it is seen that an electron moving along the line AB could have a photon of light reflected from it into the microscope M_1, by which it is

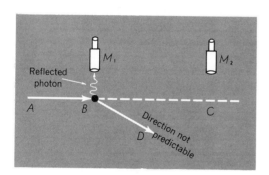

Fig. 5-9. Hypothetical experiment to measure electron velocity between **B** and **C**. Recoil of electron from photon collision at **B** sends it off in an unpredictable direction and prevents the measurement at **C** from being made.

detected at position B. If the time of observation were noted and if the time of observation at a second position C by means of microscope M_2 could be noted, the velocity of the electron could be obtained. However, we know from Compton's experiment that the photon reflected into the microscope at B in its collision with the electron gives the electron momentum and diverts it in some unpredictable direction D from its original path. The location of the electron at position C by the microscope M_2 is thereby defeated, and the velocity measurement becomes indeterminate. In this experiment the precise location of the electron at point B prevents the making of a precise measurement of the velocity (or momentum).

Let us try again by another method. We may locate the position of the electron by observing the point at which it strikes a fluorescent screen. The tiny flash of light given by the screen may with considerable precision locate the position of the electron but only at the expense of knowledge of its velocity (or momentum). When the electron strikes the screen and produces a scintillation it either loses its velocity completely or has its velocity greatly changed in a way that cannot be directly measured. Thus again, in localizing the position of the electron, we sacrifice the capacity to measure its velocity or momentum.

From the converse viewpoint an attempt to measure the velocity of the electron can only be made at the expense of an attempt to locate its position accurately. Take, for instance, the determination of the velocity of an electron by deflecting it in a uniform magnetic field. From the radius of path and the strength of magnetic field, together with the value of e/m, the velocity can be determined with precision, but the location of the electron in its path is now indeterminate.

It is evident that this kind of uncertainty has nothing to do with the uncertainty always present in the measurement of any physical quantity because of experimental limitations. This uncertainty is a quantum phenomenon belonging to the realm of microphysics and it applies only to a few *conjugate pairs* of quantities in which measurement of one quantity affects the capacity to measure the other. It can be shown, for instance, that energy E and time t are such a pair and that

$$\Delta t \, \Delta E \geq \frac{h}{2\pi} = \hbar \qquad \text{[5–26a]}$$

The effect on the width of spectral lines is given in Section 8-7 (see problem 8-15).

The Heisenberg principle marks the breakdown of classical determinism in the atomic realm but it does not mean that science has given up *causality* in the larger sense, involving as it does the reproducibility of phenomena (*uniformity of nature*) without which no science would be possible. When strictly deterministic methods applied to individual particles fail, science falls back on the statistics of large groups and applies other causal principles to predict the probabilities involved. So long as we rely on light quanta for observation there must always be a complementary relation between experimental measurements of position and momentum. This complementarity is more fully displayed in attempts to represent both the position and the momentum of the electron simultaneously by the wave picture.

5-13. Wave Description of the Electron in Free Space

Let us first approach the description of the electron from the wave viewpoint in an elementary manner. For an electron traveling with a definite velocity the de Broglie equation gives a sharply defined wavelength $\lambda = h/mv$. For a wave train to represent a sharply defined wavelength, that is, to be a truly "monochromatic" wave, it must be infinite in extent. Consequently when the velocity of an electron is precisely described by an infinite wave train, as in Fig. 5-10a, the possibility of locating the electron has been lost.

On the other hand, if we desire to locate the electron more definitely we can represent it by means of a shorter wave train or wave group. It is a common phenomenon of wave motion, readily observed when a pebble is dropped into water, that a series of ripples travels outward. This series of ripples is not a single wave train of infinite length but is called a *wave group* or packet. The amplitude rises to a maximum in the middle, as shown in Fig. 5-10b, and decreases to zero in a finite region. The Fourier analysis of such a wave group shows it to be the summation of a set of different infinite wave trains, each having a different frequency or wavelength and consequently each representing a different velocity. These component wave trains add together constructively to give the wave group as indicated but at all other points add up destructively to zero. The shorter the wave group is, the larger will be the number of component wave trains and the wider will be the spread of velocities represented.

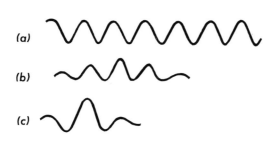

(a)

(b)

(c)

Fig. 5-10. a, An infinite train of de Broglie waves represents the velocity of an electron exactly, but its position is then completely indeterminate; b, a wave packet represents the position of an electron more definitely, but the velocity is then less sharply defined; c, a shorter wave packet increases the precision of location of position but decreases the definiteness in velocity.

If we now seek to represent an electron by a wave group, we can increase the precision of locating the electron in the region occupied by the wave group by choosing a shorter group. However, the shorter the group is, as in Fig. 5-10c, the larger is the range of wavelengths involved, and by the de Broglie formula the larger is the range of velocities involved. Thus in making the location of position more precise the velocity becomes less precise, and vice versa, and the wave description of the particle has led us directly to the complementary relation of the wave and particle descriptions.

To obtain the velocity of a component de Broglie wave we may multiply the wavelength by the frequency. The wavelength is (by Eq. 5–21)

$$\lambda = \frac{h}{mv}$$

To get the frequency we consider the usual quantum relation where the energy E of the quantum equals $h\nu$. To represent the equivalent energy of an electron of mass m we borrow the energy-mass relation, $E = mc^2$, from the theory of relativity (§6-9). Then

$$\nu = \frac{E}{h} = \frac{mc^2}{h} \qquad [5\text{--}27]$$

and the velocity u of the "monochromatic" de Broglie wave is

$$u = \lambda\nu = \left(\frac{h}{mv}\right)\left(\frac{mc^2}{h}\right) \qquad [5\text{--}28]$$

and

$$u = \frac{c^2}{v} \qquad [5\text{--}29]$$

This presents a surprising answer. If the electron travels with a speed v less than c, the speed of light, as any material particle must do, then the speed u of the de Broglie wave by which the electron is described must be greater than the speed of light. According to this result it would seem that the de Broglie wave train representing the electron would travel faster than the electron and would leave it far behind. At this point the wave description again appears somewhat unsatisfactory, and the waves evidently cannot be physical waves in real space since a speed greater than that of light would violate a basic principle of the theory of relativity (Chap. 6). They must then be only mathematical waves in some kind of mathematical space.

However, the wave picture is greatly improved by using the idea of a wave group instead of a single de Broglie wave train. It is well known that the velocity of a wave group (group velocity) may be entirely different from the velocity of the component waves making up the group, and the group velocity may be much less than the phase velocity of the components. The way in which the phase waves in water travel faster than the group and seem to move through the group can be seen by anybody observing closely. Such a wave group, with a velocity different from the component waves, can only be formed when the component waves of the group themselves have different velocities, that is, when the waves occur in a dispersive medium. This is true for waves in water, but light waves in empty space all travel with the same velocity and cannot form a group which travels at a different velocity. In air, light waves can form such a group, and though the effect is small it must often be taken into consideration in measurements of the velocity of light.

The way in which the group velocity is affected by the dispersive qualities of the medium is well known and is given by the equation

$$v(\text{group}) = u - \lambda \frac{du}{d\lambda}$$ [5-30]

where u is the velocity of the individual waves in the group. If there is no dispersion $du/d\lambda = 0$ and $v = u$; that is, the group and individual wave velocities or *phase velocities* are the same.

The new description of the electron in terms of a wave group, chosen to have its group velocity the same as the velocity of the electron, now much better represents the complementary character of its wave and particle aspects. Furthermore, the student is perhaps comforted to have the wave and particle aspects of the electron travel together at the same speed even though the waves travel as if in a dispersive medium.

5-14. Resolving Power of Electron Microscope

The subject of electron optics is chiefly concerned with the formation of images by electron beams. When diffraction effects are negligible the particle picture is satisfactory, but frequently in electron optics the wave picture is required to give more complete information. For instance, the limit of useful operation of any optical device is given in terms of its resolving power, and this depends upon the wavelength involved.

The nonrelativistic formula for the de Broglie wavelength (Eq. 5–21) of an electron accelerated by a potential of V volts is

$$\lambda = \frac{12.3}{\sqrt{V}} 10^{-8} \text{ cm} = \frac{12.3}{\sqrt{V}} \text{ Å}$$ [5-31]

For a 50,000-volt electron $\lambda = 0.055$ Å, and if the relativistic correction is made it will be a few per cent less than this. The customary formula for the resolving power of a light microscope is

$$d = \frac{0.61 \lambda}{\sin \alpha}$$ [5-32]

where d is the least distance between two points that can be resolved and α is half the angle at the object subtended by the objective lens. Applying this formula to the electron microscope the limit of its resolving power should be nearly 100,000 times better than that of the best optical microscope, since the de Broglie wavelength just stated is approximately 1/100,-000 that of visible light. If this upper limit to the resolution were possible, objects far smaller in size than atoms could be seen. Unfortunately the magnetic and electric lenses of an electron microscope have inherent limitations and cannot be shaped anywhere nearly so accurately as optical lenses.

Consequently electron beams may only be permitted to diverge through angles a hundredth or less of those for light beams. This reduction in α decreases the practical upper limit of resolving power proportionately, but even this limit has not been reached, and the best to be expected at present is something like a thousandth of the ideal limit or a hundred times better than an optical microscope. This would mean magnifications of 200,000 diameters, and since an optical microscope may be able to resolve an object of 1000 Å (10^5 cm) diameter an electron microscope would then have a resolving power of about 10 Å, and very large molecules would be within its range. Some of these have already been observed.

Problems

1. A faint star is just visible if 2000 photons/sec enter the eye. What energy per second in watts does this represent in terms of sodium light? ($\lambda = 5890$ Å.)

2. For a particular surface the threshold frequency of incident radiation for photoelectric emission is 6×10^{14} sec^{-1}. What is the work function of the surface in joules and eV?

3. Light from the strong line in the ultraviolet of a mercury arc has a wavelength of 2537 Å (0.00002537 cm). With what maximum kinetic energy will this light emit photoelectrons from a clean sodium surface? (Refer to Table 5-1.)

4. What is the maximum speed of photoelectrons ejected from a surface by light of frequency 8×10^{14} sec^{-1} if the work function of the surface is 2 electron volts? What is the threshold frequency?

5. The stopping voltage for the fastest photoelectrons emitted by a tantalum surface is 1.6 volts. What was the frequency of the absorbed light? In what region of the spectrum would this frequency occur? (Refer to Table 5-1.)

6. What stopping voltage is required for photoelectrons from a surface having a work function of 3.6 electron volts if the electrons are produced by absorption of light having three times the frequency of the D line ($\lambda = 5890$ Å) of sodium light?

*7. Light from a source falls on a clean zinc surface. If 95 per cent of the light is reflected and if only 5 per cent of the incident light has a frequency above the threshold for photoelectric emission, what maximum number of photoelectrons could be emitted per second per cm^2? Assume the amount of radiant energy falling on the surface per cm^2 is 10^{-6} joule/sec. Why is your answer too large?

8. Compute the Planck constant h from the following data obtained from an experiment on photoelectric emission from the surface of potassium. When irradiated with wavelengths of 5896 Å, the maximum required stopping potential for the emitted electrons was 0.361 volt, and when irradiated by wavelengths of 2537 Å from a mercury arc, the maximum stopping potential was 3.13 volts.

9. Using data of the previous problem, find the work function of potassium and the threshold frequency for photoelectric emission.

10. Would it be possible for a photon to eject a photoelectron from a photoelectric surface with a speed of 0.9c? What wavelength would be required? Use relativistic energy.

11. Demonstrate that when a photon ejects a photoelectron from the surface of a metal, if energy and momentum are conserved, the energy of recoil of the target is negligible. In other words practically all of the energy of the photon is available to eject an electron.

12. A beam of 10^6 photons of wavelength 5890 Å is incident upon a surface in 10^{-3} sec and is totally reflected. How many photons of wavelength 2537 Å would be required in the beam to exert the same radiation pressure?

13. Compute the energy in joules and in eV of one photon of electromagnetic radiation at the radio-frequency of 10^6 cycles/sec. Why are quantum effects not noticed with radio waves?

14. Find the nonrelativistic de Broglie wavelength for an electron of 100,000-eV energy. Find the relativistic wavelength.

15. Find the de Broglie wavelength (nonrelativistic) for a proton after being accelerated by passing through a region where there is a difference of potential of 100 volts.

16. What would be the de Broglie wavelength of a 1-milligram particle moving with a speed of 1 cm/sec? Are wave properties of any importance for such a particle?

*17. What speed in m/sec would an electron need in order that its de Broglie wavelength be of the order of magnitude of an atomic diameter (10^{-8} cm)? What energy in eV?

18. A neutron, having the same kinetic energy ($\frac{3}{2} kT$) as a gas molecule at room temperature 300°K, would have what de Broglie wavelength?

19. Suppose the speed of an electron has been measured as 10^8 cm/sec with a probable error of 1 per cent. What would be the uncertainty in the position of the electron?

20. An electron moving with a velocity of 10^6 m/sec in the x direction cannot be located more closely than $x \pm 0.001$ cm. What is the uncertainty in its velocity?

21. In a fantastic land of midget fleas one of the fleas has invented a gun to shoot a 1 microgram bullet with a speed of 1 cm/sec. What would the de Broglie wavelength of the bullet be, and would the fleas be likely to discover the wave properties of the bullet?

22. A photon of what wavelength would have its wavelength increased by 50 per cent on colliding head-on with an electron?

23. In a G. P. Thomson type of experiment a narrow pencil of electrons of 10^3-eV energy are shot through a thin metal foil. If the first diffraction maximum ring is found at an angle of 6° with the incident beam, what is the lattice spacing of the crystal planes from which reflection occurs?

24. Electrons of 50-eV energy are incident perpendicularly on the face of a crystal and are reflected. The first-order diffraction maximum will be found at what angle from the normal to the surface, if the spacing of the crystal planes is 2.5 Å?

25. An electron initially at rest is hit "head-on" by an x-ray photon of wavelength 0.5 Å. What are the energy and the momentum given to the electron?

26. An x-ray photon has a wavelength of 0.2 Å. Compute its equivalent mass and momentum.

27. An x-ray photon of wavelength 0.2 Å is reflected at an angle of 135° with its original direction after colliding with an electron at rest. What is the Compton shift in wavelength and what is the wavelength of the reflected photon?

28. An x-ray photon of wavelength 0.1 Å is reflected at an angle of 90° with its original direction after colliding with an electron at rest. What energy does it lose and what is the frequency change of the photon?

29. If the maximum magnification of an ordinary microscope is 2000 using light of average wavelength 5000 Å, what would be the upper limit of magnification with an electron microscope using 10,000-volt electrons? (Neglect relativistic corrections.)

30. Find the resolving power of an electron microscope in the ideal case of $\alpha = 1°$ if 40,000-volt electrons are used (§5-14).

31. If waves in deep water travel with a phase velocity $\mu = (g\lambda/2\pi)^{1/2}$ where g is the acceleration of gravity, find the group velocity v of the waves.

Recommended Reading

De Broglie, L., *Physics and Microphysics*. New York: Torchbooks, Harper and Row, Publishers, 1960.

Heisenberg, W., *The Physical Principles of the Quantum Theory*. New York: Dover Publications, Inc.

Born, M., *Atomic Physics*, 7th ed. New York: Stechert-Hafner, 1962.

Thomson, G. P., and W. Cochrane, *Theory and Practice of Electron Diffraction*. London: Macmillan & Co., Ltd., 1939.

Maurer, R. J., "Photoelectric Effect," in *Handbook of Physics*, edited by E. U. Condon and H. Odishaw. New York: McGraw-Hill Book Company, Inc., 1959.

Hughes, A. L. and L. A. DuBridge, *Photoelectric Phenomena*. New York: McGraw-Hill Book Company, Inc., 1932.

Zworykin, V. M., and E. G. Ramberg, *Photoelectricity and Its Applications*. New York: John Wiley & Sons, Inc., 1949.

Gamow, G., "The Principle of Uncertainty," *Scientific American*, Vol. 198, No. 1, p. 51 (1958).

Franck, P., *Between Physics and Philosophy*. Cambridge, Mass.: Harvard University Press, 1941.

Bohm, D., *Quantum Theory*, Englewood Cliffs, N.J.: Prentice-Hall, Inc., 1951.

Relativity

Einstein developed his theory of relativity in an attempt to solve what had become one of the greatest dilemmas of all physical science. This dilemma arose from apparent contradictions both in theory and in experiment. Popular emphasis on the mathematical intricacies of Einstein's theory has sometimes obscured the fact that much of the basic theory can be stated without the use of advanced mathematics. Furthermore, an understanding of the nature of the problem and its chief results is essential in modern science.

6-1. Galilean-Newtonian Relativity; Inertial Systems

The ancients interpreted many phenomena in terms of the basic concepts of space (especially length) and time, and they most certainly had a rough working concept of speed. However, the ideas of *average velocity* and *instantaneous velocity* did not receive full clarification until after the development of the calculus. When the concept of a *limit* came to be better understood, then $\Delta s/\Delta t$ was recognized as average velocity with respect to an observer who could measure a displacement Δs in an interval of time Δt. From this, instantaneous velocity (velocity at a point) could be defined as

$$v(\text{inst}) = \lim_{\Delta t \to 0} \frac{\Delta s}{\Delta t} = \frac{ds}{dt} \qquad [6\text{--}1]$$

The fact that all motion is relative to a frame of reference is implied in the very definition of velocity. If velocity in the x direction is defined as

dx/dt, the x is a measurement of displacement from some reference point. From the same reference point measurements could also be made in the y and z directions. The familiar x, y, z axes of space assumed to exist at the reference point form the *frame of reference*. *All measurements are made in some frame of reference.* Usually it is simplest to choose a frame of reference at rest with respect to the observer. However, the frame of reference may be in motion with respect to the observer, and the basic problem to be discussed is how measurements made relative to a moving system are related to those made by an observer in his own "rest system."

According to Newton's first law of motion, whenever an object is accelerated the acceleration is assumed to be the result of some applied force. According to the second law of motion, the assumed force is proportional to the rate of change of momentum of the object. If the rate of change of momentum is zero no force is assumed to act. Indeed, force in the Newtonian sense is that which produces change in momentum. For an object at rest with respect to an observer, or moving with respect to him with a constant velocity, there is no observed change of momentum, and he assumes that there is no force acting upon it. A second observer moving with constant velocity with respect to the first, that is, moving in a non-accelerated system, would observe the body in a state of relative motion with a constant velocity, and so to him also there would be no implied net force acting on the body.

If, however, the object is seen by one of these observers to be accelerated it will be seen to have the same acceleration by any other observer moving with constant velocity with respect to the first observer. In other words, all such observers will obtain the same acceleration from their measurements of a given body if the observers are moving with constant velocities with respect to one another.

For instance, observer A notes at time t_1 that the object is moving with velocity v_1, and at time t_2 he notes that it is moving with velocity v_2. If observer B is moving with constant velocity k with respect to observer A he notes at the same moments that the velocities are $v'_1 = v_1 + k$ and $v'_2 = v_2 + k$, respectively. The observed accelerations a are then equal since

$$a \text{ (observed by A)} = \frac{\Delta v}{\Delta t} = \frac{v_2 - v_1}{t_2 - t_1}$$

and

$$a \text{ (observed by B)} = \frac{\Delta v'}{\Delta t} = \frac{(v'_2 - v'_1)}{(t_2 - t_1)} = \frac{(v_2 + k) - (v_1 + k)}{t_2 - t_1}$$

$$= \frac{v_2 - v_1}{t_2 - t_1}$$

Since such observers obtain the same accelerations they will also assign the same implied force as the requirement for the measured rate of change of momentum. From this we conclude that Newton's second law of motion applies to phenomena noted by all observers moving with constant velocity with respect to each other. Since in any such system of reference a body apparently offers the same inertial resistance to a change in its state of rest or motion such systems are often called *inertial systems*. In all such systems moving with constant velocity with respect to one another the simple laws of Newtonian mechanics apply, and we may say that in such inertial systems descriptions of phenomena according to Newtonian mechanics are *equivalent*.

On the other hand, a third observer not moving with uniform velocity with respect to either of the first two, but moving with an acceleration, would see things differently. His observations would not lead to the same implied forces but to entirely different forces depending upon the acceleration of his own frame of reference with respect to the frames of reference of the other observers. Consequently descriptions of phenomena in terms of Newtonian mechanics by observers in differently accelerated systems would not agree. Such accelerated systems are not inertial systems, and they do not belong to the group of *equivalent inertial systems*. To avoid embarrassing questions as to what the "actual" velocity or acceleration of a system was, Newton felt forced to assume the existence of an absolute and universal frame of reference to which all other measurements could in theory be referred. Thus an object could be in a state of absolute rest or motion with respect to such a system, but with the coming of the Einstein theory such a privileged frame of reference became obsolete, and it was now seen that there could be no state of absolute rest or motion. But first let us consider the type of relativity of motion as recognized by Galileo and Newton.

This Galilean-Newtonian type of relativity applies to strictly mechanical phenomena. This is the relation involved when we say that, if one automobile traveling 40 miles per hour is passed by an automobile traveling in the opposite direction 60 miles per hour, the relative velocity of one car with respect to the other is 100 miles per hour. In obtaining this result we have shifted the frame of reference from an observer by the roadside to an observer in one of the cars. The only difference noted by observers in each car is the difference in direction of the relative motion. This is the common type of relativity, more or less clearly recognized by everyone as a matter of highway safety if nothing more. It is not the type of relativity developed by Einstein although it is included in it as a special case when the velocities are small compared with the speed of light.

6-2. Origin of the Einstein Theory

Einstein developed his theory of relativity in response to a definite and urgent need. The need arose from two sources, one experimental and the other theoretical. Although Galilean-Newtonian relativity seemed to be all that was required to describe ordinary mechanical phenomena it did not work in certain extreme cases, and it did not work when applied to optical or other electromagnetic phenomena. The simple relativity of motion commonly observed with moving objects was not found at all in the motion of light waves. Here, indeed, there seemed to be no relativity at all. The measured velocity of light waves was found to be apparently independent of the motion of the observer. Such a contradiction of the common-sense application of Galilean-Newtonian relativity could not be tolerated. If light waves moved as mechanical waves move, then the measured velocity should depend on the motion of the observer. However, no such dependence could be found, although many experiments were tried.

Suspicion had also arisen from theoretical considerations that all was not well in the over-all viewpoint of Galilean-Newtonian relativity.

6-3. The Theoretical Dilemma

It was gradually becoming apparent that the equations of transformation from one reference system to another system moving with a constant velocity with reference to it were in general unsatisfactory. For one thing, they did not take into consideration the fact that intervals of time measured in the two systems might not be the same. Worse yet, although the fundamental relations of mechanics were invariant in form for the Galilean-Newtonian transformation, Maxwell's well-known equations of the electromagnetic field were completely changed by the transformation, and consequently different observers would be led to different and conflicting results. In other words, the forms of the laws of electromagnetic theory were not invariant for the Galilean-Newtonian transformation.

Now it is common knowledge that a game of billiards or other mechanical processes could be carried out in the parlor car of a smoothly riding train moving at constant velocity just as well as if the train were at rest. Why should not electromagnetic phenomena in such a moving laboratory likewise conform to the usual relations, and why should this not appear in the invariance of the appropriate equations expressing fundamental laws? Here was a dilemma indeed.

6-4. The Experimental Dilemma

A number of experiments have been performed in an attempt to detect any Galilean-Newtonian relativity in the motion of light waves. Of these the first and most famous was that of Michelson and Morley, begun in 1883. The Michelson and Morley experiment was an attempt to test the hypothesis that all space is filled with some mysterious medium, called the *ether*, which has the property of transmitting visible light and other electromagnetic waves. Ever since light had been recognized as a form of wave motion it had been thought to be a wave motion of *something*. It had been considered unthinkable for a wave to exist without existing in something material. In the days when light was considered to be a mechanical wave, the *ether*, presumed to fill space, was thought of as a mechanical medium. Since other types of transverse waves were known to be transmitted only through the body of a solid substance, that is, a substance capable of sustaining a shearing stress, the conclusion seemed inescapable that the ether of space had to be a solid though at the same time it was too tenuous to be directly detected and, in addition, it would have to be assumed to have a tensile strength greater than steel to account for the transmission of the enormous forces of gravitation. All in all, such an explanation of the propagation of light was highly objectionable because of the irrational and contradictory properties which had to be assigned to this apparently solid but indetectable medium.

Upon the development of the electromagnetic theory of light in the latter half of the last century it became necessary to replace the assumed *mechanical ether* by an assumed *electromagnetic ether*. However, it was difficult also not to carry over into the new theory some irrational requirements of the old and the problem of the transmission of the force of gravitation remained regardless of attempts to somehow combine gravitational and electromagnetic theories.

Furthermore, if light waves in the electromagnetic ether behaved like all other known forms of wave motion their speed with respect to a given frame of reference should be a function of the medium, and any measured speed should depend upon the state of rest or motion of the observer and his frame of reference, as in Galilean-Newtonian relativity. It was this dependence on the state of rest or motion of the observer that Michelson and Morley set out to test, for according to the ether hypothesis the motion of the earth through space should affect the measurements of the speed of light. They made use of Michelson's newly invented *interferometer*, which was the most precise scientific instrument devised for this kind of work up to that time and one with which it should have been quite possible to detect the predicted changes in the measured speed of light.

Michelson who originated the experiment reasoned that, if the electromagnetic ether exists and penetrates all objects, the earth in its orbital motion must pass through this ether, producing the effect of an "ether wind" blowing past the earth in the opposite direction. Light waves traveling in a direction opposite to this ether wind would be slowed down. Light waves traveling in the same direction as the ether wind would be speeded up. Light waves traveling in paths that cross the ether wind would be affected, though to a somewhat lesser degree than waves traveling directly with or against it.

The essence of the Michelson-Morley experiment was the comparison of the times of travel of two trains of light waves, one traveling down and back along the ether wind, the other traveling across and back. Since the train of light waves traveling along the ether wind would lose more on the slow part of the journey than it would gain on the fast part of the journey, it would have a net loss of time because of the "ether wind." The wave train moving the same distance across the ether wind and back would also lose a little time but not so much. If the wave trains had started exactly in phase they would be out of phase on their return.

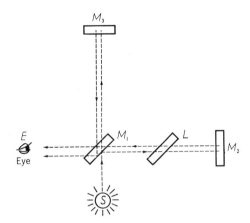

Fig. 6-1. Michelson-Morley experiment. Light from source S is split into two beams by partial reflection at half-silvered mirror face M_1. Beams reunite in eye to give interference or reinforcement depending on relative phase. L is an equalizer plate to make both beams travel same distance in glass.

The principle of the interferometer is shown in Fig. 6-1. Monochromatic light from a source S is split into two beams by partial reflection at mirror M_1. The reflected beam goes to mirror M_2 where it is reflected, and some of the light passes through M_1 to the eye at E. The beam transmitted by M_1 goes to mirror M_3 and is reflected to M_1 where some of the beam is reflected to the eye at E. If the two beams reach the eye in phase a bright field is observed. If they reach the eye in opposite phase they interfere destructively and a dark field is observed. Any change in velocity of one beam more than of the other would shift the field of view from light to dark, or vice versa. If the experiment is arranged with one of the mirrors M_2 or M_3 slightly tipped so as to produce light and dark bands (fringes) in the field of view the effect of any ether stream would be to shift these bands or fringes a measurable amount.

If we assume the apparatus of Fig. 6-1 to move with the earth in its orbit with velocity v so that the line of motion is from M_1 to M_3 then, if light travels from M_1 to M_3 and back again, it is essentially going first upstream against a presumed "ether wind" and then downstream. If l is the distance between M_1 and M_3 and if v is the velocity of the "ether wind" the total time t_1 for the round trip for light traveling in this direction is

$$t_1 = \frac{l}{c-v} + \frac{l}{c+v} = \frac{2lc}{c^2-v^2} = \frac{2l/c}{\left(1-\dfrac{v^2}{c^2}\right)} \qquad [6\text{--}2]$$

where c is the velocity of light. If we expand $1/(c^2-v^2)$ by the binomial theorem and keep only the two most important terms of the series,

$$\frac{1}{c^2-v^2} = c^{-2} + v^2 c^{-4} + \ldots\ldots \qquad [6\text{--}3]$$

from which

$$t_1 = 2lc(c^{-2} + v^2 c^{-4}) \qquad [6\text{--}4]$$

$$= 2l\left(\frac{1}{c} + \frac{v^2}{c^3}\right) \qquad [6\text{--}5]$$

We will assume that the light which travels at right angles to this path goes from M_1 to M_2 and back again in time t_2. The light going in this direction will also be delayed some by an "ether wind" but not so much. To compute the delay let us refer to Fig. 6-2.

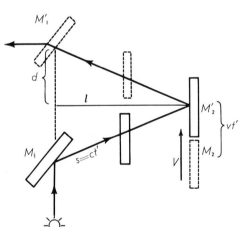

Fig. 6-2. To show delay of transverse light beam in Michelson-Morley experiment.

When light from M_1 meets M_2 the latter will have advanced a distance d. When the light gets back to M_1 it is at the position M'_1, this mirror having advanced a distance $2d$. If the light takes time t' to travel to the mirror M_2 along the line s the mirror has advanced a distance vt'. The distance the light travels is consequently the hypotenuse s of the triangle shown where $s = ct'$ and

$$(ct')^2 = l^2 + (vt')^2 \qquad [6\text{--}6]$$

Solving for t' and again expanding the numerator in series form

$$t' = \frac{l}{(c^2 - v^2)^{1/2}} = \frac{l/c}{\left(1 - \dfrac{v^2}{c^2}\right)^{1/2}} = l\left(\frac{1}{c} + \frac{1}{2}\frac{v^2}{c^3}\cdots\right) \qquad [6\text{--}7]$$

The total time for this light to go over and back again is $2t' = t_2$. We now see that the difference in time $t_1 - t_2$ for the two light beams is the difference between Eq. 6–7 and Eq. 6–2.

$$t_1 - t_2 = t_1 - 2t' = \left[\frac{2l}{c} + \frac{2lv^2}{c^3}\right] - \left[\frac{2l}{c} + \frac{lv^2}{c^3}\right] \qquad [6\text{--}8]$$

$$= \frac{lv^2}{c^3} \qquad [6\text{--}9]$$

Thus there is a difference in time for the two light beams and this should appear as a shift in the fringes seen in the interferometer if there is a medium (such as the ether) through which the earth moves. If there is no medium then there would be no effect of the motion and the two beams would suffer no relative time retardation.

To make the effect as large as possible Michelson and Morley reflected both beams back and forth a number of times by means of mirrors so that the total length of path was about 20 meters. To further increase the effect they made measurements in two positions by rotating the apparatus 90° so that in one position one beam would suffer relative delay while in the other position the other beam would. The total time delay would then be twice that given by Eq. 6–9 and during this time the light would advance a distance $c(2lv^2/c^3)$. To find how many wavelengths of light this path difference represents, assume that visible light with a wavelength $5000\,\text{Å} = 5 \times 10^{-7}$ m is used, and divide the path difference by this wavelength. Recalling that the earth's speed in its orbit is nearly 30×10^3 m/sec, then $v/c \cong 10^{-4}$ and assuming v to be the relative speed of earth and ether, the expected difference in effective light paths may be readily computed and comes out to be 0.4 of a wavelength. This would produce an easily observable shift in the fringes. Michelson and Morley observed no such shift and their experiment achieved everlasting fame for its negative result.

Seldom has an experiment in which the observers failed to find what they were looking for had such an effect on later scientific development. Other experimenters working with even greater precision have since obtained similar null results, and still others have tried entirely different experimental arrangements, but all have failed to demonstrate the existence of an ether stream. One of the more famous of the latter experiments was performed in 1902 by Trouton and Noble. Instead of an optical method they devised a sensitive electromagnetic experiment with capacitor plates. Electromagnetic theory showed that a torque should be exerted on these plates if the ether-wind theory were correct, but no such effect was found. When no experiment can be devised to detect a quantity, it rapidly loses its physical reality and the way is open for an alternative and more successful theory.

6-5. Possible Solutions of the Problem

The problem that we have just outlined was not new with Einstein. Scientists had been wrestling with it for some time, and several possible solutions had been suggested. For one thing, the assumed existence of an ether wind might be a mistake. The ether might be dragged along with the earth, and there would be no relative motion to detect. This would explain the null result of the Michelson-Morley experiment. However, it would be presumed that all stars and planets would also drag ether with them, thus producing slippage or distortion of the ether some place in the space between. This would have detectable effects on the passage of light through space. Consequently that explanation was unsatisfactory.

Fitzgerald and later Lorentz proposed a clever but questionable solution, known as the *Lorentz-Fitzgerald contraction* hypothesis. If the measuring apparatus is assumed to contract in the direction of motion by an amount proportional to $\sqrt{1 - (v^2/c^2)}$ the contraction would exactly cancel the expected variation in measured velocity of light waves so that no effect would be observed. But the shrinkage could never be detected since all measuring standards would shrink similarly.

It is like Lewis Carroll's old man who was always thinking of a plan for dyeing his whiskers green and using a fan so large they could not be seen. Since this explanation seemed to be too much "made to order," it was not generally accepted. The more satisfactory answer came from Einstein's interpretation of a set of equations that Lorentz had derived for the transformation from one system to another, moving with constant relative velocity. Out of these equations came the same shrinkage factor $\sqrt{1 - (v^2/c^2)}$, but now the interpretation was quite different. These equations were not at all like those of the Galilean-Newtonian transformation, and they embodied the new idea that time intervals measured in the two systems are not the same.

6-6. The Lorentz Transformation Equations

Let us first consider the equations of the Galilean-Newtonian transformation. The equations of transformation from a system of reference in uniform motion with respect to the observer, to the system in which the observer is at rest, are easily derived for Galilean-Newtonian relativity.

Let us take x',y',z' as the coordinates of a point in the moving system and x,y,z as the coordinates in the "rest system." Now assume that the velocity of the moving system with respect to the observer's system is v, taken along the x axis for simplicity (Fig. 6-3). A distance x' to a point in the moving

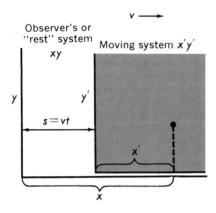

Fig. 6-3. Relation between the x coordinates of a point in the observer's or "rest" system (x,y,z) and in a system (x',y',z') moving to the right, with respect to the observer, with velocity v. For simplicity z coordinates are omitted.

system of coordinates must be added to the space $s = vt$ passed over by the moving system since the two systems were in coincidence, in order to obtain the distance x to the same point measured in the observer's rest system. Then

$$x = x' + vt$$

where t is the elapsed time since the zeros of the two systems coincided. Similarly the distance x in the observer's stationary or rest system of coordinates must have the distance vt subtracted from it to give the distance to the same point in the moving system.

$$x' = x - vt$$

Since motion along the x direction does not affect the y and z coordinates,

$$y = y' \qquad \text{and} \qquad z = z'$$

In Galilean-Newtonian relativity it is assumed that time intervals measured in both systems are the same; consequently,

$$t = t'$$

Thus, for the equations of the Galilean-Newtonian transformation we have

$$
\begin{aligned}
x &= x' + vt' & \text{and} \qquad x' &= x - vt \\
y &= y' & y' &= y \\
z &= z' & z' &= z \qquad \text{[6--10]} \\
t &= t' & t' &= t
\end{aligned}
$$

Yet, how are these equations to be modified if we are to solve the dilemma with which Lorentz was faced? Perhaps time intervals need not be the same in the two systems, but the speed of light must be the same to accord with the results of the Michelson and Morley experiment. If we modify the equations of transformation so as to preserve invariant the laws of electromagnetic theory, we may do violence to the laws of mechanics, but if we try to preserve Newtonian mechanics we may do violence to electromagnetic theory. Can the equations be so modified as to satisfy both requirements?

Einstein, applying the Lorentz transformation, emphasized the universal constancy of the velocity of light by making it a starting point rather than an objective to be attained. Take two reference systems of coordinates x,y,z and x',y',z' which are moving uniformly with different speeds. Assume that the origins of the two systems coincide at time $t = 0$. Further assume a source of light at the origin of the two systems at time $t = 0$ emits a flash of light. Because the speed of light will be the same in all directions the wave front to an observer in the first system will be a sphere and the distance to any point on this wave front after a time t has elapsed would be ct where c is the speed of light. Consequently the equation of the wave front will be

$$x^2 + y^2 + z^2 = c^2t^2 \qquad [6\text{--}11]$$

But if, as we know, the speed of light is not affected by the motion of the observer, then to an observer in the x',y',z' system which is moving at a different speed, the light should also form a spherical wave front the equation of which is

$$x'^2 + y'^2 + z'^2 = c^2t'^2 \qquad [6\text{--}11a]$$

The velocity of light c must be, of course, the same in both systems. This is directly contrary to classical theory. By writing t' for t in the second equation a radical step is taken in assuming that time intervals measured in one system may not be the same as time intervals measured in the other system. The desired transformation equations from the system x,y,z and t to x',y',z' and t' must then be such as to give

$$x^2 + y^2 + z^2 - c^2t^2 = x'^2 + y'^2 + z'^2 - c^2t'^2 \qquad [6\text{--}12]$$

If we limit motion to the x direction only and assume the x',y',z' axes coincide with x,y,z at $t = 0$ we lose nothing of importance in generality as we are always free to choose the x axis in any desired direction. We then find that the required equations of the Lorentz transformation are as follows, and since these are symmetrical with respect to observers in both systems we may write a similar set for quantities in the system at rest with respect to the observer, only making a change in signs representing the change in direction of motion.

$$x = (x' + vt') \frac{1}{\sqrt{1 - \dfrac{v^2}{c^2}}} \qquad\qquad x' = (x - vt) \frac{1}{\sqrt{1 - \dfrac{v^2}{c^2}}}$$

$$y = y' \qquad\qquad\qquad y' = y \qquad\qquad\qquad [6\text{--}13]$$

$$z = z' \qquad\qquad\qquad z' = z$$

$$t = \left(t' + \frac{vx'}{c^2}\right) \frac{1}{\sqrt{1 - \dfrac{v^2}{c^2}}} \qquad\qquad t' = \left(t - \frac{vx}{c^2}\right) \frac{1}{\sqrt{1 - \dfrac{v^2}{c^2}}}$$

For a simple derivation of the Lorentz transformation we may limit Eq. 6–11 and Eq. 6–11a to one dimension. Then the equations for the distance that light waves travel along the x axis in each system in a given time interval are

$$x = ct \qquad \text{and} \qquad x' = ct' \qquad\qquad [6\text{--}14]$$

These equations imply the constancy of the speed of light in the two systems. Let us now make a provisional assumption as to what transformation equations might be used that would be of a more general nature than those of the Galilean-Newtonian transformation. It seems reasonable to try the assumption that measured quantities in one system are proportional to measured quantities in the other; therefore, let us write

$$x = k(x' + vt') \qquad\qquad [6\text{--}15]$$

$$x' = k(x - vt) \qquad\qquad [6\text{--}15a]$$

where k is a constant of proportionality to be evaluated, x and t belong to the system in which the observer is at rest, and x' and t' belong to the system that is moving with respect to the observer. As before, v is the velocity of the moving system, which for simplicity is presumed to move in the x direction. Substituting Eq. 6–15a in Eq. 6–15 we obtain

$$x = k^2(x - vt) + kvt' \qquad\qquad [6\text{--}16]$$

and solving this for t' we have

$$t' = kt + \left(\frac{1 - k^2}{kv}\right)x \qquad\qquad [6\text{--}17]$$

Putting the values of x' (Eq. 6–15a) and t' (Eq. 6–17) into the second of Eqs. 6–14 we have

$$k(x - vt) = c\left[kt + \frac{x}{kv}(1 - k^2)\right] \qquad\qquad [6\text{--}18]$$

Since all terms are now in the unprimed system, in order that the constancy of the velocity of light be preserved, an x in this equation should have the value $x = ct$. Setting the x on the right equal to ct, the other on the left becomes equal to ct if k has the value

$$k = \frac{1}{\sqrt{1 - \dfrac{v^2}{c^2}}} \qquad\qquad [6\text{--}19]$$

Making use of this value of k, we can reduce Eq. 6–17 to

$$t' = k \left(t - \frac{vx}{c^2} \right) \qquad [6\text{--}20]$$

and we have equations for x' (Eq. 6–15a) and t' (Eq. 6–20) in terms of x and t.

We may now write the equations of the Lorentz transformation, as in Eqs. 6–**13**. Since the motion is confined to the x direction $y' = y$ and $z' = z$.

6-7. Einstein's Restricted Theory of Relativity

The equations of the Lorentz transformation led Einstein to his restricted or special theory of relativity, published in 1905. This theory is based on two postulates:

1. The speed of light in space is a universal constant independent of the motion of the observer.

2. Those mathematical relationships which we speak of as the laws of physics should have the same form for all systems moving with a constant velocity with respect to one another, or, in other words, they should be invariant for all inertial systems.

These two postulates may be combined in the single statement that "all inertial systems are equivalent."

Some implications of the special theory, as obtained from a further analysis and application of the equations of the Lorentz transformation, seemed at first revolutionary and even paradoxical. One of the most surprising is that since time intervals are not the same in two systems moving with constant speed with respect to one another, two events which appear to be simultaneous to an observer in one system will not appear simultaneous to an observer in another system. This brings up the whole question of what do we mean when we say two events are *simultaneous?* This will be discussed later in the present chapter (§6-12), but if we are to make measurements on moving objects we must have at least a working definition of *simultaneity*. This is evident if we consider how we might measure the length of a moving object. The length of the object can be measured by two observers noting the coincidence of the two ends of the object with points on a scale as the object moves past them or as they move past it. But this only gives the length correctly if both readings are taken at the same moment, that is, if they are made *simultaneously*. If measurements which are simultaneous in one system are not simultaneous in another system two sets of observers in measuring the length of a rigid rod would get different results.

Take for example a rigid rod at rest in the x,y,z,t system and lying along the x axis with its ends at points x_1 and x_2. The length to observers in that system is $l_0 = x_2 - x_1$. Observers in the $x'y'z't'$ system moving past the rod would determine its length by reading the position of the ends of the rod at x'_1 and x'_2 at the same instant t'. By the Lorentz transformation where $\beta = v/c$

$$x_1 = \frac{x'_1 + vt'}{\sqrt{1 - \beta^2}}$$

[6–21]

$$x_2 = \frac{x'_2 + vt'}{\sqrt{1 - \beta^2}}$$

Since t' is the same in both equations, because the measurements were made simultaneously in that system, we may subtract one measurement from the other obtaining

$$x'_2 - x'_1 = (x_2 - x_1)\sqrt{1 - \beta^2}$$

[6–22]

or

$$l_v = l_0 \sqrt{1 - \beta^2}$$

[6–22a]

where l_v is the measured length at speed v and l_0 is the *rest length* or length as measured by an observer at rest with respect to the rod. Thus the rod will appear to contract by the factor $\sqrt{1 - v^2/c^2}$ as it moves past an observer with a speed v, and as the speed of the body approaches that of light the measured length approaches zero. For instance, the length of a meter stick moving at a speed of 259,000 km/sec (161,000 mi/sec) would be measured as 50 cm, but, measured by an observer moving with it, it would have its normal rest length of 100 cm (Fig. 6-4).

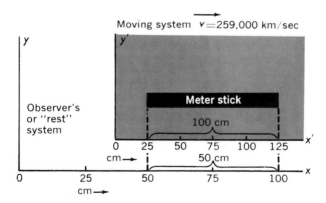

Fig. 6-4.   Measurements on a meter stick moving with a speed of 259,000 km/sec (161,000 mi/sec) with respect to the observer would show it to be 50 cm long.

It is further deduced from the Lorentz transformation that the mass of a body in motion with respect to an observer will increase with increasing speed according to the equation

$$m_v = \frac{m_0}{\sqrt{1 - \dfrac{v^2}{c^2}}} \qquad [6\text{-}23]$$

where m_v is the mass at velocity v and m_0 is the so-called *rest mass* or mass measured by an observer moving with the object. Consequently, as the relative speed of the body approaches the speed of light, the observed mass of the body approaches infinity. For instance, an electron accelerated to an energy of 10^9 eV (1 beV) has an effective mass nearly 2000 times its rest mass.

If the mass of an object varies with the speed of the object we must be careful not to define force as ordinary mass times acceleration but we must return to Newton's original definition of *force* as *rate of change of momentum p.*

$$F = \frac{dp}{dt} = \frac{d(mv)}{dt} \qquad [6\text{-}24]$$

and in terms of the rest mass the momentum p at any velocity v is

$$p = m_v v = \frac{m_0 v}{\sqrt{1 - \dfrac{v^2}{c^2}}} \qquad [6\text{-}25]$$

If we try to apply the right-hand side of this equation for relativistic momentum to a photon which according to Eq. 5–6 has a momentum h/λ we have

$$\frac{h}{\lambda} = \frac{m_0 v}{\sqrt{1 - \dfrac{v^2}{c^2}}} \qquad [6\text{-}26]$$

and since now $v = c$ for a photon

$$m_0 = \frac{h}{v\lambda} \sqrt{\frac{c^2 - c^2}{c^2}} = 0 \qquad [6\text{-}27]$$

From this we may conclude that the rest mass of a photon or anything traveling with the speed of light must be zero.

Time intervals show a dilation similar to the relativistic increase of mass. Moving clocks will apparently slow down according to the relation

$$t_v = \frac{t_0}{\sqrt{1 - \dfrac{v^2}{c^2}}} \qquad [6\text{-}28]$$

The dilation of time was first reportedly confirmed by Ives in 1938 by observing the light emitted by rapidly moving positive rays in an electric discharge tube. If the atom emitting light is considered to be an "atomic clock" the frequency of the light should be shifted because of the relativistic time dilation. Since the shift is only about 0.001 per cent for as high a speed as 1000 mi/sec, a method of extreme precision had to be developed and it was necessary to distinguish this effect from the much larger Doppler shift resulting directly from motion toward or away from an observer. The results seem to confirm the time dilation of Eq. 6–28.

MU-MESON DECAY

More satisfactory confirmation of relativistic time dilation has come from observing rates of decay of certain radioactive particles called mu mesons (§17-4) in the cosmic rays in our atmosphere. These particles may move with speeds nearly that of light. If the decay rates of these particles are measured at high speeds and again after they have slowed down to much lesser speeds a large scale effect can be obtained. The measurements confirm that the decay rate has increased at the lower speeds. This means that at the faster speeds the atomic processes have slowed down as predicted by relativistic theory.

CONCLUSIONS

To summarize some of the chief conclusions derived from the special theory of relativity;

1. The velocity of light in free space is an upper limit which can only be approached but not exceeded by any material particle.
2. The measured length of an object is less if the relative velocity of the observer is greater (Eq. 6–22a).
3. The measured mass of an object increases as the relative velocity of the observer increases (Eq. 6–23).
4. Time intervals indicated by a moving clock become longer as the relative velocity of the clock becomes greater (Eq. 6–28).

Although it is true that a moving particle can never travel faster than the speed of light in free space, this is not true in a material medium. Very high energy particles may travel faster in glass or water, or lucite, than the light does in the same medium. This is the origin of the Čerenkov radiation (§17-5).

The old quantities of classical mechanics which had been thought of as always invariant regardless of the motion of the observer are now found according to relativity theory to depend upon the relative motion of the frame of reference in which they are measured and they have had to be redefined so as to be invariant under the Lorentz transformation. Thus classical mechanics has had to be modified but only small violence has been done to classical concepts except when relative speeds are extremely large. For the ordinary speeds of everyday life these relativistic variations are entirely negligible and the more general relativistic formulas reduce to those of ordinary mechanics for the special case of moderate speeds. For this small sacrifice the gain is enormous for now Maxwell's equations of the electromagnetic field may be readily put in relativistic form invariant to the Lorentz transformation and in general Einstein's second postulate may be satisfied.

Lorentz had thought that his equations referred to the "true" values of a rest system and the "apparent" values of a moving system but Einstein showed that there was no logical way of telling which system was moving and which was at rest. Consequently the distinction vanishes and there can be no state of absolute rest or motion. Likewise there is no absolute length, mass or time but only those values appropriate to the state of motion of the observer.

Great as these changes have been it is a mistake to say that the Einstein revolution has overthrown the Newtonian world. More properly it has extended the range of application of that system by refining it and correcting it for high speeds, and Newtonian mechanics is seen to be a special case of the more general relativistic mechanics when the speeds are low.

6-8. The Addition Theorem for Velocities

Since the mass of a moving body increases in such a way as to approach infinity as the speed or velocity approaches that of light, it becomes evident that the velocity of light is thus an upper limit which may be approached but not surpassed by any material object. If this is true, very high velocities or speeds may no longer be added directly, as in the Newtonian transformation.

Consider a particle moving with a large velocity v with respect to an observer in the laboratory, the velocity v being to the left. It may have any value up to c the velocity of light. Now consider another particle moving similarly to the right with a large velocity v_2 with respect to the same observer. There is no question about the validity of these measurements in the laboratory frame of reference. The problem is to find what happens if we place an observer in a frame of reference moving with one of the particles. The second observer is now at rest with respect to that particle and he wishes to know what the velocity of the other particle is with respect to the first particle with which he is traveling.

If the particles were automobiles the observer in one would think that the other car passed him at a speed $v + v_2$ since relativistic effects are negligible. However, if the particles are high-speed electrons the sum of

$v + v_2$ might be greater than the velocity of light and this is prohibited by relativity theory. Let us see how these velocities must be added relativistically, that is in a manner consistent with the Lorentz transformation. If we represent quantities observed by the person moving with the first particle by the subscript 1 such as x_1, t_1 then he "sees" the second particle moving away from him with a velocity v_1. In accordance with Eq. 6–13

$$x_1 = k(x_2 + vt_2) \qquad [6\text{--}29]$$

and

$$t_1 = k\left(t_2 + \frac{vx_2}{c^2}\right) \qquad [6\text{--}30]$$

where

$$k = \frac{1}{\sqrt{1 - \dfrac{v^2}{c^2}}} \qquad [6\text{--}31]$$

One way of obtaining v_1 from these equations is to differentiate each with respect to t_2. We then have

$$\frac{dx_1}{dt_2} = k\left(\frac{dx_2}{dt_2} + v\right) = k(v_2 + v) \qquad [6\text{--}32]$$

$$\frac{dt_1}{dt_2} = k\left(1 + \frac{v}{c^2}\frac{dx_2}{dt_2}\right) = k\left(1 + \frac{vv_2}{c^2}\right) \qquad [6\text{--}33]$$

If we divide Eq. 6–32 by Eq. 6–33, we obtain

$$v_1 = \frac{dx_1}{dt_1} = \frac{v_2 + v}{1 + \dfrac{vv_2}{c^2}} \qquad [6\text{--}34]$$

From this v_1 is the relativistic sum of v and v_2. It is the velocity of the second particle as measured by an observer moving with the first particle. If we try this addition theorem, we find that even when v and v_2 each are equal to the velocity of light their sum is also equal to the velocity of light.

      Equation 6–34 may be arrived at in a more direct manner, without the necessity of using calculus, by dividing Eq. 6–29 by Eq. 6–30. Then x_1/t_1 is v_1, and x_2/t_2 is v_2, if x_1 is the space passed over in time t_1 and x_2 is the space passed over in time t_2.

Example   Consider a frame of reference in which an observer detects two electrons with velocities $-0.7c$ and $+0.8c$ moving in opposite directions along the x axis, c being the velocity of light. In a Galilean system their velocity relative to one another would be $1.5c$, which is impossible according to the basic postulate of restricted relativity. According to the Einstein law of addition, the relative velocity for an observer moving with one of the particles, is

$$v = \frac{0.8c + 0.7c}{1 + \dfrac{0.8(0.7)c^2}{c^2}} = \frac{1.50}{1.56} c = 0.96c$$

6-9. Equivalence of Energy and Mass

Let us take Eq. 6–23

$$m_v = \frac{m_0}{\sqrt{1 - \dfrac{v^2}{c^2}}}$$

for the relativistic mass at a given velocity v in terms of m_0, the rest mass. The right-hand side of this equation may be expanded by means of the binomial theorem to give a rapidly converging infinite series

$$m_v = m_0 + \frac{\frac{1}{2} m_0 v^2}{c^2} + \frac{\frac{3}{8} m_0 v^4}{c^4} + \cdots \qquad [6\text{--}35]$$

Considering only the first two terms, since the third is usually very small, we have

$$m_v = m_0 + \frac{\frac{1}{2} m_0 v^2}{c^2} = m_0 + \Delta m \qquad [6\text{--}36]$$

where Δm is the increase in mass due to the increase in velocity. From this

$$\Delta m = \frac{\frac{1}{2} m_0 v^2}{c^2} = \frac{\text{kinetic energy}}{c^2} \qquad [6\text{--}37]$$

Since $\frac{1}{2} m_0 v^2$ is the kinetic energy of the particle it is seen that the increase in mass to which this energy is equivalent is obtained by dividing by c^2 (the square of the velocity of light). Conversely the energy to which this increase in mass is equivalent is obtained by multiplying by c^2. Multiplying both sides of Eq. 6–36 by c^2 we may interpret the result as meaning that the energy equivalent of the rest mass is $m_0 c^2$ and of the mass in motion is $m_v c^2 = m_0 c^2 / \sqrt{1 - v^2/c^2}$. The difference between these is the kinetic energy of motion of the moving body. In the case of an electron which has gained an energy eV by falling through a potential difference V we may then write

$$m_v c^2 - m_0 c^2 = \frac{m_0 c^2}{\sqrt{1 - \dfrac{v^2}{c^2}}} - m_0 c^2 = eV \cdot \qquad [6\text{--}38]$$

This is Eq. 2–21 of Chap. 2.

Einstein concluded that in general mass and energy are equivalent and that the energy equivalent E of any mass m is

$$E = mc^2 \qquad [6\text{--}39]$$

This is the famous Einstein *energy-mass relation*.

$$E(\text{joules}) = m(\text{kg})c^2(\text{m/sec})^2$$
$$E(\text{ergs}) = m(\text{gm})c^2(\text{cm/sec})^2$$

From this relation 1 gram of matter of any kind has an energy equivalent of 9×10^{13} joules or 9×10^{20} ergs. If liberated in one second this would be 9×10^{13} watts or 0.12 million million horsepower. Thus it is evident that a very small amount of mass is equivalent to an extremely large amount of energy. This accounts for the fact that in the "atom bomb," even though the energy of only a fraction of the mass of the atoms is released by "fission" or by "fusion," it represents an extraordinary amount of energy (§16-7). The first nuclear explosion was direct confirmation of the Einstein relation and no theory ever had such a large-scale and startling experimental confirmation.

6-10. Dirac's Theory of Electrons

In the early theories of atomic structure (Chap. 7) the effects of relativity were either omitted or added as a small correction. But with the introduction of quantum-mechanical methods (Chap. 8) atomic theory took a new direction. Where classical methods failed, great success was attained by assuming every particle is describable by a form of de Broglie wave having an amplitude ψ from which many properties may be deduced. The most common form of the equation for ψ is the Schrödinger equation (§8-1) which describes the energy states of a particle. After intensive search Dirac in 1928 found similar equations which were invariant to the Lorentz transformation. Thus relativity was put into atomic theory as a basic requirement and this led to the many new developments of modern atomic theory.

Applying his theory to electrons Dirac started with the obvious fact that there is a plentiful supply of electrons in the world and that they are in positive energy states. For instance, in order to exist at all an electron must have a positive energy equal to its rest mass energy $m_0c^2 = 0.51$ meV. If it has kinetic energy this will make its total positive energy still more. However, Dirac's equation seemed equally well to indicate the existence of negative energy states and the least possible negative energy state for an electron would consequently be -0.51 meV (Fig. 6–5). But an electron in such a state should possess a positive charge. Thus to create a negative electron it would be necessary at the same time to create a positive electron. This would be equivalent to raising a negative electron from a negative energy state to a positive energy state and would require a minimum of 1.02 meV (Fig. 6-5).

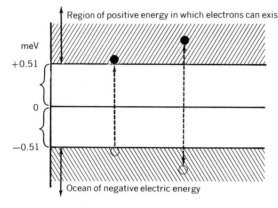

Fig. 6-5. A graphical representation of the Dirac theory of electrons.

A difficulty now arose. If the world was full of negative electrons and also full of negative energy states there would be no reason why the electrons would not fall back to negative states and disappear. To avoid this Dirac assumed that all negative states are filled and that the world is essentially a "sea of negative electricity." On this view, when a negative electron is created by raising it to a positive energy state, this leaves a "hole" in the ocean of negative energy. This "hole" has properties opposite to those of the electron created and thus represents the *antiparticle* of an electron, that is, a positive electron or positron. In brief, this is Dirac's theory of electrons, and in its broadest sense it describes pair formation and annihilation, along with implying the existence of positive electrons.

6-11. Pair Production and Annihilation; Particles and Antiparticles

PAIR PRODUCTION

According to the Einstein energy-mass relation it might be expected that a gamma-ray photon of sufficient energy might be transformed into matter of equivalent energy. Since the photon has zero charge the production of a negative electron would also require the simultaneous production of the antiparticle, a positive electron or positron. Such a positive and negative electron constitutes an *electron pair*, and its production has often been observed (Fig. 6-6). Indeed in any kind of pair production only a particle and its antiparticle can be produced.

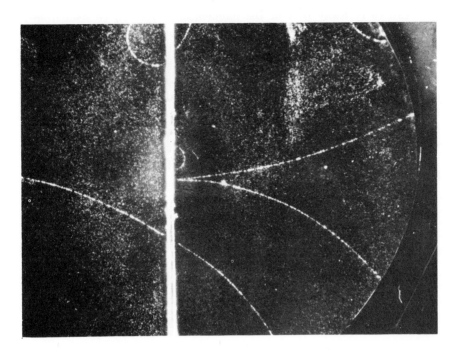

Fig. 6-6. Cloud-chamber photograph, showing production of an electron pair. Gamma-ray photon coming from left leaves no track but forms electron pair when it encounters metal plate. The paths of the positive and negative electrons are curved in opposite directions by a magnetic field perpendicular to plane of photo. (Courtesy, University of Illinois, Department of Physics.)

Since the energy equivalent of the rest mass of an electron pair is 1.02 meV, this is the minimum energy of the gamma-ray photon capable of forming a pair. The particles would have zero kinetic energy and momentum. This would not satisfy conservation of momentum. Therefore a higher-energy photon is required and excess energy can go into kinetic energy of motion of the two electrons of rest mass m_0, giving them velocities v_1 and v_2. For a gamma-ray photon of energy $h\nu$ then, to a first approximation conservation of energy gives

$$h\nu = 2m_0c^2 + \frac{1}{2} m_0 v_1^2 + \frac{1}{2} m_0 v_2^2 \qquad [6\text{--}40]$$

If the excess energy is large, a more complete relativistic treatment must be given.

However, momentum must also be conserved and conservation of energy and momentum forbid pair production to take place in empty space. The phenomenon can only occur in the presence of a nuclear mass that can carry away part of the momentum. This can be seen from a simple non-relativistic calculation. Each gamma-ray photon has momentum equal to h/λ (Eq. 5–6). If it were possible to produce an electron pair in which the particles of the pair had zero velocity they would have zero momentum and the momentum of the gamma-ray photon would have to go somewhere. If the particles had oppositely directed velocities of equal magnitude the net momentum of the particles would still be zero. If the particles both had similarly directed velocities of equal magnitude v and if $v \cos \theta$ is the component of each in the direction of the photon momentum we can then write for conservation of momentum in the simplest non-relativistic case

$$\frac{h}{\lambda} = 2m_0 v \cos \theta \qquad\qquad [6\text{--}41]$$

where m_0 is the mass (rest mass) of each electron. But if the energy $h\nu$ of the photon is conserved

$$h\nu = 2m_0 c^2 + 2\left(\frac{1}{2}m_0 v^2\right) \qquad\qquad [6\text{--}42]$$

Since $h\nu = hc/\lambda$ this gives (by Eq. 6–41)

$$2m_0 v \cos \theta = 2m_0 c + \frac{m_0 v^2}{c} \qquad\qquad [6\text{--}43]$$

or

$$v \cos \theta = c + \frac{v^2}{2c} \qquad\qquad [6\text{--}44]$$

This is greater than the velocity of light and violates relativity theory. The presence of another body is therefore required to conserve momentum and if its mass is large the energy lost to this body may be negligibly small.

More recently with the much higher-energy gamma rays now obtainable it has been possible to produce pairs of heavier particles and in particular proton pairs have been produced. This revealed that in addition to the ordinary positively charged proton which commonly exists in nature it is possible to create a much rarer kind of proton with a negative charge. This is called the *antiproton* (§17-6) just as the positron is the *antiparticle* of the electron. Other particle-antiparticle pairs have been produced but the subject of fundamental particles and antiparticles will be dealt with later (Chap. 17).

The production of a proton pair involves very much higher energies than the production of an electron pair, consequently it is a highly relativistic reaction and the production of the required high energy gamma rays is much less efficient. The relativistic masses involved in the conservation of momentum are much larger than the rest masses, and minimum energies of bombarding particles in the neighborhood of 5000 meV are required to produce two protons each with a rest mass equivalent of 938 meV.

ANNIHILATION

The opposite of pair production is pair "annihilation" though the word annihilation only applies to the disappearance of separate particles. The total energy remains unchanged and is merely transferred to the form of radiation. Indeed the equivalent mass of the radiation is the same as the mass of the original particles. Just as pair production applies only to a particle and its antiparticle so also only a particle and an antiparticle can annihilate one another. For instance, a proton and an electron possess charges of equal magnitude and opposite sign but one is not the antiparticle of the other and when they come close together they form a stable hydrogen atom.

If an electron and a positron come close together they attract each other, their charges may cancel, and they may no longer exist as separate particles. Total energy along with total charge would be expected to be conserved, and the energy equivalent of the masses of the two electrons should appear in the form of radiation. The relatively large amount of energy involved indicates that the radiation would be in the form of gamma radiation. For momentum also to be conserved two gamma rays will be radiated in opposite directions. Since the rest mass of each electron has an energy equivalent of 0.51 meV the minimum energy of each gamma-ray photon is 0.51 meV, and the frequency of each photon may be computed by the Planck equation $E = h\nu$. This gives, for the maximum wavelength possible, 0.024 Å.

The phenomenon of pair annihilation has been observed, and not only has the existence of two simultaneous photons traveling in opposite directions been experimentally verified by means of coincidence counters (§13-17) but the wavelengths of the photons have been found to agree closely with the computed values.

The phenomena of pair production and annihilation afford further dramatic experimental confirmation of the Einstein energy-mass relation.

POSITRONIUM

Speculation on how an electron and a positron might come together before annihilation led to the idea that if energy conditions were favorable the particles might first "capture" each other by going into orbit about one another to temporarily form an "atom" called *positronium* in much the same way that a proton may be said to capture an electron to form a hydrogen atom. Such an "electronic atom" if formed was expected to be quite unstable and have a very short life before annihilation occurred. In 1951 Deutsch passed a beam of positrons through nitrogen gas and found evidence that positronium is formed but that on the average half of the two-particle systems so formed would be annihilated in 10^{-7} sec or less. De Benedetti and Siegel confirmed this with further measurements the following year.

6-12. Concept of Simultaneity; Operational Viewpoint

Einstein found that not only do our common ideas of mass, length, and time have to be revised but that other concepts hitherto unquestioned require rigorous definition and must be submitted to searching analysis. Chief of these is the concept of *simultaneity*. Before Einstein pointed the finger of suspicion at this concept it had been taken for granted by most people that they knew intuitively what was meant by two events being simultaneous or not being simultaneous. According to older standards there seemed to be a definite meaning to the statement that two events are *simultaneous*.

Yet, if we observe two events occurring at the same moment we may forget that the light signal coming to us from one event may have come further than from the other. Since it takes finite time for light to travel, two events which appear to be simultaneous may not be simultaneous. So, also, of two events which we define as simultaneous, either may appear earlier than the other depending on conditions of observation. Einstein has pointed out the effect on the observer when the observer is moving.

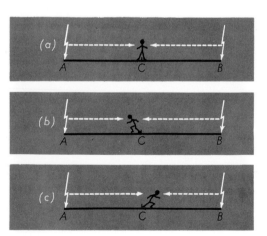

Fig. 6-7. Effect of motion of observer on apparent simultaneity of two events.

Assume that lightning strikes simultaneously at points A and B (Fig. 6-7). If the observer is at point C, halfway between A and B, and if the velocity of light is finite and is assumed to take the same time in going from A to

C as in going from B to C, the observer will see both flashes of light at the same moment, and the events will appear simultaneous (Fig. 6-7a). However, if the observer at C is moving in the direction of A (Fig. 6-7b) he will move enough to receive the flash from A sooner, and he will think the lightning stroke at A occurred before that at B. If moving toward B (Fig. 6-7c) he will think the stroke at B occurred before that at A. Yet the assumption that the events are simultaneous when the observer is at the midpoint C and receives the light flashes at the same time may be false, for the whole ABC system may be moving to the right or the left. If moving to the left the light from A again does not have so far to go, and the light from B has further to go. Events that seemed to be simultaneous to the observer at C may not be so. Consequently simultaneity is not something absolute but something to be carefully defined.

Two observers some distance apart may conclude that events are simultaneous if they refer to their clocks, but only if their clocks are running in synchronism. It is then necessary to define what is meant by *synchronism*. How can we define two clocks as being in synchronism? Einstein has given us a definition of simultaneity and a method of setting two clocks in synchronism according to the definition. Consider two clocks at positions A and B. If an observer at A sends a light signal to an observer at B, B may reflect it back to A. The clocks may be defined to be in synchronism when A and B are at rest with respect to one another, if B starts his clock on receiving the light signal and if A adjusts his clock so that it would have read zero at the middle of the time interval between sending and receiving the light signal. Yet, although A and B are at rest with respect to one another both may move along the line AB. In that event one observer may be moving toward the signal and will receive it sooner, and the other may move away from the reflected signal and will receive it later. Consequently there can be no concept of absolute simultaneity. Events can only be simultaneous or not, depending on how simultaneity is defined.

The definition of simultaneity as given by Einstein thus becomes a part of the restricted theory of relativity. It also is one of the great examples of Einstein's demonstration that definitions are only valid and precise in terms of the operations required to be performed. This is known as the *operational method* or the *operational viewpoint*. For instance, we may ask what is the *real* length of the object as it passes us? Is it the length which we obtain if we have been moving with the object? The answer is that from the viewpoint of relativity either answer is equally valid though the two may differ. There is no such thing as a *real* or *absolute* length of an object, just as there is no *real* or *absolute* time or mass. These things depend on the state of rest or motion of the observer with respect to the object, and they have meaning only in terms of the operations which have to be performed to obtain them.

6-13. The General Theory of Relativity; Expanding Universe

Einstein developed his special or restricted theory of relativity on the assumption that physical laws should be invariant in form for all systems of reference moving with constant velocity with respect to one another (inertial systems). The question arose in Einstein's mind as to whether or not this might be extended to include systems of reference which were accelerated with respect to one another. This attractive idea would involve a much more generalized theory and would mean that laws of physics were invariant in form for all systems of reference regardless of their relative motion. The development of this theory presented great mathematical difficulties, and to follow it far involves the use of the calculus of tensors. However, some aspects of the general theory are of particular interest.

Einstein was able to incorporate in his more general theory a consideration of the mysterious force of gravitation. In this he was led to his principle of equivalence, which states that it is impossible to distinguish between the effects of a gravitational field of force acting in one direction and the acceleration of a frame of reference in the opposite direction. If a system of reference is accelerated, objects in this system would seem to have forces acting on them in the direction opposite to the direction of acceleration of the system of reference. For instance, if a man were in an elevator car in a region of space far removed from appreciable gravitational force and if the car were suddenly accelerated in the direction of the arrow (Fig. 6-8), the man could equally well make two assumptions: (*a*) that a mysterious force had pulled him downward, or (*b*) that the car had suddenly been accelerated upward. Between these assumptions he could not possibly make a choice by means of any experiments carried on inside the car.

Einstein was finally led to the possibility of a new interpretation of gravitation. Instead of thinking of gravitation as a force, perhaps it could

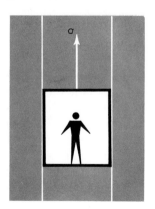

Fig. 6-8. Principle of equivalence. Man in elevator cannot distinguish between gravitation force pulling downward and an acceleration of car upward.

be treated as a property of space. A further development of the theory indicated that it was possible to consider three-dimensional space about a gravitational body as being warped or distorted in a fourth dimension of space. Since there is no way in which man, who is strictly a three-dimensional creature, can directly detect a fourth spatial dimension if it exists, there can be no direct test of this idea. However, the theory led to certain conclusions that could be tested, and we are entitled to believe that we live in a multidimensional world, having as many dimensions as are required to explain observed phenomena, unless a simpler theory is available.

Since the difference between the results predicted by ordinary Newtonian theory and those by general relativity is so small for most of the situations that can be readily investigated, a complete proof of the general theory is difficult. However, tests of the following predictions from the theory have been made: (*a*) that light passing near a star in an intense gravitational field would be bent more than it should be according to Newtonian theory (Fig. 6-9); (*b*) that certain discrepancies in the periods of rotation of the planets (advances of perihelia) could be explained; (*c*) that light radiated from a star would be affected by the gravitational field of the star in such a way as to have its frequency lowered. The last effect would give what is called a *gravitational red shift* and has been extremely difficult to detect experimentally as it would be masked by any red shift (Doppler effect) caused by recession in the line of sight. However, striking confirmation has recently come from a new direction involving the *Mössbauer effect* (§15-3).

These tests appear to confirm the general theory but they are hardly final. Since there is no unique solution to the equations of general rela-

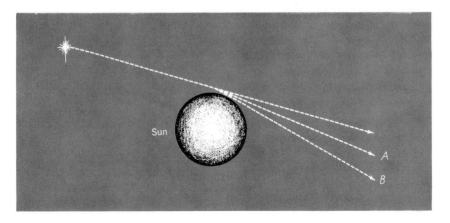

Fig. 6-9. According to relativity theory, light passing through the intense gravitational field near the sun should be bent so as to follow path *B*, whereas classical theory would predict a smaller bending along *A*.

tivity, a number of modifications of the theory have also been suggested. In contradistinction to this, the validity of the special or restricted theory of relativity is not only generally accepted but has become an integral part of the basic theories of physics.

Einstein himself in his general theory reached the conclusion that the universe instead of being infinite is actually finite, that it curves about on itself in a fourth dimension to form a closed region, much as the two-dimensional surface of a sphere curves about itself in a third dimension to form a closed region which is limitless though finite.

In a somewhat different development, Lemaître and others arrived at the conclusion that the universe is not in a stable state but that it is expanding like a giant bubble. Apparent confirmation of this astonishing idea comes from the study of the light coming to us from distant stellar galaxies. In every instance a shift of known spectral lines toward the red end of the spectrum is found. This, according to the Doppler principle, indicates that these galaxies all are moving away from the earth, and the more remote they are, the faster they are moving. Speeds of recession of the most distant galaxies have been recently reported by R. Minkowski to be as high as 0.6 the speed of light. Until a different interpretation of this *red shift* is reached we seem to be forced to accept the concept of an *expanding universe*. Such cosmological speculation, however, must be left for the student to follow in more specialized books.

Problems

1. Two automobiles each travel 100 miles but on different roads. The first travels the whole distance at a constant speed of 50 miles/hour. The second at a later time is hindered by a head wind and travels half the distance at 40 mi/hr, for the other half it is aided by a tail wind and travels at 60 mi/hr. Which one takes the lesser time and by how much?

2. A man in a rowboat on a river rows downstream 2 miles and back to the starting point. If he can row at a rate of ¾ mi/hr and if the current in the water is ¼ mi/hr, how long does it take him to go down and back? In how much shorter or longer time could he make a round trip of the same length in still water?

3. A spherical particle moves toward a similar particle at rest and makes a perfectly elastic collision with it. Except for a head-on collision show that the angle between the paths of the particles after collision is always 90°.

4. A piece of plywood 1 meter square moves away from an observer at a speed of 0.9c in the direction of one of the edges. What shape would it appear to the observer and what would be the apparent length of the diagonal? What would be the angle between a diagonal and the direction of motion?

5. A student in the laboratory sets an inclined plane at an angle of 37° with a horizontal line running east and west. The inclined plane is 1 meter long and rises to the east. An observer moving east with a speed of 0.9c would "see" the length of the plane as what? He would see the angle of inclination as what?

6. An ocean liner weighs 25,000 tons and travels 30 mi/hr. What is its relativistic increase in mass?

7. If an observer in a space ship approaches the moon, at what speed of approach would the diameter in line of motion appear ⅓ the diameter at right angles to the line of motion?

*8. A spherical wave of light is emitted from the origin of one coordinate system just as it coincides with origin of another similar system moving with constant speed with respect to the first. By means of the Lorentz transformation show that the wave front appears spherical at some later time in either system.

9. At what speed in m/sec and mi/hr will an electron have an effective mass 3 times its rest mass?

10. Compute the velocity for which an object would apparently shrink to three-fourths its length in the direction of motion.

11. At what fraction of the speed of light is a particle moving if it has a rest-mass energy m_0c^2 and a total energy mc^2?

12. Find (in per cent) the relativistic increase in mass of a proton and an electron each of which has been accelerated through a difference of potential of 10 million volts.

13. Show that Newton's second law of motion ($F = ma$) is invariant in form under the Galilean transformation for all inertial systems, but that it is not invariant for an accelerated system of coordinates.

14. Assuming the total light path to each mirror in a repetition of the Michelson and Morley experiment is 20 m, what would be the maximum expected path difference for the two beams in one position of the apparatus if the earth's orbital velocity is 30 km/sec? How many wavelengths would this be of the D_1 line of sodium ($\lambda = 5896$ Å)?

15. Light can cross the earth's orbit in approximately 1000 sec. A particle (approaching the earth) with a speed 0.9c would take how much time to cross the orbit as judged by a clock traveling with the particle?

16. The "paradox of the twins" has been much talked about. If one of a pair of identical twins travels in a space ship for 10 years at a speed of 0.5c and returns to earth, what difference will there be in the ages of the twins? What assumptions did you make?

*17. Two observers A and B set their clocks in synchronism as they pass one another. B is traveling 161,000 mi/sec with respect to A. At the end of 10 minutes by A's clock, A looks at B's clock through a telescope. The elapsed time indicated by it is what? If at the end of 10 minutes by B's clock B looks at A's clock, what time does he read?

*18. Two observers A and B set their clocks in synchronism as they pass one another. Each is traveling 104,000 mi/sec with respect to the other. After 10 minutes by B's clock A holds up a clock and signals with a flashlight for B to look at it through a telescope. What is the time by A's clock as B sees it, and at what time by B's clock does B view the signal?

19. Compute the energy equivalent of a proton pair at rest.

20. A proton and antiproton each have a kinetic energy of 0.1 beV before annihilating each other. If two gamma rays are formed by the annihilation, what will be the wavelength of each?

21. Compute the average binding energy in eV per molecule between molecules of water if the heat of vaporization is 540 cal/gm. Show that the mass this represents is ordinarily negligible.

22. Aluminum crystallizes in a face-centered cubic crystal and melts at 658°C. What is the average binding energy in eV of each atom in the crystal lattice at that temperature? The heat of fusion is 77 cal/gm. How much energy in eV per atom is required to reach the melting point starting from 0°C if the average specific heat is 0.23 cal/gm?

23. The total intensity of radiation from the sun falling on the earth's surface is 8×10^4 joules per m² per min. Find the total energy radiated from the sun in one million years. Find the equivalent mass in metric tons which must disappear. What fraction is this of the sun's total mass? The mean distance to the sun is 1.55×10^8 km and the present mass of the sun is 2×10^{30} kg.

24. Show that $\frac{1}{2}m_v v^2$, where $m_v = m_0/\sqrt{1 - v^2/c^2}$, does not give the relativistic kinetic energy $m_v c^2 - m_0 c^2$ of a particle as might appear. (Hint: Use binomial expansion.)

25. A nuclear submarine traveling at a certain low speed uses energy at the rate of 10^8 joules/kilometer. Assuming a conversion efficiency of mass to energy of 0.01 per cent, how much nuclear fuel is required per 1000 kilometers (approx. 600 miles)?

26. A battleship displaces 30,000 metric tons of water (1 metric ton = 1000 kg). If one-tenth of one per cent of the mass of a 20-gm ice cube were converted to energy to what maximum height could it lift the battleship if the latter were in dry-dock?

27. If a quantum of visible light has a wavelength of 5000 Å, what would be its "effective mass" according to the relation $E = mc^2$? How does this compare with the rest mass of an electron?

28. If any kind of matter were converted to energy, what would be the rate of energy release per gram of matter converted per hour?

29. A particle of rest mass m_0 approaches another similar particle with a speed $v = 0.8c$. What is the total energy of the two particles: (a) in the rest system of one of the particles, and (b) in the system of coordinates for which the momentum is zero (center of mass system)?

*30. Measurements were made by Fizeau in 1851 on the speed of light c' in a flowing liquid. He believed there would be an "ether drag" which would affect the speed of the light and he obtained the formula

$$c' = \frac{c}{n} + v\left(1 - \frac{1}{n^2}\right)$$

where v is the speed of the liquid and n is its index of refraction. Show that this agrees with the relativistic formula for addition of velocities if terms in $(v/c)^2$ and higher powers are neglected. Why is the idea of "ether drag" no longer needed?

Recommended Reading

Einstein, A., *The Meaning of Relativity*. Princeton, N.J.: Princeton University Press, 1953.

Einstein, A. and L. Infeld, *The Evolution of Physics*. New York: Simon & Schuster, Inc., 1938.

Eddington, A. S., *Space, Time and Gravitation*. London: Cambridge University Press, 1923; also reprinted in Torchbooks, Harper and Row, Publishers, 1959.

Sherwin, C. W., *Basic Concepts of Physics*. New York: Holt, Rinehart & Winston, Inc., 1961.

Lindsay, R. B., and H. Margenau, *Foundations of Physics*. New York: Dover Publications, Inc., 1957.

Bergmann, P. G., *Introduction to the Theory of Relativity*. Englewood Cliffs, N.J.: Prentice-Hall, Inc., 1942.

Bondi, H., *Cosmology*. London: Cambridge University Press, 1952.

Early Work and Historical

Michelson, A. A., *Studies in Optics*. Chicago: Phoenix Books, University of Chicago Press.

Whittaker, Sir Edmund, *A History of the Theories of Aether and Electricity*. London: Thomas Nelson and Sons, 1951.

The Nuclear Atom;
Hydrogen Spectrum

With the coming of Maxwell's electromagnetic theory and the recognition that light is an electromagnetic wave motion it became evident that something of an electromagnetic character must exist in the atom to act as a "vibrator" or source of these waves. In 1896 Zeeman found that when atoms are excited sufficiently to give off light, they may be affected by a magnetic field. This is called the *Zeeman effect* (§9-5) and was taken to be direct evidence that moving electric charges in an atom produce the light emitted. Going back as far as Faraday, previous attempts to detect such an effect had failed for want of optical instruments with sufficient resolving power. With the discoveries of radioactivity and the electron, the evidence for electric charges within the atom became more definite.

Since a neutral atom must contain equal amounts of positive and negative electricity the question arose as to the distribution of positive electricity in the atom and the location of the electrons. J. J. Thomson had considered the possibility that the positive electricity might be spread through the atom with electrons embedded in it in what he lightly referred to as a kind of "plum-pudding" atom. The successful theory would have to explain among other things the stability of atoms and the characteristic spectral lines emitted by the atoms of an element. Thomson could not explain the latter and a successful theory had to await the critical experiments that located the positive electric charge in the atom. These were called *scattering* experiments.

It had been observed that when a high-speed alpha particle from a radioactive source strikes a fluorescent screen it produces a flash of light, and when a narrow pencil of these particles falls on the screen a sharply defined bright spot will appear. But if a piece of thin metal foil is put in the path of the rays, although most of the rays penetrate the foil, the luminous spot becomes larger and more diffuse. The explanation was that some of the alpha particles are deflected (or *scattered*) by collision with particles in the metal foil. In 1910 Geiger, working in Thomson's laboratory, showed that although the small-angle scattering of alpha particles could be accounted for by current theory a small number of alpha particles were scattered through such large angles as to be completely inconsistent with theory. The alpha particles had speeds of about 2×10^7 m/sec.

This dilemma was solved by E. Rutherford (1911) in a brilliant analysis when he showed that for such large-angle scattering to occur, the positive charge in the atom must be concentrated in an extremely small region in the atom with a radius of approximately 10^{-12} cm. Large-angle scattering of a single ray by successive impacts (multiple scattering) was shown to be highly improbable because of the thinness of the metal foil. Furthermore, since electrons possessed too little mass to be effective in producing deflections of the far more massive alpha particles, nearly all of the mass of the atom must be concentrated at the center of the atom along with the positive charge. This revolutionary viewpoint marked the beginning of the concept of the *nuclear atom*. More accurate measurements by Geiger and Marsden (and later by Chadwick in 1920) confirmed the new theory and even showed that a small number of alpha particles were deflected more than 90° and a few almost 180°.

Rutherford's analysis led to his well-known *scattering formula* by which the number of alpha particles scattered through any angle could be computed and then compared with the experimental results. Although Rutherford obtained his formula by an application of classical mechanics and classical electrical theory the same formula has now been obtained by quantum-mechanical methods and it is noteworthy as being one of the few instances in which classical methods give valid results in the atomic realm. For simplicity we limit ourselves in what follows to the classical method.

In addition to the extraordinary results of the so-called Rutherford scattering experiments the importance of such experiments in general can hardly be overestimated. Many different types of scattering of different kinds of particles have been studied since then and are still being studied with results unattainable by other methods. A recent example is the work of Hofstadter in studying the scattering of very high energy electrons by atomic nuclei (§ 14-13).

7-1. Rutherford's Scattering Experiment; The Nuclear Atom

If a small particle with positive charge approaches another small positive particle the force of repulsion between the two according to Coulomb's law should vary inversely as the square of the distance between them as shown in Fig. 7-1. There was, of course, no guarantee that classical laws would hold at such small distances. However, if they did and if the positive charge of an atom were concentrated in a *nucleus* which is very small compared to the atom itself, the distance of approach of a high-speed alpha particle could be small enough (and the repulsive force could be large enough) to account for the observed occasional large-angle scattering (Fig. 7-2).

The angles of scattering may be measured as indicated in Fig. 7-3. In Fig. 7-4 the path of a single particle is represented showing how the particle is scattered (deflected) by Coulomb repulsion through an angle θ. Rutherford assumed a typical alpha particle might move toward a gold nucleus along a line which would carry it within a distance a (called the *impact parameter*) of the nucleus if it were not deflected.

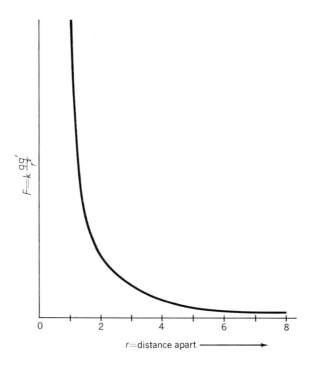

Fig. 7-1. The Coulomb force of repulsion between two positively charged particles as a function of their distance apart.

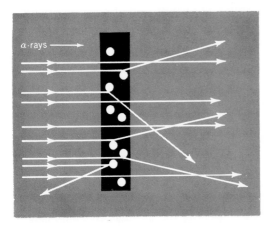

Fig. 7-2. Alpha particles scattered by nuclei in metal foil with occasional large-angle scattering if nuclei are very small.

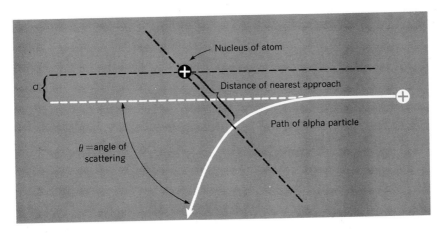

Fig. 7-3. The Rutherford experiment to measure scattering of alpha particles at angle θ from initial direction. M is a microscope to observe scintillations on fluorescent screen S.

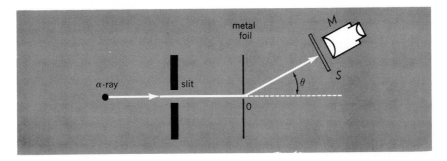

Fig. 7-4. Scattered alpha particle, deflected by repulsion of atomic nucleus.

Applying the law of conservation of energy, and also of conservation of angular momentum of the alpha particle about the nucleus, it is not too difficult to arrive at the angle θ through which the alpha particle of mass M_α moving with velocity v will be deflected for a particular value of a. This is given by

$$\tan \frac{\theta}{2} = \frac{k2Ze^2}{M_\alpha v^2 a} \qquad [7\text{--}1]$$

where k is a constant depending on the units employed and Z is the number of positive charges of electronic magnitude on the target nucleus.

But of course no one alpha particle could be aimed at any particular nucleus and statistical methods had to be applied. If we assume that only one gold nucleus is present in an area A of the foil and that this area is bombarded with N_0 alpha particles, then on the average we would expect $N_0(\pi a^2/A)$ to be aimed so that if undeflected they would pass within a distance a of the nucleus. By the same reasoning we would expect $N_0 2\pi a da/A$ to pass at distances between a and $a + da$ of the nucleus and if there are N' gold nuclei in the area A of foil then $N'N_0 2\pi a da/A$ would be expected to pass (if undeflected). This may be written $nN_0 2\pi a da$ where n is the number of atomic nuclei per unit area of the target.

The angle of scattering (deflection) for alpha particles passing at this distance from a nucleus can be computed if we assume that repulsion occurs according to the Coulomb inverse square law. It is also assumed that the nucleus in its recoil takes little energy from the alpha particle. The computation then gives for the fraction f of impinging particles scattered through an angle θ into the angle $\theta + d\theta$

$$f = k^2 \frac{N_0 n Z^2 e^4}{M_\alpha^2 v^4} \frac{(2\pi \sin \theta \, d\theta)}{\sin^4 \dfrac{\theta}{2}} \qquad [7\text{--}2]$$

where $\frac{1}{2} M_\alpha v^2$ is the classical energy of the alpha particle.

Although Eq. 7–2 is the basic scattering equation it is desirable for the practical purposes of experimental measurement to carry the mathematical development a little further. Since the scattering is in all directions it is simpler to say that the paths of the scattered alpha particles lie just beyond a cone of solid angle $\omega = 2\pi \cos \theta$, the plane section of which is θ, and lie on the increment $d\omega$ of ω, the plane section of which is $d\theta$, where $d\omega = 2\pi \sin \theta \, d\theta$. The area subtending the solid angle $d\omega$ at a distance r from the origin is $r^2 d\omega$. To obtain the number of scattered particles per unit area we divide Eq. 7–2 by $r^2 d\omega = r^2 2\pi \sin \theta \, d\theta$, giving for the number per unit area at angle θ and distance r from the origin

$$N_A = k^2 \frac{n N_0 Z^2 e^4}{r^2 M_\alpha^2 v^4} \frac{1}{\sin^4 \dfrac{\theta}{2}} \qquad [7\text{--}3]$$

This is the quantity measured by Geiger and Marsden who observed the scintillation of each alpha particle as it struck a fluorescent screen, and counted the number of scintillations per unit area for different angles of scattering.

The nearest distance d that the alpha particle can approach the nucleus when moving directly toward it, is

$$d = k \frac{4Ze^2}{M_a v^2} \qquad [7\text{-}4]$$

This formula is readily obtained from classical theory by recalling that at any distance r from a point charge Ze, representing the charge of the nucleus of an atom, the potential V is

$$V = k \frac{Ze}{r} \qquad [7\text{-}5]$$

where k is a constant depending on the units used. In mks units $k = 9 \times 10^9$, approximately. The potential energy, E_p, of the alpha particle with charge $2e$ at a distance d from the target nucleus is therefore

$$E_p = k \frac{2Ze^2}{d} \qquad [7\text{-}6]$$

If the velocity of the alpha particle is v its kinetic energy is $\frac{1}{2} M_a v^2$ and when the opposing field around the nucleus brings the alpha particle momentarily to rest its kinetic energy has been changed to potential energy,

$$\frac{1}{2} M_a v^2 = k \frac{2Ze^2}{d} \qquad [7\text{-}7]$$

from which Eq. 7-4 can be obtained and d can be computed. Of course the alpha particle continues to be accelerated backwards, reverses its motion, and is said to be scattered 180°.

In Chadwick's repetition of these experiments the precision was sufficient to enable the charge on the nucleus of the scattering atom to be determined, confirming the idea that nuclear charge increases with increasing atomic weight. In one experiment gold leaf was bombarded by alpha particles of 2×10^7 m/sec speed. If the nuclear charge Ze for gold is $79e$ Rutherford calculated that the distance of nearest approach to the nucleus of a gold atom must be about 3.2×10^{-12} cm. For the nucleus of a silver atom (for which $Z = 47$) the distance of nearest approach would be about 2×10^{-12} cm. It thus appeared that Coulomb's law of repulsion held down to these extremely small distances and that the nucleus of the atom was less than a ten-thousandth of the diameter of the atom itself.

There remained the problems of the stability of such an atom and the explanation of atomic spectra. Before discussing the break-down of classical theory in connection with the way in which these problems were solved by Niels Bohr in the case of hydrogen, it is desirable to become more familiar with the hydrogen spectrum.

7-2. The Hydrogen Spectrum

In 1888 Balmer who had been studying the visible lines of the hydrogen spectrum proposed a formula to account for the four lines that he was able to see and measure. These are known as the H_α, H_β, H_γ, and H_δ lines, the positions of which in the visible spectrum are represented in Fig. 7-5. These are now spoken of as the first four lines of the *Balmer series*. In a series of this kind the successive lines of the series become fainter but closer together as they approach what is called the *series limit*. Balmer showed that the wavelengths of these lines fitted numerically into a simple formula by means of which the wavelengths could be computed with surprising accuracy. This formula is what is known as an *empirical formula* because it was not based upon theoretical considerations, and it was not aimed at explaining anything. It was merely a formula deduced from observations in order to bring all four observed hydrogen lines into some mathematical relationship. The underlying meaning of the formula, if there was any, was yet to be found.

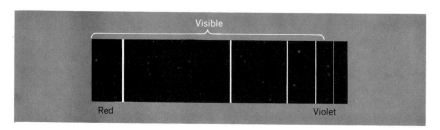

Fig. 7-5. The first five Balmer series lines of hydrogen, beginning with H_α on the left.

Balmer's formula could be readily solved for the frequency $\nu = c/\lambda$ of the light instead of the wavelength λ and because spectroscopists commonly use the *wave number* $\tilde{\nu}$ instead of the frequency it is now usually given in that form. The wave number in the cgs system is the number of waves per centimeter of path of the wave (in a vacuum) where $\tilde{\nu} = 1/\lambda$. Balmer's formula for the visible lines of the hydrogen spectrum then takes the form in which it was put by Rydberg

$$\tilde{\nu} = \frac{1}{\lambda} = R\left(\frac{1}{2^2} - \frac{1}{n^2}\right)$$
[7–8]

$$R = 109{,}678 \text{ (for hydrogen)}$$
[7–9]

where R is called the *Rydberg constant*. Rydberg followed Balmer and made extensive spectroscopic measurements. With some modifications he extended the usefulness of the formula by purely empirical methods to some heavier atoms. For hydrogen R has the value just given, but for other atoms it is slightly larger for reasons which will soon appear (§7-4).

The first term in the parenthesis of the formula has a constant value for the Balmer series and n in the second term takes successive integral values, one value for each spectral line. It is called a *running constant*.

Not only did the Balmer formula predict more lines in the series than Balmer himself observed (more than 30 have been photographed in stellar spectra), but the possibility of varying the first term in the parenthesis of Eq. 7–8 also suggested other series. These are now well known; chief among them are the *Lyman series* in which the $1/(2^2)$ of Eq. 7–8 is replaced by $1/(1^2)$, and the *Paschen series* in which the $1/(2^2)$ is replaced by $1/(3^2)$. The separate formulas are as follows:

Lyman series

$$\tilde{\nu} = \frac{1}{\lambda} = R \left(\frac{1}{1^2} - \frac{1}{n^2} \right) \qquad n = 2, 3, 4, \cdots \qquad [7\text{–}10]$$

Paschen series

$$\tilde{\nu} = \frac{1}{\lambda} = R \left(\frac{1}{3^2} - \frac{1}{n^2} \right) \qquad n = 4, 5, 6, \cdots \qquad [7\text{–}11]$$

A few lines in other series also emitted by hydrogen have been found and are given by substituting for the constant term $1/(4^2)$ or $1/(5^2)$. These less intense series are called, respectively, the *Brackett series* and the *Pfund series*. The Lyman series is in the ultraviolet region of the spectrum, the Balmer series is in the visible and ultraviolet, and the Paschen series is in the infrared (Fig. 7-6). The remaining series are still further in the infrared region. In each of these series the most striking feature is the orderly relation of the lines and the way they approach a limit.

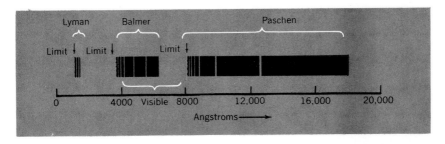

Fig. 7-6. Location of principal series of spectral lines of hydrogen in terms of wavelengths.

Of particular importance was the recognition that the specific formulas for each series were only modifications of one general formula

$$\tilde{\nu} = \frac{1}{\lambda} = R\left(\frac{1}{n_1{}^2} - \frac{1}{n_2{}^2}\right) \qquad [7\text{--}12]$$

Then n_1 takes the values 1, 2, 3, 4, etc. for the Lyman, Balmer, Paschen, Brackett, etc. series respectively, while in each series the separate lines are given by letting n_2 take successive integral values.

7-3. The Bohr Theory of the Hydrogen Atom

The great "break-through" in atomic theory came in 1913 when Niels Bohr (1885–1963) proposed his now famous theory of the hydrogen atom and showed that he could derive Eq. 7–12 from purely theoretical considerations. Starting with the new idea of the nuclear atom Bohr showed that classical principles of mechanics and electricity failed to provide a solution to the problem. Only by the radical innovation of introducing quantum methods to supplement classical theory could success be attained. Although present-day methods do not begin with classical theory and then modify it, there is much to be learned from what Bohr did.

Since the wave character of the electron was unknown at that time, Bohr treated the electron as a charged particle and this immediately led to certain contradictions. Because the hydrogen atom is the lightest and simplest one of all, Bohr assumed it to consist of a single proton as the nucleus and a single external electron revolving about the proton. The electron was then assumed to be held in its orbit by the electrical attraction between the nucleus and the electron, such that the centripetal force mv^2/r just equals the Coulomb force of attraction ke^2/r^2, where k is a constant depending on the choice of units.

$$\frac{mv^2}{r} = \frac{ke^2}{r^2} \qquad [7\text{--}13]$$

However, such a revolving electron is continuously accelerated toward the center of path and by classical theory such an accelerated charge should radiate energy like any electric oscillator. This would cause a continual loss of energy which would make the electron spiral into the nucleus and be absorbed. Thus the atom would be unstable and could only exist briefly. Bohr then boldly introduced the assumption of stable *non-radiating orbits*. Although he had no very good reasons he assumed, contrary to classical electrodynamics, that the atom possesses certain possible orbits in which the electron can revolve without radiating and that an electron can never revolve in an intermediate orbit.

To explain radiation and absorption of energy Bohr further assumed that radiation only happens when an electron transition or "jump" occurs, in which the electron passes from an outer orbit of higher energy to an inner orbit of lesser energy, or, as we now say, since orbits are no longer sharply defined, from a *higher energy level* or *energy state* to another, *lower energy level*. Absorption of energy would then occur when the transition is in the opposite direction.

That an electron would possess more energy in an orbit of larger radius was fairly evident, since work would have to be done against the attraction of the nucleus just as work is done in raising an object above the surface of the earth. Later we shall see that according to wave-mechanical theory the position of the electron in an atom is not sharply defined and the idea of exact orbits loses much if not all of its meaning. However, in many instances the electron behaves as if it possesses orbital angular momentum which can be sharply defined and we often find it convenient to refer to orbits as if we could define them also.

Bohr next introduced the Planck quantum hypothesis and assumed that in a transition between two energy levels a single quantum of energy $h\nu$ is emitted or absorbed in the form of radiation of frequency ν, where the quantum of energy is equal to the difference between the energy E_2 in some initial state and the energy E_1 in the final state.

$$h\nu = E_2 - E_1 \qquad [7\text{-}14]$$

Equation 7–14 defines the frequency of a spectral line in terms of the difference between two energy levels just as in Eq. 7-12 it is given by the difference between two terms. It remained for Bohr to satisfactorily define the correct set of energy levels or in other words in terms of the particle concept to locate the required non-radiating orbits. How this was to be done was not immediately evident and surmounting this obstacle was perhaps Bohr's chief accomplishment.

What was difficult for Bohr to do can now be very easily done by means of the de Broglie wave concept which was not known until a decade after Bohr's work. According to the wave picture a stable orbit would be one in which there would be an integral number of whole wavelengths in a complete circumference of the orbit (Fig. 7-7a). In other words the de Broglie waves should form a repeatable or stationary pattern. The pattern in Fig. 7-7b does not do this as the circumference is not an integral number of wavelengths and the wave displacement at any point is multi-valued instead of single-valued as it should be for a stable orbit. For a stable orbit then the circumference $2\pi r$ should be equal to $n\lambda$ where n is any integer and λ is the de Broglie wavelength.

$$n\lambda = 2\pi r \qquad [7\text{-}15]$$

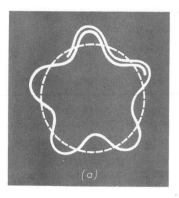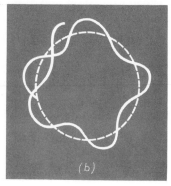

Fig. 7-7.   The orbit for n = 5 in hydrogen, according to the de Broglie wave concept.

From Eq. 5–21 for the de Broglie wavelength, then

$$\frac{nh}{mv} = 2\pi r \qquad [7\text{--}16]$$

Treating the electron as a particle as Bohr did, the speed of the electron is determined by the required centripetal acceleration. Then Eq. 7–16 defines a unique set of quantized orbits, one for each of the integers from one to infinity represented by n where n is called the *principal quantum number*.

In Fig. 7-7a there are 5 whole wavelengths around the orbit and $n = 5$ for this orbit. The innermost orbit (ground state) should have only one wavelength ($n = 1$). Although more difficult to picture, there can be no smaller repeatable wave pattern, the atom is stable in the lowest level or *ground state*, and the electron cannot spiral into the nucleus.

Although we have just shown how Eq. 7–16 can be readily reached by means of the wave concept of the electron, Bohr derived the same relation in a quite different manner. Reasoning in part by analogy he came to the conclusion that it would be necessary to extend the idea of quantization to angular momentum as well as to energy, and that the fundamental unit of angular momentum was $h/2\pi$. The electron in its orbital motion could then only have integral multiples of this unit. Since the angular momentum of the electron in a circular orbit of radius r is mvr the allowed angular momentum must be given by

$$mvr = n\frac{h}{2\pi} = n\,\hbar \qquad [7\text{--}17]$$

where n takes on integral values. But this is exactly the same relation as Eq. 7–16 which was arrived at more directly. At the time it was thought to be a radical extension of the idea of quantization but it was later found to be in harmony with Planck's ideas. For instance, from the definition of the quantum of radiation, h has the dimensions of *action* (energy multiplied by time) but these can be shown to be the same as the dimensions of angular momentum. The symbol $\hbar$ stands for $h/2\pi$.

To adequately describe the hydrogen spectrum it is necessary to be able to compute the various possible energy states. Actually these are states of the atom as a whole and not just of the electron although it is often convenient to just talk about the electron.

Although to Bohr the determination of the radii of the possible non-radiating orbits was a major problem which had to be solved before he could compute the energy of an electron in any orbit, these radii have lost their importance because of the change from the older quantum physics of the particle picture to the more complete analysis afforded by the wave picture (next chapter). However, for reasons of physical simplicity as well as historical interest, it is desirable to follow through with the particle picture in the derivation of the Bohr equation.

THE RADIUS OF THE HYDROGEN ATOM

If Eq. 7–16 is solved for v and then squared, the value of v^2 may be substituted in Eq. 7–13. The resulting equation may be solved for the radius r, giving for any integral value of n the appropriate radius r_n.

$$r_n = \frac{n^2h^2}{k4\pi^2e^2m} \qquad\qquad [7\text{--}18]$$

If n is put equal to 1 in Eq. 7–18, it then gives the radius for the innermost orbit, which is the normal orbit for the unexcited hydrogen atom. This radius can be readily computed, and in terms of the known values of the quantities involved it turns out to be

$$r \text{ (first Bohr orbit)} = 0.529 \times 10^{-8} \text{ cm or } 0.529 \text{ Å}$$

This is in good agreement with the best values for the radius of the hydrogen atom obtained by experimental methods, such as those involving the kinetic theory of gases. It is also closely checked by later more complete quantum-mechanical methods.

THE BOHR EQUATION

Bohr derived his equation for the hydrogen spectrum by making four basic assumptions the first two of them classical and the second two non-classical.

1. The electron is held in an orbit about the proton by Coulomb attraction (Eq. 7–13).
2. The binding energy of the electron is the difference between its kinetic energy and its Coulomb potential energy (Eq. 7–19).

3. The electron can revolve in certain orbits (stationary states) without radiating energy. The radii of these orbits are determined by quantizing the angular momenta (Eq. 7–17).

4. The frequency ν of radiation emitted (or absorbed) is determined by quantizing the energy difference ΔE between two states so that $\Delta E = h\nu$ (Eq. 7–14).

The energy an electron possesses in any orbit is the sum of its potential and kinetic energies. The potential energy of an electron of charge $-e$ at a distance r from a proton of charge e is $-ke^2/r$. The minus sign means this is energy lost with respect to infinity. The kinetic energy $\frac{1}{2}mv^2$ of orbital motion must be less than this in magnitude otherwise the electron would escape from the nucleus. The net energy E is equal to

$$E = \frac{1}{2}mv^2 - \frac{ke^2}{r} \qquad [7\text{–}19]$$

From Eq. 7–13 it can be seen that $\frac{1}{2}mv^2$ is equal to $ke^2/2r$. Therefore

$$E = \frac{ke^2}{2r} - \frac{ke^2}{r} = -\frac{1}{2}\frac{ke^2}{r} \qquad [7\text{–}20]$$

This is the binding energy of an electron in its orbit. It is the amount of energy which must be supplied to remove the electron completely from the nucleus.

The energy difference between two orbits r_1 and r_2 can now be written equal to $h\nu$ (Eq. 7–14) as follows

$$h\nu = E_2 - E_1 = \frac{ke^2}{2}\left(\frac{1}{r_1} - \frac{1}{r_2}\right) \qquad [7\text{–}21]$$

If we put expressions for two different radii, r_1 and r_2, from Eq. 7–18 into Eq. 7–21 we may solve for ν the frequency of the radiation, but it is more common to solve for the wave number $1/\lambda = \nu/c$. This gives the Bohr equation,

$$\frac{1}{\lambda} = \frac{\nu}{c} = R\left(\frac{1}{n_1{}^2} - \frac{1}{n_2{}^2}\right) \qquad [7\text{–}22]$$

in cgs units where $k = 1$ and where

$$R = \frac{2\pi^2 me^4}{ch^3} \qquad [7\text{–}23]$$

Putting in the appropriate values, $R = 109737 \text{ cm}^{-1}$.

In mks units

$$k = \frac{1}{4\pi\epsilon_0} = 8.98776 \times 10^9$$

and

$$R = 1.09737 \times 10^7 \text{ m}^{-1}$$

Since Eq. 7–23 was found to give a satisfactory value for the Rydberg constant after a small correction was made (next section) Eq. 7–22 was seen to be the same as Eq. 7–8.

Equation 7–22 gives the frequencies of spectral lines emitted in electron transitions from any higher energy level n_2 to a lower level n_1. Such transitions produce *bright line* or *emission spectra*. Transitions in the opposite direction can remove these lines from a continuous bright spectrum and produce the dark lines of an absorption spectrum. The transitions representing the first five lines of each of the three series, Lyman, Balmer and Paschen, are shown in Fig. 7-8.

Early investigators had puzzled over how an atom of hydrogen could emit so many different spectral frequencies at one time. It now became clear that different atoms undergoing different transitions were responsible for the different lines, and that any one atom could only emit one frequency at a time. The brightness of any line is a measure of the probability that the particular transition will occur.

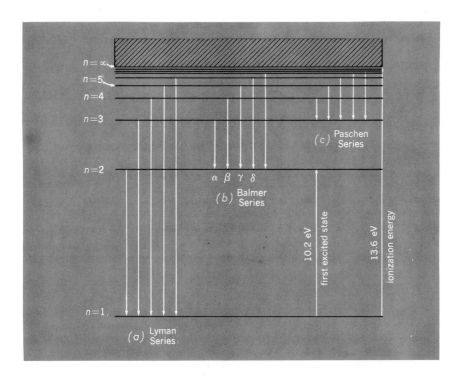

Fig. 7-8. Energy levels of hydrogen (horizontal lines). The transitions (arrows) represent the first few lines of *a*, the Lyman series; *b*, the Balmer series; *c*, the Paschen series.

7-4. Successes of the Bohr Theory

The derivation of Eq. 7–22 by Bohr was a theoretical achievement of the first order. It marked the end of one era and the beginning of another in which, in time, quantum methods were to supplant classical methods in the atomic realm. In brief summary the more important successes of the Bohr theory were as follows.

1. It accounted for the Balmer and other hydrogen series.
2. It derived the Rydberg constant from known physical quantities.
3. It gave a satisfactory value for the radius of the hydrogen atom.
4. It accounted quantitatively for ionization and excitation potentials.

It had several other successes, such as the explanation of the normal Zeeman effect (§ 9-5) and the explanation of the spectra of hydrogen-like atoms.

IONIZATION AND EXCITATION POTENTIALS

The Bohr theory was also successful in making it possible to compute theoretical values of the ionization potential and excitation potentials for the hydrogen atom. The ionization potential of hydrogen represents the energy required to remove the electron completely from its nucleus. In terms of the Bohr orbital picture this is equivalent to raising the electron up to that orbit for which n equals infinity. Putting n equal to infinity in Eq. 7–22, we have, since $n_1 = 1$,

$$E_\infty - E_1 = h\nu = \frac{k^2 2\pi^2 m e^4}{h^2}\left(\frac{1}{n_1} - \frac{1}{\infty}\right) \qquad [7\text{--}24]$$

or

$$= \frac{k^2 2\pi^2 m e^4}{h^2} \qquad [7\text{--}25]$$

This may be reduced to electron volts by dividing by 1.6×10^{-12} erg/eV (when the energy is computed in ergs) or 1.6×10^{-19} joule/eV (depending on the units used). Putting in the appropriate values for the different quantities and making the computation, we find for the hydrogen atom H^1

$$H^1 \text{ Ionizing potential} = 13.56 \text{ eV}$$

This is in good agreement with the ionization potential of atomic hydrogen obtained experimentally when molecular hydrogen is dissociated.

Excitation potentials may be similarly computed and are in close agreement with experimental values. For instance, the energy required to raise the electron from its normal state to the next energy level or first excited state, is the *first excitation potential* and is found to have a computed value of 10.2 eV for hydrogen.

It is often desirable to write the Bohr equation in terms of electron volts. The energy of an electron in any level of principal quantum number n, when referred to infinity as zero energy, is

$$E_n = \frac{-13.60}{n^2} Z^2 \text{ (eV)}$$

The difference in energy between any two energy levels n_1 and n_2 is then

$$\Delta E \text{ (eV)} = E_{n_1} - E_{n_2} = -13.60 \, Z^2 \left(\frac{1}{n_1^2} - \frac{1}{n_2^2}\right) \qquad [7\text{--}26]$$

HYDROGENIC ATOMS

The Bohr theory applied particularly to an atom composed of a positively charged nucleus with one external electron. The helium atom has two external electrons; however, if a helium atom has been singly ionized, it now has only one electron and it is said to be *hydrogen-like* or *hydrogenic*, the difference being only in the charge on the nucleus. Similarly, lithium which has three planetary electrons per atom would be hydrogenic if it were doubly ionized. The Bohr formula gives the correct frequencies for the lines observed from these hydrogenic atoms, but since the charge on the nucleus is $2e$ for helium, $3e$ for lithium, and so on for heavier atoms the Bohr equation for the wave number becomes

$$\frac{1}{\lambda} = Z^2 R \left(\frac{1}{n_1^2} - \frac{1}{n_2^2}\right) \qquad [7\text{--}26a]$$

where Z is the number of positive electronic charges on the nucleus. For corresponding transitions the formula now predicts higher frequencies. This has been confirmed by experiment, and two well-known series of lines, called the Fowler and Pickering series (observed astronomically) whose origins had been unknown, were found to be produced by ionized helium.

THE RYDBERG CONSTANT. REDUCED MASS

The value of the Rydberg constant for hydrogen R_H can be obtained with great precision from spectroscopic measurements. It is

$$R_H = 109,677.58 \text{ cm}^{-1}$$

Eq. 7–24 is slightly in error because the original assumption that the electron moves about a motionless proton would only be true if the proton had infinite mass. Actually they each move about their common center of mass, and this is appreciable even though the larger mass of the proton makes its motion slight. The correction for this may be accomplished by assuming that the effective mass of the electron, assuming the proton is stationary, is slightly less than the actual mass. The correction can be made in the Bohr formula by replacing the mass of the electron with what is called the *reduced mass* μ where

$$\mu = \frac{Mm}{M + m} \qquad [7\text{--}27]$$

M being the mass of the nucleus and m the mass of the electron.

This formula may be obtained readily by "balancing masses" about the center of mass. If the distance between electron and nucleus is r and if the center of mass is assumed to be at a distance x from the electron then it is at a distance r-x from the nucleus. By balancing masses $M(r\text{-}x) = m(x)$. From this

$$\frac{Mm}{M + m}\, r = mx \qquad [7\text{--}28]$$

and instead of multiplying the distance x by the full mass m we can equally well multiply the distance r by the reduced mass $\mu = Mm/M + m$.

Since the reduced mass of the electron depends upon the mass of the nucleus the Rydberg constant varies slightly for different atoms and should be written with μ instead of m in Eq. 7–23. Values of the Rydberg constant R determined from spectroscopic data for different atoms of the hydrogenic type are given in Table 7-1. Without the correction for the reduced mass the value of R is called R_∞, meaning the value that it would have if the electron rotated about a fixed center of infinite mass. Spectroscopic measurements are made with such precision that these differences are important.

TABLE 7-1. RYDBERG CONSTANT FOR DIFFERENT ATOMS

Atom	Rydberg Constant (cm^{-1})
Hydrogen ($_1H^1$)	109677.58
Deuterium ($_1H^2$)	109707.42
Helium ($_2He^4$)	109722.27
Lithium ($_3Li^7$)	109728.72
Oxygen ($_8O^{16}$)	109733.54
Infinite mass	109737.31

7-5. Isotope Shift and Deuterium

The fact that the reduced electron mass in the corrected Bohr formula depends upon the mass of the nucleus to an appreciable degree means that a sufficient variation of the mass of the nucleus of an atom would appear as a small frequency shift and a slight displacement of the spectral lines. If the isotopes of an element differ sufficiently in mass this shift, called the isotope shift, should be detectable. The largest shift would of course be between isotopes having the largest relative difference in nuclear mass. Even after isotopes were discovered, the possibility that hydrogen itself might have isotopes was not at first considered, but when slight unaccounted variations of chemical atomic weights suggested it, Urey, Brickwedde, and Murphy, in 1932, by sensitive spectroscopic means found a faint trace of a spectral line of hydrogen displaced slightly from the normal. Succeeding experiments confirmed their hypothesis that this was due to the heavy hydrogen atom H^2, thus it was the isotope shift that led to the discovery of heavy hydrogen or deuterium.

7-6. Limitations of the Bohr Theory

Despite the extraordinary success of the original Bohr theory it had serious limitations which in time became more evident. This led to the search for a more thorough-going quantum mechanical theory. In brief:

1. It failed to account for the spectra of complex atoms.

2. It could not deal with atoms as simple as neutral helium having more than one electron.

3. It did not permit the calculation of the intensities of lines.

4. It failed to give correct results in the more complicated conditions of splitting of lines by a magnetic field, known as the anomalous Zeeman effect (§9-5).

5. It did not account for the fine structure observed in the hydrogen lines, and it did not account for such simple matters as the doublet structure of the alkali metal spectra.

7-7. The Fine Structure of Hydrogen Lines; Quantum Numbers

A defect of the simple Bohr theory as applied to hydrogen becomes apparent when observations are made by means of spectroscopic apparatus of very high resolving power. Some of the principal hydrogen lines were then found not to be single lines, as they at first seemed to be, but were actually composed of several lines extremely close together. This is what is known as the *fine structure* of hydrogen lines. The discovery that the first line H_α (red line) of the Balmer series is not a single line but is composed of at least two components (perhaps more) was made by Michelson and Morley in 1887.

Actually no spectral line is the ideally narrow line it may appear to a casual observer. Instead, spectral lines are broadened for several reasons and the intensity usually follows a curve such as in Fig. 7–9a. Most of the broadening results from thermal agitation. Some atoms are moving toward and some are moving away from the observer producing a small

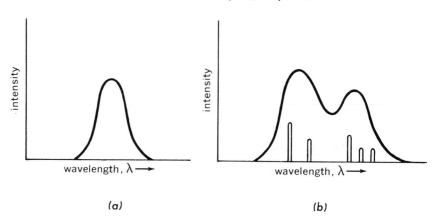

Fig. 7-9. *a,* Represents the usual broadening of an ideal narrow spectral line. *b,* Represents the "fine structure" of the H$_\alpha$ line of hydrogen as found by Michelson and Morley. Quantum theory predicts the five separate lines indicated below the broad curve.

spread of frequencies (Doppler shift) instead of a single frequency for a given line. Michelson and Morley found the structure of the H$_\alpha$ line to have two marked peaks (Fig. 7-9*b*) and a weaker third component was later noticed more or less hidden by the other two. Modern quantum theory predicts that there are three weaker components, five in all, but the overlapping makes it very difficult to distinguish them experimentally.

The particle model of the atom though destined to be displaced by the wave-mechanical model was all that was available for a considerable period. Attempts to modify the Bohr theory (particle model) so that it would be more useful had only small success.

Bohr had recognized that a circular orbit is not the most general form of an orbit for a particle under the action of a central force. However, he also knew that by classical mechanics particles in elliptic orbits all having the same major axis (that is, the same principal quantum number n) would all possess the same energy. In this connection Arnold Sommerfeld did two things of interest today in putting relativity into the atom and by inventing a new set of quantum numbers. By means of the latter he restricted the number of possible elliptic orbits for a given principal quantum number n to just those having angular momenta that are integral multiples of the fundamental unit $\hbar$ equal to or less than $n\hbar$.

Then by making a relativistic correction for the varying speeds of electrons in elliptical orbits he was able to show that orbits of different degrees of ellipticity would possess slightly different energies. This "splitting of the energy levels" enabled him to give an approximate explanation of the fine structure of the hydrogen lines according to which the Balmer lines should have three components. But when similar ideas were applied to the spectra of the alkali metals there was something definitely lacking and it became evident that a third set of quantum numbers was required even though only capable of possessing two values. And when the behavior of atoms in a magnetic field was studied still more was lacking. A fourth set of quantum numbers was required.

The solution of these difficulties came when the "old quantum theory" based on the particle-like character of the electron was given up for the "new quantum theory" based on the wave-like character of the electron. Classical and semi-classical theory was then replaced by quantum-mechanical theory and the description of the energy states of an atom in terms of unobservable orbits was given up in favor of their description in terms of quantum numbers. To adequately do this it was found that 4 sets of quantum numbers were required. Three of these sets came out of the solution of the problem of the hydrogen atom by means of the Schrödinger wave-mechanical equation (next chapter). The fourth set (along with the others) came out of the more complete relativistic theory of Dirac in 1928 (§8-8). Instead of inventing quantum numbers as needed and making up a "patchwork system" the required sets of quantum numbers were found to come naturally out of quantum-mechanical theory. This subject will be developed in the following chapter.

7-8. The Correspondence Principle: Fine Structure Constant

Going back to the orbital picture of the atom, if we consider the frequency with which an electron must be assumed to rotate in a Bohr orbit of low principal quantum number we see it is far removed from the frequencies of the emitted light. This is a good reason why classical physics could not explain the emission of light in terms of the orbital rotation of the electron in its inner orbits. But where classical physics failed, quantum physics succeeded as we have just seen.

On the other hand, by the Bohr principle of correspondence classical theory and quantum theory should be indistinguishable for large quantum numbers. If we solve Eq. 7–13 for the velocity of the electron in its orbit we may compute the frequency of rotation. We may then compare this frequency of rotation with the frequency of the emitted light according to the Bohr theory for small quantum jumps (n to $n - 1$) when the principal quantum number n is very large. If Eq. 7–22 is written for the frequency ν in the form

$$\nu = \frac{c}{\lambda} = ck^2R \left(\frac{1}{n_1{}^2} - \frac{1}{n_2{}^2} \right) = ck^2R \left(\frac{n_2{}^2 - n_1{}^2}{n_1{}^2 n_2{}^2} \right) \qquad [7\text{–}29]$$

then by factoring and substituting n for n_1 and $n - 1$ for n_2 we obtain

$$\nu = ck^2R\,\frac{[n - (n - 1)][n + (n - 1)]}{n^2(n - 1)^2} \qquad [7\text{--}30]$$

and for n very large

$$\nu \cong ck^2R\,\frac{(2n - 1)}{n^4} \cong \frac{2ck^2R}{n^3} \qquad [7\text{--}31]$$

This is the frequency obtained for a small quantum transition.

To show that this is the same as the orbital frequency of the electron when the radius is very large, take Eq. 7–13 and put $v = 2\pi\nu r$; then

$$\frac{ke^2}{r^2} = \frac{mv^2}{r} = \frac{4\pi^2\nu^2r^2m}{r} \qquad [7\text{--}32]$$

Solving for ν the frequency of rotation

$$\nu = \sqrt{ke^2/4\pi^2r^3m} \qquad [7\text{--}33]$$

Putting in the value of the radius r from Eq. 7–18 we have

$$\nu = \frac{2ck^2}{n^3}\left(\frac{2\pi^2me^4}{ch^3}\right) = \frac{2ck^2R}{n^3} \qquad [7\text{--}34]$$

Since the quantity in parenthesis in Eq. 7–34 is the Rydberg constant R (Eq. 7–23), the classical orbital frequency of the electron for very large n is the same as the quantum frequency given by Eq. 7–31 in accordance with the correspondence principle. Bohr himself showed that quantization of energy (provided one accepts the correspondence principle) makes quantization of angular momentum necessary.

FINE STRUCTURE CONSTANT

The speed of the electron in any circular orbit of principal quantum number n can be readily found according to the Bohr theory from the quantum condition for angular momentum (Eq. 7–17) $mvr = nh/2\pi$ and from Eq. 7–13. For the first orbit $(n = 1)$

$$v = \frac{h}{2\pi mr} = k\,\frac{2\pi e^2}{h} \qquad [7\text{--}35]$$

The ratio of this quantity to the speed of light c is

$$\frac{v}{c} = k\left(\frac{2\pi e^2}{hc}\right) = k\alpha \qquad [7\text{--}36]$$

where the quantity in parenthesis is called the *fine structure constant* α. It turns up in so many atomic computations and in quantum electrodynamics that it has unusual significance. If numerical values are substituted into Eq. 7–36, α is found to have the approximate numerical value of $1/137$.

Problems

1. Find the number of silver atoms per cm^2 of silver foil if the thickness of the foil is 10^{-5} cm. The density of silver is 10.6 gm/cm^3 and the atomic mass is 108.

2. Find the number of gold atoms per cm^2 of gold foil if the thickness of the foil is 10^{-5} cm. The density of gold is 19.3 gm/cm^3 and the atomic mass is 197.

3. What is the nearest distance a 7-meV alpha particle can approach to a silver nucleus? What would be the minimum distance of approach for a proton of the same energy?

4. An alpha particle of velocity 1.6×10^7 m/sec is scattered through an angle of 20° by a gold nucleus. What was its *impact parameter a?*

5. At what minimum impact parameter would an alpha particle having a velocity of 2×10^7 m/sec be scattered 5° or less by a gold nucleus? What would be the effective area of the gold nucleus for scattering at this and larger angles?

6. If we assume that half the atoms in the gold foil of problem 2 are not obscured by nuclei in front of them, what is the total target area of nuclei in a cm^2 of the foil? What is the probability of a direct hit by a bombarding particle hitting the area if the probability is proportional to the area and if the particle is undeflected? Take the diameter of a gold nucleus to be roughly 8×10^{-13} cm. Would the particle be likely to make a significant number of multiple collisions?

7. Compute the radius of the normal hydrogen atom (first Bohr orbit).

8. Compute the Rydberg constant by the Bohr formula for singly-ionized helium.

9. Show that for the electron in a deuterium atom the reduced mass is approximately $\mu = 2Mm/(2M + m)$ where M is the mass of a proton.

10. Compute the first and second excitation potentials of hydrogen.

11. What is the gravitational attraction between the electron and proton in a hydrogen atom if the distance between the two is 0.5 Å? How does this compare with the electric force of attraction?

12. The ionization energy of a neutral helium atom is 24.46 eV. How much energy is required to remove the second electron and produce a doubly-ionized atom?

13. Compute the energy required to remove the third electron from a doubly-ionized lithium atom Li^7.

14. Find the energy in eV required to raise a hydrogen atom from the ground state to the third excited state. What spectral line is emitted when the atom returns to the ground state?

15. Find the angular momentum in kg m^2/sec of the electron in the third Bohr orbit of hydrogen.

16. A hydrogen atom undergoes multiple inelastic collisions with electrons. The first collision raises the atom to the first excited state. The second collision raises it to the second excited state. What energy in eV was required in the second collision? What possible spectral lines may be emitted on return to the ground state?

17. An electron is in the energy level for $n = 3$ of hydrogen. Compute the energy in joules and eV required to ionize this atom.

18. Plot a curve representing the radii of electron orbits in hydrogen for $n = 1, 3, 5, 7, 9$ in units of 10^{-8} cm.

19. Plot a curve representing the radii of electron orbits for singly-ionized helium for $n = 1, 3, 5, 7, 9$ in units of 10^{-8} cm.

20. What is the ratio of the de Broglie wavelength for an electron in the nth orbit of hydrogen to the wavelength in the first orbit?

21. Find the limiting value of the ratio of the de Broglie wavelength of an electron in the nth orbit of hydrogen to the circumference of the orbit as n approaches infinity.

22. If the average life-time of an atom in an excited state is 10^{-8} sec, how many revolutions according to the Bohr theory would an electron make in the first excited state of hydrogen ($n = 2$) before returning to the ground state with the emission of a photon?

*23. Will the H_α line for deuterium be higher or lower in frequency than H_α for hydrogen? Why? What will be the wavelength difference in angstroms?

24. Compute the wavelengths in angstroms of the first three lines of the Lyman and of the Paschen series by the simple Bohr formula.

25. Compute the wavelengths in angstroms of the first four lines of the Balmer series of hydrogen by means of the Bohr formula.

26. Compute, by means of the simple Bohr formula, the wave numbers and the wavelengths in angstrom units of the limits of the Lyman and Paschen series of hydrogen.

27. Compute the limit of the Balmer series in wave numbers, in angstrom units, and in electron volts.

*28. Find the radius of the first and second Bohr orbits for a positronium "atom." Can you say which particle moves around the other? (The reduced mass should be used.) What would be the ionization energy?

29. Construct an energy level diagram for atomic hydrogen for the first three energy levels. Compute the energies in eV for each level taking the energy for $n = \infty$ equal to zero, and for $n = 1$ it will then be -13.6 eV.

30. Repeat the previous problem for singly-ionized helium. The first level is -24.5 eV and for $n = \infty$ it is zero.

31. Show which spectral lines for singly-ionized helium will fall almost exactly half-way between those for the Lyman series of atomic hydrogen.

32. Suppose an electron is so far from a proton that it is effectively separated from it (the atom is ionized). If the electron is moving toward the proton with a kinetic energy of 2 eV and is captured by it, what is the frequency of light radiated if the electron goes to the ground state?

33. At what temperature would a hydrogen atom be excited to the first excited level by collision with another atom, assuming a collision in which half the kinetic energy of one atom is transferred to another? The energy of thermal agitation is $3/2 \, kT$.

Recommended Reading

White, H. E., *Introduction to Atomic Spectra.* New York: McGraw-Hill Book Company, Inc., 1934.

Herzberg, G., *Atomic Spectra and Atomic Structure.* New York: Dover Publications, Inc., 1944.

Born, M., *Atomic Physics,* 7th ed. New York: Stechert-Hafner, 1962.

Johnson, R. C., *Atomic Spectra.* London: Methuen & Co., Ltd., 1950.

Andrade, E. N., "The Birth of the Nuclear Atom," *Scientific American,* Vol. 195, No. 5, p. 93 (1956).

Wave Mechanics and the Hydrogen Atom

There are two chief forms of quantum mechanics, one based on the famous wave-mechanical differential equation proposed by Erwin Schrödinger in 1926, and the other based on methods developed by Werner Heisenberg the previous year, involving matrix algebra. Later the two mathematical methods of approach were proved to be equivalent. Additions to the theory by Born, Jordan and Dirac brought it to a high degree of development, and it has proved to be the only successful theory in dealing with the whole realm of atomic and subatomic phenomena.

8-1. The Schrödinger Wave Equation

The Schrödinger equation is the fundamental equation of *wave mechanics*. In its simplest one-dimensional form (non-relativistic), in which the time does not appear as one of the variables, the equation for a particle of mass m is

$$\frac{\partial^2 \psi}{\partial x^2} + \frac{8\pi^2 m}{h^2}(E - V)\psi = 0 \qquad [8\text{-}1]$$

where h is the Planck constant, E is the total energy of the particle and V is its potential energy. In general the potential energy V would not be a constant but would be a function of the coordinates. The quantity ψ called the *wave function* remains to be understood or at least to be given a useful interpretation, but from the equation it is evident that ψ is that quantity that varies just as the displacement of a particle in a mechanical wave varies from point to point at any given time.

In three dimensions the Schrödinger equation would be

$$\left(\frac{\partial^2\psi}{\partial x^2} + \frac{\partial^2\psi}{\partial y^2} + \frac{\partial^2\psi}{\partial z^2}\right) + \frac{8\pi^2 m}{h^2}(E - V)\psi = 0 \qquad [8\text{-}2]$$

or

$$\nabla^2\psi + \frac{8\pi^2 m}{h^2}(E - V)\psi = 0 \qquad [8\text{-}3]$$

where ∇^2 represents the operator

$$\nabla^2 = \frac{\partial^2}{\partial x^2} + \frac{\partial^2}{\partial y^2} + \frac{\partial^2}{\partial z^2} \qquad [8\text{-}4]$$

The derivation of the Schrödinger equation goes back to the familiar equation of wave motion in classical physics. In its one-dimensional form for a wave traveling in either direction along the x axis it may be written

$$\frac{\partial^2 A}{\partial x^2} = \frac{1}{u^2}\frac{\partial^2 A}{\partial t^2} \qquad [8\text{-}5]$$

In this equation A is the "wave function" and it could represent the displacement in a mechanical wave or it could represent the electric or magnetic field components of an electromagnetic wave. Indeed it was when Maxwell found equations of this well-known type involving electric and magnetic fields that he at once saw that such combined fields could be propagated as waves. This led him to the electromagnetic theory of light and to the prediction of the existence of electromagnetic waves.

The Schrödinger equation is closely related to the classical wave equation but involves quantum physics. It includes the de Broglie wavelength of a particle $\lambda = h/mv$, which itself includes the fundamental constant h of the quantum theory. To derive the Schrödinger equation let us put ψ for A in Eq. 8-5. Then

$$\frac{\partial^2\psi}{\partial x^2} = \frac{1}{u^2}\frac{\partial^2\psi}{\partial t^2} \qquad [8\text{-}5a]$$

A simple solution of this equation is well known to be

$$\psi = a \sin \omega t = a \sin\left(\omega\frac{x}{u}\right) \qquad [8\text{-}6]$$

where a is the amplitude of the wave and u is its velocity in the x direction. That this is a solution of the equation can be readily checked by differentiating ψ with respect to x and also with respect to t and substituting back into the original equation. The second derivative of ψ with respect to t is

$$\frac{\partial^2\psi}{\partial t^2} = -\omega^2 a \sin \omega t = -\omega^2\psi \qquad [8\text{-}7]$$

Putting this into Eq. 8–5a we have

$$\frac{\partial^2 \psi}{\partial x^2} + \frac{\omega^2 \psi}{u^2} = 0 \qquad [8\text{--}8]$$

In this equation ω is the usual symbol for angular velocity, and

$$\omega = 2\pi f = 2\pi \frac{u}{\lambda}$$

where u is the linear velocity of the wave and λ is the wavelength. Substituting this value of ω in Eq. 8–8 we have

$$\frac{\partial^2 \psi}{\partial x^2} + \frac{4\pi^2 \psi}{\lambda^2} = 0 \qquad [8\text{--}9]$$

If we now interpret λ not as the wavelength of a classical wave but as the de Broglie wavelength of a particle of mass m, moving with velocity v, we have $\lambda = h/mv$. By classical mechanics the momentum mv of a particle moving with velocity v may be written

$$mv = \sqrt{2m(E - V)} \qquad [8\text{--}10]$$

where E is the total energy, kinetic plus potential, and V is the potential energy. Substituting this expression for mv in $\lambda = h/mv$ and substituting for λ in Eq. 8–9, we arrive at the Schrödinger wave equation in terms of one dimension, x, as previously given (Eq. 8-1).

$$\frac{\partial^2 \psi}{\partial x^2} + \frac{8\pi^2 m}{h^2} (E - V)\psi = 0 \qquad [8\text{--}11]$$

This is what is called the *time-independent* form of the Schrödinger equation and it is the most immediately useful form of the equation. However, the most general form of the Schrödinger equation contains the time and is called the *time-dependent* form.

8-2. Born's Interpretation of ψ

The quantity ψ had at first little physical significance except that it was spoken of as the *wave function* which determines the amplitude of a vibration. Since the electron was chiefly described by the wavelength, the wave amplitude seemed a more or less indefinite if not superfluous quantity. However, a brilliant suggestion was made by Born in 1926.

Born suggested that ψ^2 may represent the probability of finding one or more particles to which it is applied in a given region. This is in direct analogy with an electromagnetic wave in which the square of E, the electric field strength in the wave (or of H, the magnetic field strength), determines the energy density in a beam of light and thus represents the probability of finding one or more photons in a given region (§5-10). For these reasons ψ^2 has been called the *probability density*, and ψ has been called the *probability amplitude*. Unlike E or H which have physical significance as well as an interpretation in terms of probability, ψ is not observable and has no physical significance other than its relation to the probability function. Instead of ψ^2 the probability density is often written $\psi\psi^*$ in more advanced texts. Since ψ itself may be a complex quantity and ψ^* is its complex conjugate, their product will always be real but for our purposes ψ^2 may be taken to be equivalent to $\psi\psi^*$.

If for instance ψ is taken to refer to a single electron, ψ^2 for a given region is interpreted as representing the probability of finding that electron in that region. Numerical values must then be adjusted so that, by integrating the probability of finding any one electron throughout all available space, the answer is unity. Since a probability of unity stands for certainty this means that the electron must certainly be somewhere at any instant. The adjustment of the numerical values so that the integral is unity is called *normalization*. The condition of normalization may be expressed (in one dimension) as

$$\int_{-\infty}^{+\infty} \psi\psi^* \, dx = 1$$

8-3. Quantized Particle in an Impenetrable Box

The description of an atomic or subatomic particle in terms of its de Broglie wavelength leads to results quite different from those reached by classical theory if the particle is confined to a limited region by boundary conditions or by a field of force. Such a particle is called a *bound particle* as distinguished from a particle in free space. For a particle in free space described by the de Broglie relation $\lambda = h/mv$ there can be no limitation on the value of the wavelength λ and consequently the particle can have any value of momentum just as in everyday life an object can be given any amount of momentum (or velocity) up to the relativistic limit. This is not so with a bound particle.

Consider the ideal case of a particle enclosed in a box making perfectly elastic collisions with the walls as it bounces back and forth. Assume that the particle is moving back and forth in the x direction with constant speed in a box of small dimensions with *impenetrable walls*. We ask then, can it move with just any speed or momentum or is it restricted to certain quantized amounts? According to the de Broglie formula, the particle has a wavelength $\lambda = h/mv$, depending on its momentum. Since the box is assumed to be impenetrable the probability of finding the particle beyond the surface of the wall is zero, and the amplitude of the wave on which the probability depends must drop to zero at the walls. For a particle to set up a stationary wave pattern in such a box, representing continual motion back and forth between opposite sides, it appears that the only possible stationary wave patterns for which the displacement falls to zero at the boundaries of the box are exactly those of a vibrating string fixed at the ends. The various modes of vibration form a series in which the length of the string is an integral number of half wavelengths. Consequently, the various simple wave patterns for a particle are those for which the various possible wavelengths (Fig. 8-1) are

$$\lambda = \frac{2d}{n} \ (n = 1, 2, 3, \ldots)$$ [8-12]

where d is the width of the box and n may have any integral value from 1 to ∞. The particular allowed values of the wavelength λ which are solutions of this problem are often called the *characteristic values* or the *eigenvalues*. In more complicated problems these eigenvalues are derived from *characteristic functions* or *eigenfunctions*.

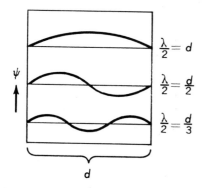

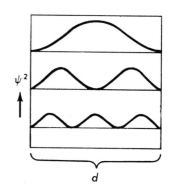

Fig. 8-1. Possible de Broglie wavelengths of amplitude ψ in an impenetrable box of side d, same as possible modes of vibration of a stretched string.

Fig. 8-2. Probability (ψ^2) curves for the wavelengths of Fig. 8-1. Unlike the ψ curve, the values of ψ^2 are always positive.

From the above it appears that for the particle moving back and forth in the box only those momenta are possible for which the de Broglie wavelengths are given by Eq. 8–12. This introduces quantization of the motion of the particle, and since momentum is quantized, only particular discrete states of kinetic energy are possible for such a particle.

There is a very good reason why with the objects of everyday life such quantization is not noticed. If we should try to apply the idea to the motion of a macroscopic particle as small as a just barely visible particle of dust, which of course is enormously more massive than an atomic particle, we would find that unless this particle were given an unreasonably small velocity the wavelength would be so small that no effects of quantization of motion would be noticeable. Thus, as we leave the atomic realm and approach the realm of ordinary events, quantum concepts lose themselves by merging into classical concepts according to the Bohr *principle of correspondence* (§7-8).

Fig. 8-1 represents the values of ψ for different allowed states and Fig. 8-2 represents values of ψ^2 for Fig. 8-1. If ψ^2 in any region is a measure of the probability of finding the particle in that region we find the result is quite different from that of classical mechanics. From the classical viewpoint, since the particle moves with constant velocity, it spends equal times in equal spaces along its path, and the probability of finding it along its path is constant. From the wave picture, although by the artificially imposed conditions the probability must drop to zero at the sides of an impenetrable box, we may be surprised to find that for the higher energy states the probability curve drops to zero at points between. This need not disturb us unduly since the conditions of the experiment are highly artificial, and in this example the wave serves chiefly to introduce quantization of momenta for a *bound* particle as distinguished from the non-quantized states of a free particle. Besides, the standing wave pattern in the box may be thought of as composed of two oppositely directed "running" waves of sharply defined wavelength $\lambda = h/mv$, and as previously noted (§5-13) such a wave train of uniform amplitude does not serve to locate an electron at all. Evidently the principle of uncertainty enters into the picture.

However, when the Schrödinger equation is applied to the hydrogen atom, as we shall see in the present chapter, the conditions are quite different, the amplitude varies from region to region and its square *does* measure the probability of finding the electron at different distances from the atomic nucleus in various energy states (§8-7).

Another important result arises from wave-mechanical analysis. Boundaries which would be impenetrable according to classical physics become penetrable to some degree at least, and the resulting predictions regarding atomic phenomena are in agreement with observations. For an introduction to these matters, let us consider the application of the Schrödinger equation to a barrier that is not assumed to be impenetrable.

8-4. Reflection at a Barrier and the Penetrable Barrier; Quantum Tunneling

Solutions of problems reached by wave-mechanical methods in the atomic or microscopic realm and by classical methods in the macroscopic realm have many striking differences. An important example is that of a moving electron (or other electrically charged particle) approaching a region of reverse electric field. The field is best described in terms of its potential distribution and is called a *potential barrier*.

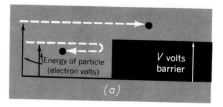 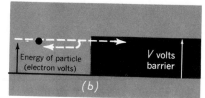

Fig. 8-3.   a, Total transmission or total reflection of electrons at a potential barrier according to classical theory; b, partial transmission (some probability of reflection and some probability of transmission) according to wave mechanics.

According to classical electrical theory, an electron approaching such a barrier will either pass the barrier or be turned back, depending on whether its energy is greater than that required to overcome the reverse field or less than it (Fig. 8-3a). A 90-eV electron approaching a 100-eV barrier can never pass it according to classical theory, and a 110-eV electron will always pass it. In the latter case the electron is said to surmount the barrier. In classical theory there is no such thing as occasional penetration of a barrier.

According to wave-mechanical analysis the results are quite different. Without going fully into the solution of the Schrödinger equation we shall indicate the nature of the solution which clearly predicts that some electrons with insufficient energy to overcome the barrier may penetrate the boundary of the barrier (Fig. 8-3b). If the barrier is infinitely wide, those which penetrate will eventually be turned back in agreement with classical conclusions, but if the barrier is of finite width there will always be some probability that the electron or other particle will penetrate the whole barrier region and escape completely. These findings have important applications in nuclear physics.

Consider an electrically charged particle moving back and forth in a confined region or "box" bounded by an electric field. The walls become a potential barrier. In the region inside the "walls," that is between the barriers, the particle is "trapped" and its potential energy is negative. Since its kinetic energy is positive and V is the potential energy inside the barrier, $E - V$ is positive. The Schrödinger equation may then be written

$$\frac{\partial^2 \psi}{\partial x^2} = -k^2 \psi \qquad [8\text{--}13]$$

where

$$k^2 = \frac{8\pi^2 m}{h^2} (E - V) \qquad [8\text{--}13a]$$

This is the familiar equation of a sine or cosine wave function, and in its simplest form the solution for the sine term may be written

$$\psi = \psi \sin kx \qquad [8\text{--}14]$$

The question now arises as to what happens to the solution of the Schrö-dinger wave equation if an electron or other particle is in the region of the barrier where its potential energy V is larger in magnitude than E. In such a case the sign of the right-hand term of Eq. 8–13 is reversed, and the equation becomes

$$\frac{\partial^2 \psi}{\partial x^2} = +k^2 \psi \qquad [8\text{--}15]$$

The solution of this equation is well known, and the useful part takes the form

$$\psi = \psi \epsilon^{-kx} \qquad [8\text{--}16]$$

showing that ψ is represented by a decreasing exponential curve.

This shows that there is a definite probability ψ^2 of the electron being found beyond the front of the barrier. Consequently the solution (Eq. 8–14) for the Schrödinger equation inside the barrier cannot be allowed to drop to zero at the surface of the barrier as if it were an impenetrable wall and as the de Broglie waves were made to do in Fig. 8-1.

We now have a mathematical problem in which there are two kinds of solutions of the Schrödinger equation, one kind showing a simple sine wave pattern inside the barrier, the other kind showing a logarithmic decay curve outside the barrier. Physical intuition tells us that for a complete solution involving the space both inside and outside the barrier these curves must be continuous. This is no more than partial fulfillment of the familiar condition for mathematical functions when applied to physical quantities, that they be single-valued, finite, and continuous. To avoid mathematical intricacies we may fulfill all these conditions by doing a job of patchwork in putting the two curves together graphically, so that where they join at the barrier they both have the *same value* and the *same slope*. This is represented in Fig. 8-4. Here we have fitted the two curves together, thus giving us a ψ graph from which a ψ^2 graph may be obtained showing the probability of finding the electron (or other subatomic particle) at any position in the "box" or outside.

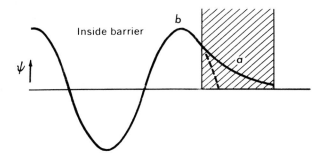

Fig. 8-4. Exponential curve, *a*, fitted to wave function, *b*, at barrier.

As before, the probability distribution inside the barrier is represented by the square of the ψ values of the wave patterns that fit into the "box." Outside the "box," however, the value of ψ drops off logarithmically, and the ψ^2 curve representing the probability drops off similarly. Although mathematically the curve does not reach zero until an infinite distance, practically the value becomes too small to be appreciable within a fairly short distance.

The case of penetration of a narrow finite barrier is represented by Fig. 8-5. Here, for instance, a few electrons may completely penetrate the barrier. When an electron emerges on the other side its velocity is less, as represented by an increased de Broglie wavelength, and the probability of finding such an electron outside the barrier is also less than inside since the amplitude ψ (and consequently ψ^2) is less outside.

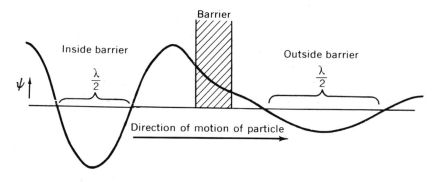

Fig. 8-5. Penetration of a potential barrier of limited extent by a particle, according to wave mechanics.

When electrically charged (or uncharged) particles are bounded by atomic or nuclear fields the ideal model of a simple "box" or of an impenetrable barrier does not apply. The exact nature of the forces and their specific distribution in space and time are unknown to us. The remarkable thing is the high degree of success that has been attained in dealing with such situations by means of quantum mechanics.

The phenomenon whereby an electron or other particle may pass a potential energy barrier even though it may not have enough energy to surmount the barrier is often called *tunneling* (or quantum tunneling) because the particle behaves as if it had found a tunnel through which it could escape.

8-5. Applications of Tunneling

This idea has many applications. It has been applied in the explanation of the emission of alpha particles from radioactive nuclei, a subject to be discussed later (§14-3). One of the ways in which electrons may be emitted from solids is by the influence of high intensity electric fields. To say that the electrons are pulled from the surface of a metal by the electric field is an oversimplification and tunneling is probably involved.

Tunneling may even occur on the inside of a solid. For instance in an insulator the electrons belonging to an atom are prevented by potential barriers from breaking away from the parent atom and giving rise to dielectric breakdown. If they pass these barriers by tunneling rather than after having gained enough energy to surmount the barrier the insulator may undergo dielectric breakdown at a lower voltage than would have been expected.

In a later chapter (§12-4) the crystal diode or solid junction rectifier is discussed. These may be modified by an extremely thin layer of insulation between the two faces in contact to form what are called *tunnel diodes* which have unusual current-voltage characteristics because of tunneling across the intervening layer at the junction.

8-6. Simple Harmonic Linear Oscillator: Potential Well

The wave-mechanical analysis of a simple linear harmonic oscillator brings up further points of interest. An ideal, simple harmonic oscillator is approximated by a ball vibrating at the end of a spring or by a pendulum swinging back and forth with not too large amplitude. By definition the motion is simple harmonic if the restoring force is proportional at each instant to the displacement from the center of path. The velocity of such an object is a maximum at its center of path. Consequently, from the classical viewpoint the probability in any small time interval of finding the body at its center of path is a minimum, and such an oscillator spends more of its time near the ends of its path than at any other points.

The probability of finding the oscillator at a given point in its path according to classical theory is represented by the curve *ABC* in Fig. 8-6. Let us now imagine an atomic particle moving back and forth with simple harmonic motion under the action of a central force. No longer do we have free motion of the particle up to a sharply defined barrier, which rises discontinuously to its full value at a given distance. A particle surrounded by such a barrier is said to be in a *rectangular potential well*, and the potential barrier may be represented graphically by a vertical wall. The harmonic oscillator, on the other hand, may be described as being in a *parabolic potential well*. In solving atomic problems by the methods of wave mechanics still other types of potential wells may be assumed for special purposes.

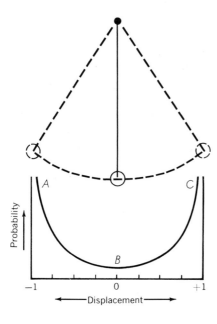

Fig. 8-6. Curve ABC represents probability of finding oscillating particle at
points along its path according to classical physics. Amplitude is assumed so small
that oscillations are essentially linear
and harmonic.

To see that the simple harmonic oscillator may be described as being
in a parabolic potential well, consider the work done in displacing the
oscillator a distance x. Just as with a stretched spring, the average force
is $kx/2$, and the work is $kx^2/2$, where k is the force per unit stretch of the
spring or per unit displacement of the oscillator. The energy required for
the oscillator to reach a distance x from the center of attraction, or in other
words to "climb" the barrier for that distance, is proportional to the
square of the distance; thus we may describe the oscillator as being in a
parabolic potential well since the walls rise parabolically with increased
distance.

To apply the Schrödinger equation (Eq. 8–1) to the problem of the
linear oscillator it is first necessary to substitute for V, the potential energy,
the particular value $\frac{1}{2}kx^2$, representing this oscillator. The solution of the
resulting equation is too involved for inclusion here, but the consequences
are of great interest. They show that the simple harmonic linear oscillator,
according to wave mechanics, is a quantized oscillator whereas the classical
oscillator is not. Therefore it can have only certain discrete amounts of
energy, and only certain wave patterns will fit into its length of path, just
as only particular wave patterns could be fitted into the box of the previous
section. That the indicated wave patterns do not fall to zero at the end of
the path but "tail off" gradually shows a definite, though frequently small,
probability that the oscillating particle may be found beyond the classical
limit. The explanation is the same as with the simpler penetrable barrier

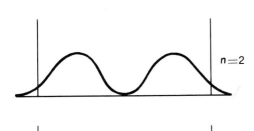

Fig. 8-7. Curves representing probability of finding linear harmonic oscillator at points along its path according to quantum mechanics. For high values of *n* the average of the curve approaches the classical distribution of Fig. 8-6.

given in §8-4. The wave-mechanical solution of the problem then differs from the classical solution in that it leads to three important and different results: the *quantization of the energy of the oscillator*, a different method of locating the oscillator, and the probability that the oscillator may be found beyond the classical limit.

The probability of finding the linear oscillator at different positions of its path is again accepted as being represented by ψ^2. For such a quantized harmonic oscillator the ψ^2 probability curve is, as before, a series of peaks depending upon the wave pattern, one for the first possible energy state, two peaks for the second, and so on. Just as with a classical oscillator, we would expect the probability of finding the particle to be greater toward the ends of the path, and this is seen to be true for the higher energy states where there are enough peaks of the curve to establish a trend (Fig. 8-7). In fact average value of the curve approaches the classical probability curve for the higher energy states in accordance with the Bohr principle of correspondence.

8-7. Application of the Schrödinger Equation to the Hydrogen Atom

The fundamental problem in atomic structure is that of the nature of the hydrogen atom. It also presents the most direct and critical test of any theory. In the solution of this problem the Schrödinger equation proves to be the most powerful tool we know.

The only disposable quantities in the Schrödinger equation are the total energy E, and the potential energy V, the difference $(E - V)$ of course being the kinetic energy of the particle. In the hydrogen atom it is the potential energy that we may now specify for the electron in terms of the central field of force around the nucleus of the hydrogen atom. Putting into the Schrödinger equation the expression $-e^2/r$ for the potential energy of the electron in the hydrogen atom in terms of its distance r from the nucleus and the product of the charges of nucleus and electron, we have the Schrödinger equation in three dimensions in the following form:

$$\nabla^2\psi + \frac{8\pi^2 m}{h^2}\left(E + \frac{e^2}{r}\right)\psi = 0 \qquad [8\text{--}17]$$

This is a differential equation the full solution of which is beyond the scope of this textbook, but some of the chief steps can be outlined. First it is easier to solve the equation if it is expressed in spherical coordinates since they have the same spherical symmetry as the potential. This is accomplished by means of the customary transformation equations,

$$x = r \sin \theta \cos \varphi$$

$$y = r \sin \theta \sin \varphi \qquad [8\text{--}18]$$

$$z = r \cos \theta$$

The Schrödinger equation for hydrogen (Eq. 8-17) then becomes

$$\frac{1}{r^2}\frac{\partial}{\partial r}\left(r^2 \frac{\partial \psi}{\partial r}\right) + \frac{1}{r^2 \sin \theta}\frac{\partial}{\partial \theta}\left(\sin \theta \frac{\partial \psi}{\partial \theta}\right)$$

$$+ \frac{1}{r^2 \sin^2 \theta}\frac{\partial^2 \psi}{\partial \varphi^2} + \frac{8\pi^2 m}{h^2}\left[E + \frac{e^2}{r}\right]\psi = 0 \qquad [8\text{--}19]$$

Fortunately this formidable appearing equation can be solved by separating it into three equations, one for each of the variables φ, θ, and r. These can be solved one at a time and a combined solution finally arrived at.

When this is done it is found that there are certain possible functions of each of the three variables which are satisfactory solutions of the original Schrödinger equation. These are the *characteristic functions* or *eigenfunctions,* and each of them involves a quantized constant, that is a number which may take only integral values if the solution is to satisfy the required physical and mathematical conditions which must be imposed. When numerical values are put into the eigenfunctions or characteristic equations in which they are involved, particular values of the solution are obtained called *eigenvalues* or *characteristic values.* The three quantized constants are represented by the letters n, l and m_l. The first of these, n, comes from the equation for the variable radius r and it evidently is the same as the principal quantum number of the simple Bohr theory.

The second constant, l, comes from the equation for the variable angle θ. It is readily interpreted to be the orbital angular momentum quantum number. The third quantized constant, m_l, is associated with the variable angle φ. It is called the *magnetic quantum number* and its chief function is to describe the possible angles which the axis of orbital motion may assume in a magnetic field. The effect is often referred to as *space quantization* and more will be said of it later (§9-4). That these three quantum numbers should come with surprising mathematical elegance from the solution of the Schrödinger equation is remarkably strong evidence of the fundamental validity of the equation and its value in attacking atomic problems.

For acceptable values of the solution of the Schrödinger equation we find that n can have any integral value from 1 to ∞; l can only have integral values from 0 to $n - 1$, and m_l can only have integral values from $-l$ to $+l$, including zero. These, together with a fourth quantum number m_s, for the spin of the electron, are just what are required to describe observed phenomena in terms of the energy states of an atom. But though the spin quantum number m_s had been used for some time to describe optical spectra (next chapter) it did not come out of the simple non-relativistic wave mechanics of the Schrödinger equation but had to be added more or less gratuitously in order to explain the doublet structure of the spectra of the alkali metals. The defect of this theory was remedied later by the more complete Dirac theory (next section).

When Eq. 8–19 is separated into three separate equations, the simplest one is the one for changes of the angle φ and the solution must therefore be a function of φ which we shall call $\Phi(\varphi)$ or just Φ. This equation is a function of φ only, just as the other two equations are respectively functions of θ and r only. This can only be true if the terms in φ are equal to a constant which by a shrewd guess is chosen to be $-m^2$. The equation in φ is then

$$\frac{1}{\Phi} \frac{\partial^2 \Phi}{\partial \varphi^2} = -m^2 \qquad [8\text{--}19a]$$

Solutions of this are well known to be $e^{im\varphi}$ and $e^{-im\varphi}$. For the solution to represent a constant state at any particular angle φ it must have the same value at any constant point such as given by the angles $\varphi + 2\pi$, $\varphi + 4\pi$, etc. This can be possible only if m has integral values

$$m = 0, \pm 1, \pm 2, \ldots \ldots \ldots$$

This illustrates the way in which integral values of the quantum numbers arise from the solution of the Schrödinger equation.

The solutions of the two remaining equations in θ and r are more involved. That for θ leads to valid solutions only in terms of a quantum number l which is limited to positive integral values. The solution for r is valid only for integral values of the quantum number n, and two further conditions are found,

$$l + 1 = n$$

and m is limited to integral values running from $-l$ to $+l$ including zero.

An important distinction must now be emphasized between the simple picture of Bohr orbits in terms of de Broglie wavelengths and the Schrödinger method. In the former the Bohr orbits were defined in terms of stationary wave patterns of whole wavelengths marked off by nodes and antinodes around a circumference. In the latter three-dimensional treatment there are n *nodal surfaces* of the stationary waves in the form of concentric spherical surfaces. There are $|m|$ *nodal planes* usually taken at right angles to the z axis and there are $l - |m|$ *conical nodes*. Thus the atom is represented by a stationary wave pattern of ψ waves in three dimensions.

It is common to speak of the angular momentum quantum number l as if the angular momentum were l times the unit $h/2\pi$ where l takes only integral values. Actually, however, in quantum mechanics the quantity $\sqrt{l(l+1)}$ appears instead of just l, and its use is required by the theory instead of simply l as the multiplier by which the amount of angular momentum is determined. For convenience, however, it is common to speak of l as if it were to be used directly whereas when a computation is made it is actually $\sqrt{l(l+1)}$ which is needed. The same mathematical relationship is generally true of the other quantum numbers obtained by wave mechanics. For instance, when the quantum number s is indicated the actual value for computing energies is $\sqrt{s(s+1)}$. This is true of all quantum numbers and sometimes a star is used to indicate the more exact values as for example $l^* = \sqrt{l(l+1)}$.

The solution of the Schrödinger equation for hydrogen not only furnishes a valid set of quantum numbers and gives valuable information about quantized states in hydrogen, but it leads, as previously stated, to the same energy levels as did the simple Bohr theory. There remains, however, the question of the location of an electron in a hydrogen atom. This can only be given in terms of probabilities as determined by ψ^2. For instance, for $n = 1$ there can only be the state $l = 0$ and the probability distribution is spherically symmetrical since there are no conical nodes or plane nodes. For $n = 2$ and $l = 1$ there will be one conical node if $m = 0$ or one plane node if $m = 1$. But because of its wide angle the cone looks like a plane until states of $n = 3$ are reached.

To make it easier to visualize the process consider the solution of the wave equation for hydrogen for ψ as a function of the radial distance r from the nucleus. If we plot the value of ψ for different distances from the nucleus when $n = 1$ and $l = 0$ we obtain curve $1a$, Fig. 8-8. When $n = 2$ and when

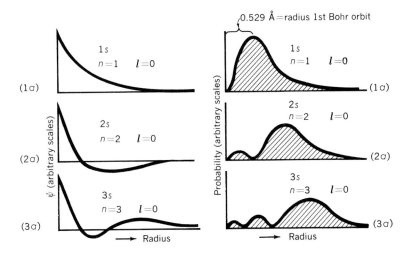

Fig. 8-8. Plots of ψ for variations of distance r from nucleus of hydrogen atom for different energy states.

Fig. 8-9. Plots of radial probability $4\pi r^2 \psi^2$ for variations of distance r from nucleus of hydrogen atom for same energy states as Fig. 8-8.

$n = 3$, with $l = 0$, we obtain curves $2a$ and $3a$. We cannot plot ψ^2 directly to get the probable space distribution around the nucleus according to Born's suggestion, since ψ^2 applies to equal volumes of space and the available space about the nucleus increases as the square of the radius. In other words, for each unit distance from the nucleus, the volume of the shell of unit thickness increases as the area of the shell. To get the probability function we must multiply ψ^2 in its radial variation by $4\pi r^2$ and thus get the curves of Fig. 8-9, where $1a$, $2a$, and $3a$ represent the probable location of the electron in hydrogen for the states given. The peaks of the curves indicate that at certain distances from the nucleus the probability of finding the electron is at a maximum, and at points between these maxima the probability falls to a minimum. These probability regions may be thought of as taking the place of the old-fashioned Bohr orbits. This is strikingly confirmed when we note that the distance from the nucleus to the top of the probability peak for $n = 1$ comes out the same as the radius of the first orbit obtained by Bohr's original method.

It may at first disturb the student that the electron in the hydrogen atom cannot always be pinned down to a particular orbit, sharply defined at any instant by a specific path each point of which is at a definite distance from the nucleus. However, it has become an axiom of scientific method that scientific theories should be based on observable quantities in so far as possible and orbits are essentially unobservable. The modern viewpoint is also in harmony with the principle of uncertainty. After all, the Bohr orbits were a little too sharply defined in light of the complementarity of the wave and particle aspects. It is not the distance of the electron from the nucleus or the orbital radius which is sharply defined; rather, the various energy states of the atom are sharply defined, as they need to be to account for the distinct frequencies of spectral lines. However, if energies are sharply defined, so also momenta will be, and momentum is conjugate to position. The more sharply the momentum is defined the less sharply is the position defined, and in the atom the ability to locate the electron is sacrificed in the interests of sharply defined spectral lines.

In the theories as given, the stationary states were assumed perfectly stable which means an infinite life. Since energy and time are conjugate quantities by the uncertainty principle

$$\Delta t \Delta E = \hbar \qquad [5\text{--}26a]$$

An infinite Δt would mean the uncertainty in the energy is $\Delta E = 0$, and the energy levels of the atom would be infinitely sharp. However, the excited states of the atom from which radiation occurs do not last indefinitely and the life time is in the neighborhood of 10^{-8} sec. By Eq. 5–26a this gives a small but finite width to the energy levels which in turn shows that spectral lines cannot be infinitely sharp but must have a natural finite width. Even the hydrogen atom itself may not be *infinitely stable*.

8-8. The Dirac Theory; The "Lamb Shift"

Despite formidable mathematical difficulties, Dirac searched for and found wave-mechanical equations which are invariant under the Lorentz transformation (§6-6). Thus he started with relativity as a basic consideration in the theory of the atom and not as a correction to be added later. Instead of a single equation such as the Schrödinger equation he found the more complete theory required four equations. Out of these equations he derived all four sets of quantum numbers n, l, m_l, m_s, required for the description of atomic states. One of the most satisfactory results of the theory was the fact that the spin quantum number m_s came out naturally and did not have to be invented ad hoc.

There were still some questions about the completeness of the theory, in particular in regard to the reaction of radiation on the radiator. A critical test of any theory of the hydrogen atom is how well it can explain the fine structure of the spectral lines of hydrogen. Lamb and Retherford were able to make measurements in 1947 to a very high degree of precision by a method involving microwave and atomic-beam techniques. They found a very slight discrepancy called the *Lamb shift* between the experimental and theoretical values for certain of the fine structure energy levels of atomic hydrogen.

These results indicated a slight upward shift of some energy levels above the theoretical expected values, the shift being 1058 megacycles/sec (0.033 cm^{-1}) above that predicted by the Dirac theory. Although this is only a variation of about 2 ten-thousandths of one per cent Kuhn and Series obtained a closely similar result the following year by more strictly optical methods. These results were taken to indicate that something had been omitted from the Dirac theory. Progress in explaining the effect has been made by Bethe who reformulated the Dirac theory to include the reaction of the radiation field on the electron when emission of radiation occurs.

8-9. Complex Atoms

As has been seen, Schrödinger's equation can be applied very directly to hydrogen or, for that matter, to any hydrogenic-type atom, but for the more complex atoms the application is more difficult. For instance, the potential-energy function which was put into the Schrödinger equation for hydrogen was simply $V = -e^2/r$, but for helium, where there are two electrons, there are at least three terms, $-Ze^2/r_1$ for one electron, $-Ze^2/r_2$ for the second electron where $Z = 2$ for helium, and e^2/r_{12} for the interaction between the two electrons where r_{12} is their distance apart. Thus

$$V = -\frac{Ze^2}{r_1} - \frac{Ze^2}{r_2} + \frac{e^2}{r_{12}} \qquad [8\text{--}20]$$

Not only the number of charges on the nucleus and their effect on each electron but also the effect of each electron on every other electron must be considered. When there are many electrons this becomes an extremely complicated problem, for which even for helium there is no complete solution. However, approximate solutions can be reached by several methods. When this is done for a heavy atom, and when ψ^2, the probability, is plotted for the total electron population, it is found to follow a curve such as is shown in Fig. 8-10. From this the average population density of the electrons around the nucleus is greatest in the immediate vicinity of the nucleus. The curve also shows definite maxima which, in the language of x-ray technology (§9-9), correspond to K, L, M, and other electron shells. After these it drops to a negligible value. Between the peaks the curve does not drop to zero because there is some overlapping of electron shells. This means that an electron in one shell may in its motion penetrate a lower shell.

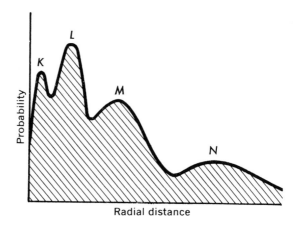

Fig. 8-10. Approximate radial electron population probability for a heavy atom, obtained by one of several wave-mechanical methods. The curve is the sum of all the separate curves for the individual electrons in the atom.

Problems

1. An electron is confined in an impenetrable box each side of which is 10 Å long. If the electron moves parallel to one of the edges of the box, what are the de Broglie wavelengths representing the first five allowed energy states of the electron?

2. Find the energies of the electron in eV in the five states of the previous problem.

3. If the length of each side of the box of problem 1 is 2 Å, what are the de Broglie wavelengths and energies in eV for the states for which $n = 1, 3, 5,$ and 7?

4. What are the three lowest energies that a neutron can have if *confined* to move along the edge of an impenetrable box 5×10^{-13} cm in length (approximate nuclear dimensions)?

*5. If an electron is to be *confined* in a nucleus and can only move along a dimension 6×10^{-14} cm long, what will be the minimum kinetic energy in eV it can have? (Hint: Try $v = c$ for an approximation, and find relativistic value of m in the de Broglie equation. Refer to Table 2-1 for approximate energies.)

6. If the average kinetic energy of thermal agitation of a gas molecule is $\frac{3}{2} kT$, show that the de Broglie wavelength is $\lambda = h/\sqrt{3mkT}$. What is the length of the smallest box in which this particle could be *confined?*

7. Show that $\psi = \psi \sin kx$ is a solution of Eq. 8–13.

8. Show that $\psi = \psi \cos kx$ is a solution of Eq. 8–13.

9. A 100-gram pendulum bob swings on a suspension of length 100 cm. As it swings back and forth can it lose energy continuously? Compare classical and quantum ideas.

10. The pendulum of the previous problem swings back and forth through an arc of 10°. Calculate the least quantum number n for the allowable wave function for the motion. Would quantization be noticeable? How can the correspondence principle be applied here?

*11. The allowed wave functions for a particle in a box of length L are $\lambda = nx/L$. The wave function ψ will then be represented by an amplitude function $\psi_n = a_n \sin(\pi nx/L)$. Since the probability of finding the particle between 0 and L is unity then $\int_0^L \psi^2 dx = 1$. Show that the "normalized" wave function representing this probability is

$$\psi = \sqrt{\frac{2}{L}} \sin(\pi nx/L)$$

12. The ratio of the amplitude of the wave function just outside a barrier to the amplitude just inside a barrier is called the "transmission coefficient." The square of this represents the probability for a particle escaping through the barrier. Measure the amplitudes as given in Fig. 8-7 and find the probability that a particle of the energy represented will escape.

13. If 10^6 electrons are incident upon the barrier of Fig. 8-7 and if they have the proper energies to be represented by the wave function as given, find the number that will probably escape and the number that will be reflected.

14. Find the expression for the fractional difference between adjacent energy levels in terms of the quantum number n for a particle confined in a box such as in problem 1.

15. An "excited" sodium atom radiates a quantum of light of wavelength 5890 Å on the average in 10^{-8} sec. Applying Heisenberg's principle for the uncertainty relation between time t and energy E ($\Delta t \Delta E = h/2\pi$) and taking 10^{-8} sec to be the uncertainty in the time of radiation, what is the uncertainty in the energy? In the frequency? This sets a limit to the sharpness of a spectral line even if there is no Doppler broadening or other effect.

16. Discuss the application of the uncertainty principle to the problem of locating a particle confined in a box.

*17. Show that for an electron in a very high energy state in a one-dimensional impenetrable box, the probability of finding the electron in any small linear interval does not depend upon the location of the interval. Interpret this in terms of the correspondence principle and compare with the classical viewpoint.

*18. An electron moves toward a potential barrier 10 eV high and 1 Å thick. Discuss the possibility of the electron penetrating the barrier according to classical theory and according to quantum theory if the energy of the electron is (a) 8 eV and (b) 12 eV. To solve the problem mathematically what conditions would have to be met?

Recommended Reading

Born, M., *Atomic Physics*, 7th ed. New York: Stechert-Hafner, 1962.
Heitler, W., *Elementary Wave Mechanics*. Oxford: Clarendon Press, 1946.

Richtmeyer, F. K., E. H. Kennard and T. Lauritsen, *Introduction to Modern Physics.* New York: McGraw-Hill Book Company, Inc., 1955.

Sherwin, C. W., *Introduction to Quantum Mechanics.* New York: Holt, Rinehart and Winston, Inc., 1960.

Lindsay, R. B., and H. Margenau, *Foundations of Physics.* New York: Dover Publications, Inc., 1957.

Gurney, R. W., *Elementary Quantum Mechanics.* London: Cambridge University Press, 1934.

Complex Atoms: Electron Spin; X-ray Spectra

9-1. Spectra of the Alkali Metals: Electron Spin

The spectra formed by the atoms of the alkali metals are more complex than the spectrum of hydrogen but less complex than most spectra formed by atoms having more than one electron. Although the atoms of each of the alkali metals possess more than one electron the spectrum of each is formed by transitions involving only one electron. The other electrons of each atom group themselves in what we shall soon find (§9-9) are filled or closed *shells*. The spectra of the alkali metals are thus spoken of as *one-electron spectra*. Spectra of atoms involving two or more electrons are still more complex. The spectra of the various alkali metals are closely related because of their one-electron origin and because in the different metals these electrons undergo similar transitions. The single electron outside a closed shell not only accounts for the optical similarity of the atoms of the alkali metals but also accounts for the chemical similarity, since these elements all have a chemical combining power (valence) of one. This electron is variously spoken of as the *optical electron* or the *valence electron*.

Upon first examining the spectrum of lithium or sodium or any of the alkali metals it appears difficult to see any order or relationship between the lines, but in 1890 Paschen and Runge, and at about the same time Rydberg, discovered that the lines could be sorted into several different more or less overlapping series. The lines of the brightest series were named *principal series* lines, those thought to be most clearly defined were called the *sharp series* lines, another group from their superficial appearance was called the *diffuse series* lines (Fig. 9-1). A fourth group of lines was badly misnamed the *fundamental series* for it turned out to be no more fundamental than any other. However, in designating the different sets of energy levels of the atom that give rise to these series the initials *S*, *P*, *D*, and *F* are now commonly applied and the transitions that give rise to these series occur between levels belonging to adjacent sets (Fig. 9-2).

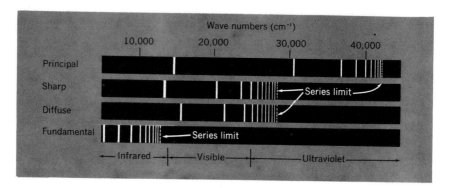

Fig. 9-1.   Spectrum of lithium. The lines of the lithium spectrum may be sorted into the overlapping series shown.

The *S*, *P*, *D*, and *F* levels are assigned *l* values of 0, 1, 2, 3 respectively. The common interpretation is that *S* levels represent zero orbital angular momentum. The *P*, *D*, and *F* levels represent increasing amounts of angular momentum. The more angular momentum an electron has the less likely it is to penetrate the inner shells of electrons, consequently the *F* levels are more like the levels of the early Bohr theory for hydrogen. Indeed computation shows them to be quite close to what the similar levels in hydrogen would be. This is because electrons in *F* levels move more nearly in a Coulomb field, being the resultant of the field due to the nuclear charge $+Ze$ reduced by the $Z-1$ electrons which form an inner "core" of filled shells and reduce the effective charge of the nucleus to approximately $+e$ as in hydrogen.

The two sets of quantum numbers of the Bohr-Sommerfeld theory could account for the over-all characteristics of the alkali metal spectra but not for their fine structure which for the most part was a fairly obvious feature. The spectral lines of the alkali metals are essentially *doublet lines* consisting of two components closer together, and in some cases a third faint component called a *satellite* may be seen. This is called the *fine structure* of the alkali metal series lines and regardless of the presence or absence of the so-called satellites the series are usually called *doublet series*. For instance, the common yellow line of sodium is easily observed to be a

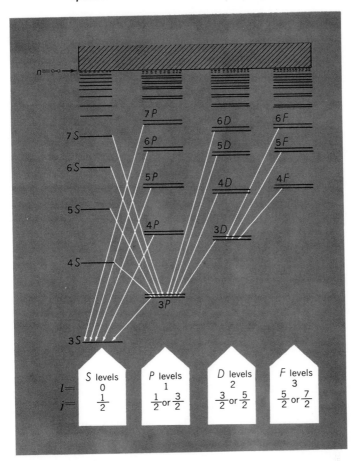

Fig. 9-2. Energy levels and transitions for sodium. *P, D,* and *F* levels are double because of electron spin. *S* levels are single (see text), and are lowest because the electron paths are most elliptical and penetrate closer to the nucleus.

doublet. One component has a wavelength of 5890 Å, and the other has a wavelength of 5896 Å. Thus the difference between the two lines of the doublet is 6 Å. The lighter the atom is, the less is the doublet separation; for lithium the doublet separation is so small as to be difficult to observe experimentally, but for the heaviest of the alkali metals, cesium, the separation is more than 400 Å.

To describe the observed doublet structure of these lines it was necessary to assume that the *P, D,* and *F* levels are doublet levels, that is, each is split into two components. However, spectroscopic evidence indicates that the *S* levels are not double but single. To adequately describe these facts it was necessary at the time to invent a third quantum number which could have either of only two values. No physical explanation of this third quantum number was forthcoming until the suggestion that the electron behaves as if it were spinning on its own axis like the earth, a very fruitful idea which Goudsmit and Uhlenbeck proposed in 1925. The angular momentum of spin and the accompanying magnetic moment are independent of orbital motion and are considered to be constant intrinsic properties of the electron just as much as mass and charge.

The magnitude of the spin angular momentum of the electron in units of $h/2\pi = \hbar$ is nominally given as $s\hbar$ where $s = \frac{1}{2}$ always. The actual wave-mechanical value is $\sqrt{s(s+1)}(h/2\pi)$ or $\sqrt{\frac{3}{4}}(h/2\pi)$ and is always the same. In the atom or in the direction of an external field there are two possible orientations represented by the magnetic spin quantum number m_s. Agreement with experiment is obtained when the component of spin momentum in the direction of the field is $m_s(h/2\pi)$ where $m_s = \pm\frac{1}{2}$.

Since the energy depends upon the total angular momentum it is convenient to represent this total by a new quantum number j (once called the *inner quantum number*). Actually j is not a new and independent quantum number but is completely determined by l and s. If we assign to l the values 0, 1, 2, 3 for the S, P, D and F levels respectively then we can find the possible j values for these levels.

The possibilities for combining l values with s are readily seen to be

$$j = l \pm \tfrac{1}{2} \quad \text{for } l > 0$$

$$j = \tfrac{1}{2} \qquad \text{for } l = 0$$

For S levels then, $j = \frac{1}{2}$. For P levels $j = 1 \pm \frac{1}{2} = \frac{1}{2}$ or $\frac{3}{2}$, and for D and F levels $j = \frac{3}{2}$ or $\frac{5}{2}$ and $j = \frac{5}{2}$ or $\frac{7}{2}$ respectively. Thus P, D and F levels under the influence of electron spin become doublet levels. It now became necessary to set up certain *selection rules* that "permit" some transitions and "forbid" others under "normal conditions" in order to obtain agreement with observed experimental data.

The selection rule for l is that l may change by plus or minus 1 but not by 0.

$$\Delta l = \pm l \qquad \Delta l \neq 0$$

For j the rule is that j may change by ± 1 or 0

$$\Delta j = \pm 1 \text{ or } 0$$

Thus transitions between levels in adjacent sets are permitted but transitions between two levels of the same group such as two S levels or two P levels are forbidden and in any transition the angular momentum must change.

The lines of any series approach a limit, the *series limit*, as the electron "falls" from higher energy levels (larger n), as n approaches infinity. This determines the series limit. For $n = \infty$, the electron is removed from the atom and the atom is said to be *ionized*. Electrons falling from the continuum of non-quantized levels "beyond infinity" (Fig. 9-2) are responsible for a faint continuous spectrum sometimes seen in certain spectra.

Although we now rather glibly speak of *electron spin* we must be careful not to think of spin as if the electron were a simple rotating charged sphere. From the wave-mechanical view we find certain terms in the equations which may conveniently be associated with the common concept of spin, but if the mechanical picture is pushed to its logical conclusions there are many contradictions.

The electron is certainly not a purely mechanical system. If l is taken to represent the orbital angular momentum of a revolving particle, the zero value would seem to indicate it is not revolving. This is difficult to explain by any classical particle model, and in early theory a state of zero angular momentum was ruled out; but in wave-mechanical theory if $l = 0$ the probability distribution is spherically symmetrical (§8-7). This means there is no axis of symmetry as would be required for ordinary orbital motion. Perhaps if there is motion of that kind it is a complex form in which there is no net circulation. In such instances the correctness of the wave-mechanical view must be accepted because it makes valid predictions even though no satisfactory mechanical model may be made.

Energy levels and transitions for the chief series of sodium are indicated in Fig. 9-2. Because for sodium the orbits with principal quantum numbers 1 and 2 are filled, the innermost orbit in which the outer electron can exist is number 3 ($n = 3$) as indicated on the diagram by the lowest available S level. Transitions to this level may be made from higher P levels. These transitions describe the *principal series* lines. The *sharp series* lines are described by transitions from any higher S level to the lowest vacant P level, known as $3P$. *Diffuse series* lines result from transitions from any higher D level to the lowest available P level. The *fundamental series* results then from transitions from F levels to the lowest D level.

To avoid complications on the diagram the doublet transitions are not represented in Fig. 9-2 but they are represented in Fig. 9-3 on a larger scale for some of the lower levels and in particular the transitions are marked for the well-known D lines. On this diagram the transitions are also marked for the first "doublet" line of the diffuse series. Although called a *doublet* there are three possible transitions with $\Delta j = \pm 1$ or 0 for a line. The $\Delta j = 0$ transition, being less probable, gives the faint line called a *satellite* which, before it was recognized as a separate line, gave a "fuzzy" (diffuse) appearance to the lines of this series. The relative intensities of the lines are represented by the numbers 9, 5, 1 marked on the diagram. The spectroscopic symbols for the levels have the following meaning: take for instance $3\,^2P_{3/2}$. The $3P$ means it is a P level of principal quantum number 3. The pre-superscript 2 means it is a doublet level. The post-subscript $\frac{3}{2}$ is the j-value. The S levels though not actually doublet levels have the superscript 2 by convention because they belong to a family of doublet levels. Capital letters are used for states of the atom as a whole.

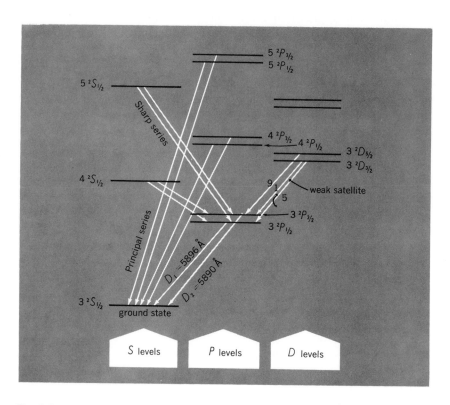

Fig. 9-3. Transitions for the sodium D lines which form the first doublet line of the principal series. The three transitions for the first line of the diffuse series are labelled with the numbers 9, 1, 5 representing relative intensities. The first two lines of the sharp series are also shown.

9-2. The Bohr Magneton

If an electron were to revolve in an orbit with one unit of angular momentum $h/2\pi$ it would have a magnetic moment which is often taken as a unit of measurement and is called *the Bohr magneton*. The numerical value is given by the following equation*

$$\mu_B = \frac{eh}{4\pi m_e} = 9.2732 \times 10^{-24} \text{ joule m}^2/\text{web} \qquad [9\text{--}1]$$

Although quantum-mechanical theory gives the result in a more general way we may derive this equation in a simple manner by classical

* This equation is often given in cgs units (where c is the velocity of light) as

$$\mu_B = \frac{eh}{4\pi m_e c} = 9.2732 \times 10^{-21} \text{ erg/gauss}$$

theory if we recall that by electrical theory the magnetic moment μ of a current loop is equal to the product of the current strength i by the area A. But for a stream of electrons, i is equal to nev where n is the number of electrons per unit length of path moving with velocity v, and nev is the amount of charge passing a point per second. For a single electron revolving in a circular orbit the number of times per second it passes a point is $v/2\pi r$ and the current is equal to $ev/2\pi r$. Then $\mu = iA$ and for a circular path,

$$\mu = \frac{ev}{2\pi r} \times (\pi r^2) = \frac{evr}{2} = \frac{e\omega r^2}{2} = \frac{e(m_e\omega r^2)}{2m_e} \qquad [9\text{-}2]$$

where ω = angular velocity ($v = r\omega$), and in the last form both numerator and denominator have been multiplied by m_e, the mass of the electron. It is now seen that $m_e\omega r^2$ is the angular momentum. If the least amount of angular momentum is $h/2\pi$, then substituting this for $m_e\omega r^2$ in Eq. 9-2, we obtain for the Bohr magneton μ_B,

$$\mu_B = \frac{e}{2m_e}\left(\frac{h}{2\pi}\right) = \frac{eh}{4\pi m_e} \qquad [9\text{-}3]$$

This is the minimum magnetic moment that an electron would possess as a result of orbital motion according to classical theory. Wave-mechanical theory gives a similar result. Although in practice measured values of magnetic moments may not come out as integral multiples of this unit, it is nevertheless a useful unit and it has been found also that the electron spinning on its axis actually possesses a magnetic moment of almost exactly one Bohr magneton. This has been confirmed by the experiment to be described in section 9-8. Precise measurements of the value of the magnetic moment μ_s due to axial spin give

$$\mu_s = 9.2840 \times 10^{-24} \text{ joule m}^2/\text{web}$$

This compares closely with the value of the Bohr magneton Eq. 9-1.

9-3. The Vector Model of the Atom

One of the simplest ways to discuss the atom is to represent the quantities involved by means of vectors. This leads to the so-called *vector model of the atom*, although such models should be accepted as only limited representations of the actual phenomena. In what follows we shall find vector methods very useful.

The orbital angular momentum of an electron may be represented by a vector 1 along the axis of rotation. It denotes the number of units $h/2\pi$ of angular momentum. The spin angular momentum of the electron may be similarly represented by the vector **s** as $\mathbf{s}(h/2\pi)$ where the magni-

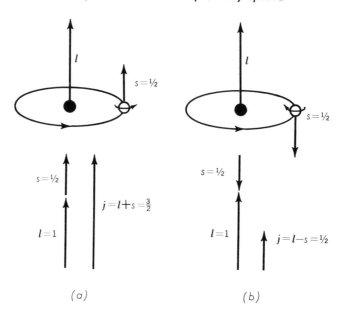

Fig. 9-4. Vector addition to get resultant angular momentum when $l = 1$ and $s = \frac{1}{2}$ according to earlier quantum theory; a, parallel, b, antiparallel.

tude of s is $\frac{1}{2}$. Then by the earlier quantum theory the two vectors may combine in two ways, as previously mentioned, to give the resultant angular momentum $j(h/2\pi)$. In magnitude either $j = l + s$ or $j = l - s$, as in Fig. 9-4a and b, depending on whether l and s are parallel or antiparallel.

Quantum mechanics, however, requires that $l^* = \sqrt{l(l + 1)}$ be used instead of l, $s^* = \sqrt{s(s + 1)}$ be used instead of s, and similarly for j^*. This leads to somewhat different results for small values of l and s not only in magnitude but in the angular relationships.

For instance in Fig. 9-5 if we take $l = 1$ then $l^* = \sqrt{1(1 + 1)} = \sqrt{2}$ and if $s = \frac{1}{2}$, then $s^* = \sqrt{\frac{1}{2}(\frac{1}{2} + 1)} = \sqrt{\frac{3}{4}}$. Since $j = l + s = 1 + \frac{1}{2}$, then $j^* = \sqrt{\frac{3}{2}(\frac{3}{2} + 1)} = \sqrt{\frac{15}{4}}$ and the spin and orbital angular momenta are presumed to precess around the resultant j^*. For larger values of l, s and j the results approach the simpler methods of Fig. 9-5. For many purposes the simpler picture is sufficient but for the more complete description, l^*, s^* and j^* should be applied rather than l, s and j.

9-4. "Space Quantization"; Larmor Precession

An ordinary magnet can only be *held* at any desired angle in a magnetic field by the application of a force to hold it there. But if it were endowed

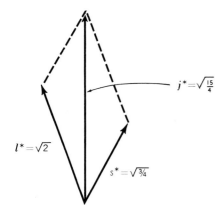

Fig. 9-5.   Resultant of l^* and s^* according to later quantum theory.

with angular momentum like a spinning top it could remain inclined at any angle to the field according to classical theory because it would precess about the direction of the field at that angle. Now, if an electron revolves in an orbit about the nucleus of an atom it is like a spinning top in that it has orbital angular momentum. Unlike a spinning top, however, if placed in a magnetic field it can only sustain itself with its axis at certain preferred (quantized) angles to the direction of the field. These are the angles which are described by the magnetic quantum number m_l and they represent a kind of quantization of position sometimes referred to as "space quantization." The effect is only observed with respect to an impressed magnetic field and the different positions represent different energy states. If theory is to be in agreement with experiment it is required that in a magnetic field the precession of the resultant orbital angular momentum (resulting from the torque exerted on the orbital dipole moment of the electron) can only occur at such angles that the projection on the field direction is an integral multiple of the unit $h/2\pi$ (Fig. 9-6a). These values are defined by $m_l(h/2\pi)$ where m_l is the magnetic quantum number and m_l can have any integral value from $-l$ to $+l$ including zero.

If l^* is used instead of l the projections will still have integral values as indicated in Fig. 9-6b but the angles are different and even for $m_l = \pm l$ the angular momentum is not quite parallel to the field direction. Since the changes in the components of angular momentum in the direction of the field occur in equal steps, the changes in the energies representing these states are also equal. The result is that each original energy level having a particular angular momentum quantum number l is split by the magnetic field into $2l + 1$ equally spaced levels (Fig. 9-7).

The several levels into which a single level is split by a magnetic field are thought of as existing (potentially at least) when the magnetic field is removed although they have the same value and are indistinguishable. Such levels are said to be *degenerate* and the magnetic field is said to remove

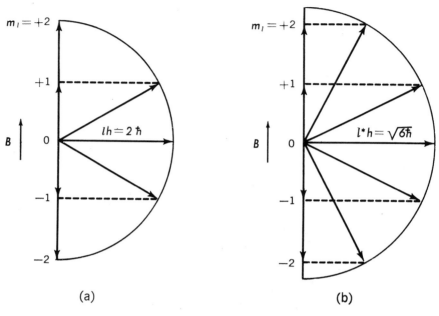

Fig. 9-6.   Orbital space quantization in magnetic field according to vector model of atom for $l = 2$. Vector representing orbital magnetic moment can only take positions for which the projection on a line in the direction of the field B is an integral multiple (or zero) of the fundamental unit according to either older model *a* or newer model *b*.

the degeneracy. The energy difference between 2 adjacent levels will be shown in what follows to be $\Delta E = (eh/4\pi m_e)B = \mu_B B$ where the quantity in parenthesis is μ_B the Bohr magneton, and B is the magnetic flux density of the field.

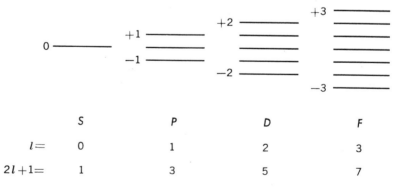

Fig. 9-7.   The splitting of energy levels for S, P, D and F states for the normal Zeeman effect (no net electron spin).

LARMOR PRECESSION

The frequency with which an atom precesses in a magnetic field is of importance in understanding a number of phenomena. It can be readily obtained from the well-known formula of classical mechanics $L = I\omega'\omega \sin \varphi$ for the precession of a gyroscope where the angular frequency of precession ω is given in terms of the rotational frequency ω', the moment of inertia I, the applied torque L, and φ, the inclination of the axis of spin. In the case of an electron revolving in a circular orbit in a field of flux density B the torque is $\mu_o B \sin \varphi$ where μ_o is the orbital magnetic moment of the electron equal to one Bohr magneton μ_B and φ is the angle between the direction of the field and the magnetic moment μ_o. We then have from Eq. 9-3 for μ_B

$$\mu_o B = \left(\frac{eh}{4\pi m_e}\right) B = I\omega'\omega \qquad [9\text{-}4]$$

But the orbital angular momentum $I\omega'$ in the lowest orbit is $h/2\pi$ and $\omega = 2\pi\nu_p$ where ν_p is the frequency of precession; therefore

$$\left(\frac{eh}{4\pi m_e}\right) B = \left(\frac{h}{2\pi}\right) 2\pi\nu_p \qquad [9\text{-}5]$$

$$\nu_p = \left(\frac{e}{4\pi m_e}\right) B \qquad [9\text{-}6]$$

This is called the *Larmor frequency*. The energy of precession it represents for $l = 1$ is obtained by multiplying by h,

$$E(\text{precession}) = \left(\frac{eh}{4\pi m_e}\right) B \qquad [9\text{-}7]$$

This will be needed in explaining the Zeeman effect.

9-5. The Zeeman Effect

The Zeeman effect is the splitting of spectral lines when the atoms which are emitting radiation are subjected to a magnetic field. In the so-called *normal Zeeman effect* a spectral line is split into three components (Fig. 9-8a) when observed at right angles to the field. The middle of line has the frequency of the original line. The other two have frequencies larger and smaller. Usually a more complicated pattern is observed (Fig. 9-8b), called the *anomalous Zeeman effect*, although in the light of modern quantum theory there is nothing really anomalous about it. The so-called normal effect is observed in *singlet lines* such as the singlet lines of helium, zinc, and mercury when electrons occur in pairs with opposite spins and the effects of spin cancel. Since singlet lines are in the minority most lines show the so-called anomalous effect. In the anomalous Zeeman effect electron spin enters in, and there is more splitting of energy levels; consequently there are more possibilities for transitions between levels, and more observed splitting of lines. Indeed, this more complex Zeeman effect gives some of the strongest evidence in support of quantum ideas and electron spin and in particular of the idea of quantization of position, or what is often called *space quantization* (next section).

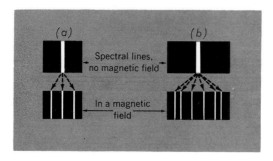

Fig. 9-8. Zeeman effect: a, Normal effect, a singlet line split into 3 components when observed at right angles to the magnetic field; b, anomalous effect, a triplet line split into several components.

The Zeeman effect is not easy to observe and requires optical equipment of high resolving power; however, it has been intensively studied because of the information that it gives about the atom. It has been frequently used to help sort out the lines belonging to one series of an element. In complex spectra the overlapping of different series often obscures the fact that there are definite series or groups, but all such closely related lines always show the same characteristic Zeeman pattern. A similar effect of splitting of the spectral lines in an intense electric field was observed by Stark in 1913 and is called the *Stark effect*. It is of much less importance in spectroscopy but can be completely explained by quantum mechanics.

We now take an example to show how quantization of position accounts for the normal Zeeman effect. For a transition between a singlet D level ($l = 2$) and a singlet P level ($l = 1$) such as are found in some atoms, the P level would be split into three levels and the D level would be split into five (Fig. 9-9). The required selection rule is that m_l can change by plus or minus 1 or zero.

$$\Delta m_l = \pm 1 \text{ or } 0$$

The nine possible transitions between these levels are grouped in threes according to the change in m_l. Since the energy differences are the same between adjacent levels the three groups represent only three different frequencies as shown. Thus what was a single spectroscopic line without the field becomes a *normal triplet* in the field when viewed at right angles to the field. For simplicity we have omitted discussion of the polarization of the light for the different lines which is correctly predicted by quantum theory, and we shall say only a little in the next paragraph of the fact

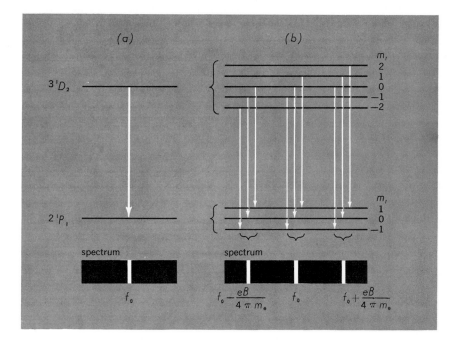

Fig. 9-9.   Explanation of normal Zeeman effect in terms of splitting of singlet energy
levels by a magnetic field: a, without field; b, with field.

that when viewed parallel to the field (through a hole drilled in the poles
of the magnet) the center line of the three is not seen.

Since l (and m_l) can only have integral values Eq. 9–6 represents the
frequency shift of the lines in the normal Zeeman effect (Fig. 9-9). If ν_o is
the frequency of the line without the magnetic field, the energy of the
precession may add to or subtract from the original energy. The observed
frequencies then are $\nu_o + \nu_p$, ν_o, and $\nu_o - \nu_p$.

It should be added that the normal Zeeman effect was given a simple
explanation in terms of classical electrical theory by Lorentz. He assumed
that the light is produced by a simple harmonic oscillating charge. If the
field is in the x direction and if the oscillatory motion is resolved into two
components, one in the x direction and the other in the yz plane, the latter
may be further resolved into two circular motions in opposite directions,
the circular motions being at right angles to the field. Since the magnetic
field would tend to expand one of these circles and contract the other, the
circular motions would result in two different frequencies different from
the original frequency of the oscillator. The light viewed along the field
would consist of two lines circularly polarized in opposite directions. The
frequency of the component vibration in the direction of the field would

be unchanged but would not be observable in that direction of motion. Why? It would be observed at right angles to the field along with the other two lines which would now appear plane polarized.

Lorentz obtained the correct frequency shift of the lines in the so-called *normal* effect but neither he nor anyone else of that day could explain the anomalous patterns usually observed.

9-6. Anomalous Zeeman Effect: Landé "*g*-factor"

The explanation of the anomalous Zeeman effect with its complex pattern of lines awaited the development of the concept of *electron spin* and the recognition that magnetic moment and angular momentum for orbital motion and spin are not in the same ratio. The orbital angular momentum p_o in the lowest orbital state is, by the usual quantum rules,

$$p_o = \frac{h}{2\pi} \qquad [9\text{--}8]$$

At the same time the orbital magnetic moment μ_o which is the same as μ_B given by Eq. 9–1 is

$$\mu_o = \left(\frac{eh}{4\pi m_e}\right) \qquad [9\text{--}9]$$

The ratio of the latter to the former is called the *orbital gyromagnetic ratio* and is

$$\frac{\mu_o}{p_o} = \left(\frac{e}{2m_e}\right) = g_o\left(\frac{e}{2m_e}\right) \qquad [9\text{--}10]$$

where the *g-factor* $g_o = 1$.

However, to successfully explain the anomalous Zeeman effect it was necessary to assume that the gyromagnetic ratio for electron spin is twice what it is for orbital motion, thus

$$\frac{\mu_s}{p_s} = 2\left(\frac{e}{2m_e}\right) = g_s\left(\frac{e}{2m_e}\right) \qquad [9\text{--}11]$$

where μ_s is the spin magnetic moment, p_s is the spin angular momentum, and $g_s = 2$. The quantities g_o and g_s are called *g*-factors for orbital motion and spin respectively. They determine the *g*-factor for the atom as a whole.

In general, in finding resultant spins and resultant magnetic moments in atoms of one or more electrons where spin is involved the magnetic moment and angular momentum are neither directed along the same line nor are they always in the same ratio. The component of magnetic moment μ_j in the direction of resultant angular momentum j is given by

$$\mu_j = j^*g\left(\frac{eh}{4\pi m_e}\right) = j^*gM_B \qquad [9\text{--}12]$$

The quantity g is called the *Landé g-factor*, or the *splitting factor* for a particular state of the atom as a whole, and it determines the separation of the energy levels in the anomalous Zeeman effect.

Although g has the values 1 and 2 for the special cases just given, in all other cases the values of g differ from 1 or 2, and may be different for different states of the same atom. Because g is different for different states the energy level differences are different for different splittings. Thus transitions which would give the same frequency if the splitting were the same for both states, now give different frequencies and a complex pattern of lines. It is of interest to note that according to quantum theory the g-factor may be computed very closely by the formula

$$g = 1 + \frac{J(J + 1) + S(S + 1) - L(L + 1)}{2J(J + 1)} \qquad [9-13]$$

where capital letters are used to indicate quantum states of the atom as a whole.

Since different energy levels may split in different ways, the patterns of lines of the anomalous Zeeman effect are complex, but it is a triumph of quantum-mechanical theory that they are all successfully explained by it.

9-7. Spin-Orbit Coupling: The Paschen-Back Effect

In any atom with one valence electron where there is orbital motion as well as axial spin, the two fields interact (Fig. 9-10) and we say that they are coupled together through this interaction. This is called *spin-orbit coupling*. Likewise the angular momenta are coupled together.

Where there are two or more outer electrons the spins usually couple together to form a resultant spin represented by quantum numbers $S = s_1 + s_2 + \ldots$, and the orbits are coupled so that $L = l_1 + l_2 + \ldots$. Then the resultant L and S combine to give the resultant J in what is known as *L-S coupling*. This is the commonest kind of spin orbit coupling. (In some atoms a different kind of coupling may be found. The spin and orbital momenta for each electron combine to give resultant j values as for instance $j_1 = l_1 + s_1$, $j_2 = l_2 + s_2$, etc. Then the j values combine to form a resultant J as $J = j_1 + j_2 + j_3 + \ldots$. This is called *j-j coupling*.)

When radiating atoms are placed in an *extremely intense magnetic field*, the anomalous Zeeman effect disappears and the multiplicity of lines reverts to the normal Zeeman pattern. This effect is called the *Paschen-Back effect*. The explanation is that in a very intense magnetic field the *L-S* coupling is broken down, and since the orbital motion and spin are decoupled the orbital precession can again occur and give rise to the normal Zeeman effect. For further details see more advanced texts.

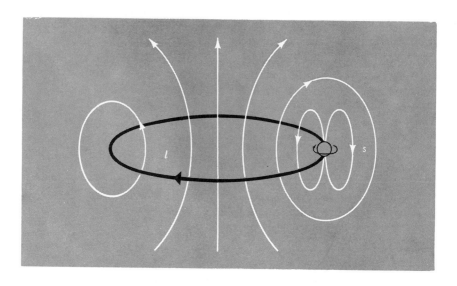

Fig. 9-10.   Interaction of magnetic fields due to orbital motion l and spin s.

9-8. The Stern-Gerlach Experiment

The idea of space quantization in a magnetic field can be very directly tested by experiment. In the work of Stern and Gerlach (1922), of great historical importance, a beam of silver atoms was passed through a non-uniform magnetic field. The beam was observed to be split into two parts, one deflected in the direction of the field, the other deflected in the opposite direction. Now, a silver atom has one electron outside a filled shell neither accompanied by nor paired with others. Since all other electrons are paired their effects cancel, and what effect there is is due to the remaining electron. The silver atom is normally in an S state, and the magnetic moment and angular momentum that it has are due entirely to the spin of this electron and not to orbital motion. According to the idea of space quantization in a magnetic field there should be only two possible positions for the direction of the spin of this electron. It should point in the direction of the magnetic field or in the opposite direction. If the atoms are in a nonuniform magnetic field they should then be pulled in one direction or the other. The experiment of Stern and Gerlach showed that the beam divided into two parts and that actually only two positions were taken by the silver atoms in the field. This is direct confirmation of space quantization since by classical theory the silver atoms, no matter what their original position, would all turn similarly to "line up" with the field, or at least to precess about it.

As is well known a magnetic dipole in a uniform magnetic field has no resultant force acting on it. However, in a non-uniform field changing in the x direction at a rate $\partial B/\partial x$ there is a net force the direction of which depends on which way the dipole is turned. In terms of the pole concept, where Δx is the separation of the poles of strength m, then $m\Delta x = \mu$ is the dipole moment. The net force on the dipole is readily found to be

$$F = \left(mB + m\,\frac{\partial B}{\partial x}\,\Delta x \right) - mB = m\,\frac{\partial B}{\partial x}\,\Delta x \qquad [9\text{--}14]$$

$$= \frac{\partial B}{\partial x}\,\mu$$

From this it is seen that only in a nonuniform field where $\partial B/\partial x \neq 0$ is there any force on the dipole, and to get maximum force the field must diverge as much as possible.

In the Stern and Gerlach experiment a strongly nonuniform field was obtained by means of a magnet with one pole in the form of a sharp edge facing an opposite pole with a broad face (Fig. 9-11). Silver atoms were evaporated from a tiny furnace and allowed to pass between the poles of

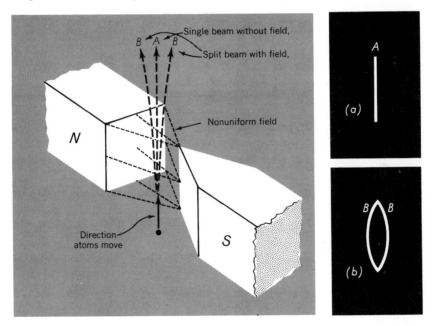

Fig. 9-11. Stern-Gerlach experiment. Shape of magnet poles to give nonuniform field in experiment. Beam of silver atoms passing through field is split into two parts. One part is deflected toward the S-pole, the other toward the N-pole.

Fig. 9-12. a, Trace of silver atoms where beam strikes detecting plate (no field); b, with field, trace shows splitting of beam.

this magnet. The vapor was detected by condensing it on a glass plate placed in the path of the beam (Fig. 9-12). From the amount of separation of the two parts of the beam when the field was on, together with the field intensity, the magnetic moment of the silver atom could be computed. This turned out to be one Bohr magneton, and therefore represents the magnetic moment of one spinning electron.

In hydrogen the situation is similar. Since the electron in hydrogen is in an S state there is no net orbital motion. If there is no orbital motion there can be no orbital magnetic moment, and any magnetic moment in hydrogen must therefore also be the result of spin of the electron about its own axis.

9-9. The Pauli Exclusion Principle and Atomic Structure

By what now seem to be awkward and difficult methods Bohr and others had arrived at the conclusion that the orbits for a given principal quantum number in an atom can contain only a certain limited number of electrons before becoming "filled." It has since become common practice to speak of such an orbital group as a *shell*, and in x-ray jargon the innermost shell with $n = 1$ is called the K *shell*, the next with $n = 2$ is called the L *shell*. After that come the M, N and O shells, etc.

All atoms with a large number of electrons would then have several filled shells, any remaining electrons being in the next outer shell. There was evidence that, for all atoms of $Z \geq 10$, in the first shell there could be only 2 electrons and that in the second there could be only 8 electrons. The question of the number of electrons in succeeding shells and how to determine when a shell was filled or not was not entirely clear, but the attempt was made to assign electrons to successive shells for heavier and heavier atoms in such a way as to fulfill the periodicity of chemical and physical properties represented in the periodic table of the elements (Table 9-1). Then came a remarkable development.

In 1925 W. Pauli discovered a rule, known as the *Pauli exclusion principle*, for determining the numbers of electrons in filled shells based on quantum theory. This rule was so successful that it was incorporated into quantum theory and it is now recognized that deductions from quantum-mechanical theory only have physical significance when interpreted in accordance with this rule. Thus it has become one of the most important principles of atomic structure. The Pauli exclusion principle states: *In any atom no two electrons may have the same set of quantum numbers n, l, m_l, m_s.* This is equivalent to saying that electrons and atoms preserve a kind of individuality which may not be infringed upon by other electrons. To see how the rule operates, consider the number of electrons permitted in the

TABLE 9-1. PERIODIC SYSTEM OF THE ELEMENTS*

(The boxed-in elements are man-made.)

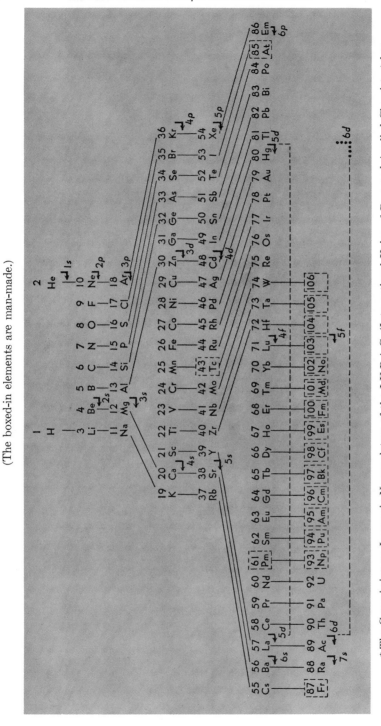

*The Commission on Inorganic Nomenclature of the I.U.P.A.C. (International Union of Pure and Applied Chemistry) has recommended the following changes in symbols: Ar for argon, not A, Es for einsteinium, not E, and Md for mendelevium, not Mv.

first shell, for which $n = 1$. It must be remembered that l may have all integral values from 0 to $n - 1$, and m may have all integral values from $-l$ to $+l$. For the first shell, since $n = 1$, $l = 0$ and $m_l = 0$, but m_s may be plus or minus $\frac{1}{2}$, there may be only two electrons, identical except that their spins are in opposite direction.

Now for the second group or shell $(n = 2)$ l may have the values 0 or 1. If $l = 0$, $m_l = 0$, and two electrons are permitted with these quantum numbers if they have spins $+\frac{1}{2}$ and $-\frac{1}{2}$, respectively. The remaining electrons for which $l = 1$ may have values of $m_l = -1$, 0, or $+1$, and for any of these, spins may be $-\frac{1}{2}$ or $+\frac{1}{2}$. This permits six electrons with $l = 1$. These together with the two for $l = 0$ make eight electrons permitted in the second shell. Similarly, for the third shell 18 electrons will be permitted, for the fourth 32, and for the fifth 50, and so on. The distribution of quantum numbers for shells one, two and three are shown in Table 9-2.

Electrons in the first shell, since they have values of $l = 0$, are known as s-electrons. In the second shell there are two subgroups. Two electrons are s-electrons, and the remaining six are known as p-electrons since $l = 1$. In the third shell there would be 2 s-, 6 p-, and 10 d-electrons. For this reason it is customary to speak of the s-, p-, and d-subshells. The L shell, for instance, has two subshells, s and p, the M shell has three subshells, s, p, and d. The N shell has four subshells, s, p, d, and f. For the heaviest atoms the outermost shell is the Q shell; there are only a few electrons in this shell. For any completely filled shell the total angular momentum is zero, since for every electron there' is one other electron with oppositely directed angular momentum and they cancel by pairs.

9-10. Periodic Table of the Elements

The Pauli exclusion principle gives the key to building the atoms and to their relations represented by the periodic table (Appendix or Table 9-1). By adding successive positive charges to the nucleus, together with an equal number of electrons surrounding the nucleus, we can account for the periodic relationship between the atoms. Only two different atoms representing two elements exist in the first period of the periodic table, since only two electrons are permitted in the first or K shell by the Pauli principle. Eight atoms representing eight elements occur in the next period of the periodic table, since only eight electrons are permitted by the Pauli principle in the second or L shell.

The third period of the periodic table also has eight atoms representing eight more elements formed by adding the 2 s-electrons and the 6 p-electrons of the third shell according to the same principle. Here, however, the first of several deviations from the regular order begins. Starting

TABLE 9-2. NUMBERS OF ELECTRONS IN GROUPS OR SHELLS ACCORDING TO PAULI'S PRINCIPLE

Orbital Group or Shell	n	l	m_l	m_s	No. of Electrons in Subgroup or Subshell	No. of Electrons in Completed Group or Shell
1	1	0	0	$+\frac{1}{2}$	2 s	2
	1	0	0	$-\frac{1}{2}$		
2	2	0	0	$+\frac{1}{2}$	2 s	8
	2	0	0	$-\frac{1}{2}$		
	2	1	-1	$+\frac{1}{2}$		
	2	1	-1	$-\frac{1}{2}$		
	2	1	0	$+\frac{1}{2}$	6 p	
	2	1	0	$-\frac{1}{2}$		
	2	1	1	$+\frac{1}{2}$		
	2	1	1	$-\frac{1}{2}$		
3	3	0	0	$+\frac{1}{2}$	2 s	18
	3	0	0	$-\frac{1}{2}$		
	3	1	-1	$+\frac{1}{2}$		
	3	1	-1	$-\frac{1}{2}$		
	3	1	0	$+\frac{1}{2}$	6 p	
	3	1	0	$-\frac{1}{2}$		
	3	1	1	$+\frac{1}{2}$		
	3	1	1	$-\frac{1}{2}$		
	3	2	-2	$+\frac{1}{2}$		
	3	2	-2	$-\frac{1}{2}$		
	3	2	-1	$+\frac{1}{2}$		
	3	2	-1	$-\frac{1}{2}$		
	3	2	0	$+\frac{1}{2}$	10 d	
	3	2	0	$-\frac{1}{2}$		
	3	2	1	$+\frac{1}{2}$		
	3	2	1	$-\frac{1}{2}$		
	3	2	2	$+\frac{1}{2}$		
	3	2	2	$-\frac{1}{2}$		

with potassium, instead of adding the d-electrons belonging to the third shell, the s-electrons of the next or fourth shell are added first, and other irregularities follow in such a manner as to explain how the next three periods are double ones involving eighteen elements each. Although the Pauli principle defines the number of possible electron states it does not specify the order in which the vacancies will be filled. The rule is that any particular electron goes to the lowest available energy state and the order in which this happens can only be determined spectroscopically.

The electronic structure of the atoms and the way in which the periodic table is built up on this basis are shown better in Table 9-2 and in Table 9-3, and the order of filling the shells is indicated. In the long period from potassium K to krypton Kr it is indicated how $3d$ electrons are filled in "underneath" $4s$ electrons with deviations from the regular order at Cr, Mn, Fe and Cu. In the group from Rb to Pd the $4d$ electrons are filled in under $5s$ electrons with some irregularities. It is likewise seen that the group of similar elements from $Z = 57$ to $Z = 72$ known as the rare-earth elements which could not be easily crowded into the older form of the periodic table, now represent the filling in of the $4f$ electrons beneath outer $6s$ and $5d$ electrons. Since the outer electronic structure is the same for all of these, this accounts for their similar chemical properties. When an added electron goes to what is called an inner shell it is actually going to the lowest available energy level. The order in which the electrons are filled in with increasing atomic number is determined from spectroscopic observations (or by analogy with known conditions).

The structure of the periodic table thus can be shown to be in agreement with the ideas of filled shells and subshells as predicted by the Pauli principle. In addition, we now have the satisfaction of having a principle based on quantization which gives results entirely in agreement with observations. We also now have an explanation of the so-called "noble" elements, which do not interact chemically at ordinary temperatures because of filled shells. These elements, beginning with helium with 2 electrons, neon with 10, and so on, represent atoms with completely filled outer shells and subshells. For many years it had been thought that because of the filled shells they could not form chemical compounds, but in 1962 at the Argonne National Laboratory much to the surprise of the scientific world it was found that this was not true at high temperatures, and the first such compound to be so formed was xenon and fluorine.

The electronic structure of an atom may be represented in terms of filled or partly filled shells; for instance, an aluminum atom would have the following electronic structure, $1s^2$, $2s^2$, $2p^6$, $3s^2$, $3p$, and the normal or ground state of the atom is said to be the P state. The symbol $1s^2$ indicates that in the first shell there are 2 s-electrons. In the second shell $2s^2$ and $2p^6$ indicate that there are 2 s-electrons and 6 p-electrons, and in the third shell there are 2 s-electrons and 1 p-electron. The lowest or normal state of an atom is the state of the last valence electron. It is frequently designated by the j value as a subscript after the letter, and a superscript before the letter indicates whether the state is a singlet, doublet, triplet, etc., as follows: oxygen ($^3P_2$), sodium ($^2S_{1/2}$). For the aluminum atom just discussed, the symbol for the lowest state is $^2P_{1/2}$.

TABLE 9-3. ELECTRON CONFIGURATIONS AND GROUND STATES OF ELEMENTS 1 TO 92

(Numbers in parentheses are uncertain.)

Element	K	L		M			N				O				Ground State
	1s	2s	2p	3s	3p	3d	4s	4p	4d	4f	5s	5p	5d	5f	
1. H	1														$^2S_{1/2}$
2. He	2														$^1S_0$
3. Li	2	1													$^2S_{1/2}$
4. Be	2	2													$^1S_0$
5. B	2	2	1												$^2P_{1/2}$
6. C	2	2	2												$^3P_0$
7. N	2	2	3												$^4S_{3/2}$
8. O	2	2	4												$^3P_2$
9. F	2	2	5												$^2P_{3/2}$
10. Ne	2	2	6												$^1S_0$
11. Na				1											$^2S_{1/2}$
12. Mg		Neon		2											$^1S_0$
13. Al		config-		2	1										$^2P_{1/2}$
14. Si		uration		2	2										$^3P_0$
15. P		(10		2	3										$^4S_{3/2}$
16. S		electrons)		2	4	—									$^3P_2$
17. Cl				2	5	—									$^2P_{3/2}$
18. Ar				2	6	—									$^1S_0$
19. K						—	1								$^2S_{1/2}$
20. Ca						—	2.								$^1S_0$
21. Sc				Argon		1	2								$^2D_{3/2}$
22. Ti				configuration		2	2								$^3F_2$
23. V				(18 electrons)		3	2								$^4F_{3/2}$
24. Cr						5	1								$^7S_3$
25. Mn						5	2								$^6S_{5/2}$
26. Fe						6	2								$^5D_4$
27. Co						7	2								$^4F_{9/2}$
28. Ni						8	2								$^3F_4$
29. Cu						10	1								$^2S_{1/2}$
30. Zn						10	2								$^1S_0$
31. Ga						10	2	1							$^2P_{1/2}$
32. Ge						10	2	2							$^3P_0$
33. As						10	2	3							$^4S_{3/2}$
34. Se						10	2	4							$^3P_2$
35. Br						10	2	5							$^2P_{3/2}$
36. Kr						10	2	6							$^1S_0$
37. Rb									—	—	1				$^2S_{1/2}$
38. Sr									—	—	2				$^1S_0$
39. Y							Krypton		1	—	2				$^2D_{3/2}$
40. Zr							Configuration		2	—	2				$^3F_2$
41. Nb							(36 electrons)		4	—	1				$^6D_{1/2}$
42. Mo									5	—	1				$^7S_3$
43. Tc									5	—	2				$^6S_{5/2}$
44. Ru									7	—	1				$^5F_5$
45. Rh									8	—	1				$^4F_{9/2}$
46. Pd									10	—	—				$^1S_0$

2   8   18

TABLE 9-3. (CONTINUED)

Element	K L M N				O			P			Q	Ground
	4s	4p	4d	4f	5s	5p	5d	6s	6p	6d	7s...	State
47. Ag				—	1							$^2S_{1/2}$
48. Cd				—	2							$^1S_0$
49. In				—	2	1						$^2P_{1/2}$
50. Sn	Palladium			—	2	2						$^3P_0$
51. Sb	Configuration			—	2	3						$^4S_{3/2}$
52. Te	(46 electrons)			—	2	4						$^3P_2$
53. I				—	2	5						$^2P_{3/2}$
54. Xe				—	2	6						$^1S_0$
55. Cs				—	2	6	—	1				$^2S_{1/2}$
56. Ba				—	2	6	—	2				$^1S_0$
57. La				—	2	6	1	2				$^2D_{3/2}$
58. Ce				(1)	2	6	(1)	(2)				—
59. Pr				(2)	2	6	(1)	(2)				$^4I_{9/2}$
60. Nd				(3)	2	6	(1)	(2)				$^5I_4$
61. Pm				(4)	2	6	(1)	(2)				—
62. Sm				6	2	6	—	2				$^7F_0$
63. Eu				7	2	6	—	2				$^8S_{7/2}$
64. Gd				7	2	6	1	2				$^9D_2$
65. Tb				(8)	2	6	(1)	(2)				—
66. Dy				(9)	2	6	(1)	(2)				—
67. Ho				(10)	2	6	(1)	(2)				—
68. Er				(11)	2	6	(1)	(2)				—
69. Tm				13	2	6	—	2				$^2F_{7/2}$
70. Yb				14	2	6	—	2				$^1S_0$
71. Lu							1	2				$^2D_{3/2}$
72. Hf							2	2				$^3F_2$
73. Ta							3	2				$^4F_{3/2}$
74. W	Shells 1s						4	2				$^5D_0$
75. Re	to 5p are filled						5	2				$^6S_{5/2}$
76. Os	(68 electrons)						6	2				$^5D_4$
77. Ir							7	2				$^4F_{3/2}$
78. Pt							9	1				$^3D_3$
79. Au							10	1				$^2S_{1/2}$
80. Hg							10	2				$^1S_0$
81. Tl							10	2	1			$^2P_{1/2}$
82. Pb							10	2	2			$^3P_0$
83. Bi							10	2	3			$^4S_{3/2}$
84. Po							10	2	4			—
85. At							10	2	5			—
86. Em							10	2	6			$^1S_0$
87. Fr							10	2	6	—	1	—
88. Ra							10	2	6	—	2	$^1S_0$
89. Ac							10	2	6	(1)	(2)	—
90. Th							10	2	6	(2)	(2)	$(^3F_2)$
91. Pa							10	2	6	(3)	(2)	—
92. U							10	2	6	(4)	(2)	$^5L_6$

9-11. Complex Spectra

Atomic spectra range from the simplest such as that of hydrogen to spectra such as that of iron, so complex that there may be several thousand lines in the visible region and as many more in the ultraviolet and infrared. Spectra of heavier atoms and those with more outer electrons become increasingly complex. In general it is convenient to classify spectra as *one-electron spectra*, with 1 electron outside a closed shell as in the alkali metals; *two-electron spectra*, with 2 electrons outside a closed shell as in helium, mercury, and calcium; *three-electron spectra*, with 3 such electrons as in aluminum, boron, etc. One-electron spectra are doublet spectra, two-electron spectra may be singlet or triplet spectra, three-electron spectra may be doublet or quadruplet spectra, and so on. These relationships which rise and fall as one passes from column to column across the periodic table are known as the *multiplicity of spectra*.

It is of interest to examine the energy-level scheme for a two-electron spectrum. Mercury is a good example (Fig. 9-13). Other elements such as zinc and cadmium in the second column of the periodic table have similar

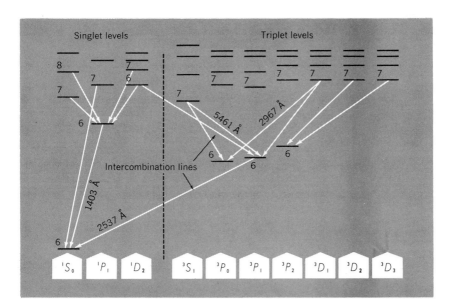

Fig. 9-13. Energy levels for a two-electron spectrum, mercury, involving singlet and triplet levels. For singlet levels the two outer electron spins are opposed, and the vector sum is zero. For triplet levels the spins are parallel, and the vector sum is 1. When the spin and orbital angular momentum vectors are combined for the triplet state there are three different values for each level shown, but in the interest of simplicity the triplet levels are here represented by single lines.

spectra. These elements show spectra, some of the lines of which arise from transitions between singlet levels and others from triplet levels. These lines all arise from the transitions of one of the two "optical" electrons. Some important lines occasionally arise from transitions of one electron between singlet and triplet levels. This means that the electron reverses its axis of spin in the transition. Certain important complex groups of lines arise from transitions involving both electrons at once. The lines so formed are called *multiplets*, and some of these groups appear as *triads of complex triplets*. They involve complications that cannot be discussed here.

In two-electron spectra, singlet levels arise from those atoms in which the spins of the two outer electrons are in opposite directions (antiparallel). The effects of spin cancel, leaving only orbital angular momentum. There will then be no splitting of levels due to spin and consequently no fine structure. In what is called the vector model of the atom the angular momentum is represented by an arrow along the axis of revolution or of spin as in ordinary mechanics. The vectors representing the orbital angular momenta l_1 and l_2 of the two electrons combine to form a resultant L (Fig. 9-14). However, according to quantum rules they only combine in such a manner that the resultant L is always an integral multiple of $h/2\pi$. Again it should be noted that it is common custom to use small letter s, l, and j to represent quantum numbers applying to a single electron. When the vector sum of the s values or the l or j values for two or more electrons is taken, the custom is to use capital letters S, L, or J for these sums. The capital letters may then be thought of as applying to the atom as a whole, whereas the small letters apply to individual electrons. For the singlet levels the electron spins are antiparallel and the total spin is represented by $S = s_1 + s_2 = \frac{1}{2} - \frac{1}{2} = 0$.

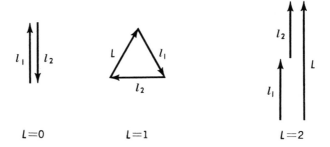

$L=0$ $L=1$ $L=2$

Fig. 9-14.   Vector model of atom with two "optical" electrons. Total orbital angular momentum L is vector sum of separate values l_1 and l_2 for each electron. If $l_1 = 1$ and $l_2 = 1$, three values of L are obtained. In the triplet state $s_1 + s_2 = S = 1$, and S combines with L to give integral values of J from $L - S$ to $L + S$. For $L = 2$ and $S = 1$, J has values 1, 2, 3, and the energy levels are designated $^3D_1$, $^3D_2$, $^3D_3$.

In triplet levels, the electron spins of the two outer electrons are in the same direction (parallel), and the resultant spin designated by S is $\frac{1}{2} + \frac{1}{2} = 1$. By the quantum rule the vectors L and S now form a resultant J which can only take integral values from $L + S$ to $L - S$. As with the alkali metals, the selections rule for J is that it may change by ± 1 or zero, excluding zero-zero transitions. By these concepts the spectra of two-electron atoms may be quite accurately described. The process may be extended to the three-electron atoms of the third column of the periodic table, and so on. Again it should be stated that to compute the energy levels properly the values L^*, S^* and J^* should be used where $L^* = \sqrt{L(L + 1)}$ and similarly with S^* and J^*.

METASTABLE STATES

When the selection rule just mentioned is applied to these atoms certain apparently plausible transitions are forbidden. For instance, transitions from the level 6^3P_2 or from 6^3P_0 are forbidden. By this rule an electron raised to either of these levels cannot ordinarily return to the normal state by radiation. It is then in what is called a *metastable state*, in which it will stay until released by some special process, such as perhaps being raised to another level from which it can return by radiation, or it may give up energy at the moment of collision with another atom. Such a collision is called a *collision of the second kind*.

9-12. Characteristic X-ray Spectra

Characteristic x-rays are particular x-ray frequencies produced by excitation of atoms in the target, and they depend on and are characteristic of the material of the target. In Fig. 9-15 the curve is shown representing the combined continuous spectrum and characteristic spectrum of x-rays produced when electrons strike a target with sufficient speed. The two peaks on the curve represent the characteristic frequencies resulting from excitation of the atoms of the target. Although Barkla and Sadler discovered characteristic x-rays in 1908 and distinguished between what they called K and L rays, it was a number of years before the origin of these rays was understood and before the names K and L were given to the electron shells of the atom. Visible spectra are produced by excitation of an atom so that one or more outer electrons are raised to higher energy states. Characteristic x-ray excitation, on the other hand, involves the displacement of an inner electron as, for instance, one in what we now call the K or L shells. Since there are usually no nearby vacant energy levels to which these electrons may be raised, such excitation involves removing them altogether from the atom (ionization). This permits transition of a nearby electron to the vacancy thus created in an inner shell.

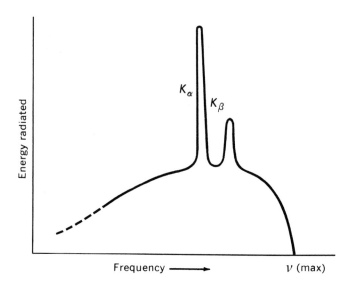

Fig. 9-15. Characteristic x-ray lines of the target (sharp peaks) superposed on the continuous background of general x-rays.

The transitions most likely to occur are those in which the vacancy is filled by a nearby electron from a higher energy state. In the transition a characteristic x-ray photon is radiated. The vacancy left by this electron is in turn filled by the transition of another electron from a still higher energy state with radiation of a photon of somewhat lower frequency. Thus the displacement of one inner electron may permit a series of transitions, with each of which emission of radiation occurs.

Since the electrons in the innermost or K shell of an atom are those most tightly bound to the nucleus they require bombardment by higher energy electrons to displace them than do electrons in L or outer shells. In Table 9-4 ionization energies are given for K and L electrons of some atoms. If displacement of a K electron is followed by transition of an electron from an L to a K shell, an x-ray quantum is emitted representing the first line of the K series of characteristic x-rays. This is called the K_α line. If the transition is from the M to the K shell, the emitted quantum represents the second or K_β line of the K series. Since the energy difference between levels is greater for the latter than for the former transition the second line of the series will have a higher frequency, and the K series will be composed of lines of increasing frequency approaching a high-frequency limit. As the probability of transition decreases rapidly for the higher-frequency members of the series only a few lines of the K and L series can be readily detected except in the elements of high atomic weight.

TABLE 9-4. SOME IONIZATION ENERGIES IN
eV FOR K AND L ELECTRONS

	K	L
Hydrogen	13.6	——
Carbon	282	——
Aluminum	1487	——
Nickel	7477	849
Copper	8047	928
Silver	22162	2984
Tungsten	59310	8396
Gold	69794	9711
Uranium	98428	13613

In the L, M, and higher shells there are electrons with different j values representing slight differences in energy. Consequently the characteristic lines may be expected to have a fine structure, and in accordance with the selection rule for Δj and Δl

$$\Delta j = \pm 1 \text{ or } 0 \qquad \Delta l = \pm 1$$

The K_α line is actually composed of two lines close together, $K_{\alpha 1}$ and $K_{\alpha 2}$. Lines in the L spectra of an element may be represented as L_α, L_β, and so on, and each of these may show a similar fine structure for the same reason.

9-13. Moseley's Rule and Atomic Numbers

In 1913, Moseley used the Bragg-type crystal spectrograph to make an extensive study of the similarities and relations between the characteristic x-ray spectra of a considerable number of the heavy elements. In passing from one element to another of higher atomic weight no simple relation is to be observed for the ordinary visible spectra. However, Moseley found a very simple relationship between the characteristic x-ray spectra of the elements. These spectra all appear very similar, and, with few exceptions, with increasing atomic weight the lines of a given element are merely shifted in the direction of higher frequencies or shorter wavelengths (Fig. 9-16). When the few exceptions were straightened out by changing the order of certain elements, the numbers given to the elements were called *atomic numbers* by Moseley.

Moseley plotted a diagram of the K series, as in Fig. 9-17, in which the square root of the wave number is closely proportional to these atomic numbers. This surprisingly simple but regular relationship of the characteristic x-ray spectra made possible at once the location of missing elements in the periodic table that have since been found. Furthermore it contributed to our knowledge of the atoms themselves.

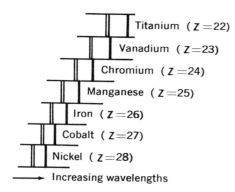

Titanium ($Z=22$)

Vanadium ($Z=23$)

Chromium ($Z=24$)

Manganese ($Z=25$)

Iron ($Z=26$)

Cobalt ($Z=27$)

Nickel ($Z=28$)

⟶ Increasing wavelengths

Fig. 9-16. Characteristic K lines of x-ray spectra of several elements. (After Moseley.)

After the success of the Bohr theory of the atom in explaining hydrogen spectra, it became evident that the simple theory might help to explain characteristic x-ray spectra if the atomic number was identified as Z, the number of charges on the nucleus. For instance, if one of the K electrons of an atom were removed, an L electron would be attracted toward the nucleus in very much the same way as the single electron of a hydrogen atom is attracted toward its nucleus, with two important differences. The attractive force is much greater for the L electron of a heavy element because of the large number of charges on the nucleus. Then the effect of the remaining K electron must be taken into consideration.

Since the remaining K electron is much nearer the nucleus than the L electron, in part it exerts a screening effect reducing the attraction of

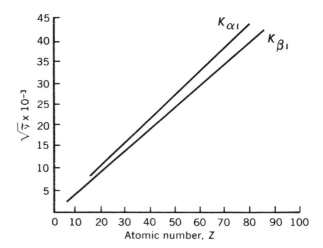

Fig. 9-17. Moseley diagram, showing uniform relation between square root of wave number and atomic number Z.

the nucleus for the L electron. This screening effect may be described in terms of reduction of the effective nuclear charge, and if the number of nuclear charges of the atom is Ze the effective charge on the nucleus, as far as the L electron is concerned, then becomes approximately $(Z - 1)e$. Putting this into the Bohr equation (Eq. 7–29), and remembering that when an L electron falls into a K orbit the quantum number n changes from 2 to 1, we find that the wave number of a K_α line of an element of atomic number Z should be

$$\tilde{\nu} = \frac{1}{\lambda} = R(Z - 1)^2 \left(\frac{1}{1^2} - \frac{1}{2^2} \right) \qquad [9\text{--}15]$$

This can be rewritten, if the constants are replaced by their numerical value, as

$$\frac{1}{\lambda} = 8.23 \times 10^4 (Z - 1)^2 \qquad [9\text{--}16]$$

From this it is seen that the Bohr theory predicts that the square roots of the frequencies or wave numbers are proportional to Z. Moseley's graph (Fig. 9-17) demonstrated this relationship, and the agreement between theory and observed values is surprisingly good. For other lines in the K series and for the lines of other series the simple Bohr theory does not so directly apply, but a simple relationship between spectra remains.

To briefly summarize the historical highlights of this aspect of early atomic theory, the work of Moseley on x-ray spectra led to the idea that an element is distinguished by the number of positive electronic charges on the nucleus of each of its atoms and that the elements can be arranged in a uniform series of increasing nuclear charge. The experiments of Rutherford, Chadwick and others on the scattering of alpha particles confirmed the idea that the number of such charges on each nucleus is the same as its number in the ascending series of the elements. The weight of evidence indicated that the simplest and lightest atom, that of hydrogen, must have 1 positive electronic charge on its nucleus, helium must have 2, lithium 3, and so on up to uranium 92. Thus developed the well-known *atomic number series* of the elements which has now been extended beyond 100 by the "man-made" elements (Appendix).

9-14. X-ray Absorption Spectra

X-ray spectra, like optical spectra, may be studied either by examining emission lines or by examining the lines absorbed from a continuous background. It has been previously indicated that x-ray absorption in any material follows a logarithmic decay curve, the intensity of the beam decreasing logarithmically as the thickness of the absorber increases. It is now possible to say more about just what causes absorption. Generally, any process by which energy is removed from an x-ray beam causes what we think of as absorption. Energy may be removed from a beam by the general process of scattering of radiation; it may be removed by x-ray photons losing energy in collision with electrons (Compton effect); or an x-ray photon may be absorbed by an atom producing a photoelectric ejection of an electron from the atom. It is the latter process which we now wish to consider.

When the absorption of any element is measured at different frequencies of the incident x-ray beam, sudden increases of absorption are noted as the frequency of the incident x-ray is increased. The sudden increase in absorption is the result of photoelectric dislodgment of L or K or other electrons from the atom, and it is represented by sudden increases in the absorption coefficient, as shown on the curve of Fig. 9-18. These points of sharp increase in absorption are called *absorption edges*. The experiment may be done by measuring with an ionization chamber or other detecting device the intensity of the x-rays that pass through a layer of absorber at different frequencies. By means of a crystal spectrograph of the Bragg type any particular frequency may be selected from the continuous spectrum

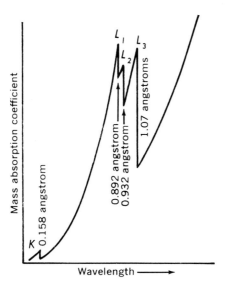

Fig. 9-18. X-ray absorption curve for platinum, showing "edges" where marked absorption begins.

produced by an x-ray tube, and if necessary the spectrum may be pushed to higher limits by an increase in the voltage applied to the x-ray tube.

It will be noticed, for instance, that in the curve representing the absorption by platinum, as the wavelength is decreased (or as the frequency is increased) three absorption edges represented at L_3, L_2, L_1 appear. Then as the frequency is further increased the rays become more penetrating, and the absorption drops to a low level until another sudden increase occurs representing the ejection of K electrons.

The three peaks marked L_1, L_2, L_3 represent successive ejections of L electrons of slightly different energies, and the fact that there are three absorption edges for L electrons, whereas there is only one for K electrons, indicates that in the K shell there is one energy level whereas in the L shell there are three energy levels. Experimental studies show that for M electrons similarly there are five absorption edges and consequently five energy levels.

In the L shell there are only two kinds of electrons, s-electrons and p-electrons; however, there are three different possible combinations of quantum numbers, l and m_s.

$$l = 0 \qquad m_s = +\tfrac{1}{2} \qquad L_1 \text{ level}$$
$$l = 1 \qquad m_s = -\tfrac{1}{2} \qquad L_2 \text{ level}$$
$$l = 1 \qquad m_s = +\tfrac{1}{2} \qquad L_3 \text{ level}$$

Since the three represent slightly different energies this gives three energy levels L_1, L_2, and L_3, thus explaining the three absorption edges in the L shell. The five edges for the M shell may be similarly explained.

In the region of the x-ray spectrum between the groups of levels represented by the absorption edges it will be noticed from Fig. 9-18 that, with increasing frequency (to the left in the figure), the absorption coefficient decreases rapidly, approximately as the inverse cube of the frequency. Penetration, in other words, increases as the cube of the frequency over a considerable range.

Problems

1. Which two series of the alkali metals approach the same series limit? Why?

2. Which outer electrons s, p, d, or f according to the Bohr-Sommerfeld theory would have the more elliptic orbits and might be expected to penetrate other shells? Which of these would be more uniformly screened from the nucleus by the inner electrons?

3. In a sodium atom which of the S, P, D, F energy levels corresponds more closely to the hydrogen energy levels? Why?

*4. Compute the ionization energy for a sodium atom on the assumption that the valence electron "sees" the nuclear charge reduced by all the electrons in the inner shells and that it acts like a hydrogen-type atom with the valence electron in orbit $n = 3$. Compare this with the observed ionization energy of 5.14 eV and account for any discrepancy. How could the ionization energy be computed more accurately?

5. Look at the energy-level diagram for sodium and account for the fact that in the absorption spectrum of sodium only principal lines are usually seen. Remember that the lifetime of an excited state is of the order of 10^{-8} sec.

*6. Show that if s, p, d, f sets of energy levels are set up for the hydrogen atom according to the simple Bohr theory the "sharp series" and "diffuse series" are degenerate (give the same frequencies and are hence indistinguishable) and that these frequencies form the Balmer series.

7. Make diagrams to show how the normal Zeeman effect can be explained by classical electromagnetic theory. Why can the anomalous Zeeman effect not be similarly described?

8. Show that in *mks* units the Bohr magneton $M_B = eh/4\pi m_e$ is measured in the units (joule m²)/weber.

9. Compute the value of the Bohr magneton in mks units from the known physical constants which define it.

*10. If the Landé g-factor for electron spin is 2, how can you account for the fact that the spin magnetic moment is one Bohr magneton?

11. If the magnitude of the angular momentum of the spinning electron is given by $s^* (h/2\pi)$ where $s^* = \sqrt{s(s + 1)}$, what is the angle between it and the allowed projection given by the spin quantum $m_s = \frac{1}{2}$?

12. With which of the following elements could the normal Zeeman effect occur: Al, K, Ca? Why?

*13. According to the vector model of an atom, show that the angle between the total angular momentum j and the orbital angular momentum l for a single electron is given by

$$\cos (l, j) = \frac{l(l + 1) + j(j + 1) - s(s + 1)}{2\sqrt{l(l + 1)} \sqrt{j(j + 1)}}$$

14. Show that the magnetic moment resulting from orbital motion of an electron having one unit $(h/2\pi)$ of angular momentum is one Bohr magneton. Discuss whether or not this applies to a hydrogen atom in the ground state.

*15. Discuss whether or not the magnetic moment of an electron due to spin could be explained by assuming the electron is a rotating sphere with a uniform surface charge.

16. Apply the Pauli exclusion principle to show that for an atom of an element possessing closed electron subshells, the total angular momentum must be zero. What is the total magnetic moment?

17. Show that the force on a magnetic dipole (such as that due to electron spin) in a non-uniform magnetic field is

$$F = \mu \frac{\partial B}{\partial x}$$

where μ is the dipole magnetic moment and $\partial B/\partial x$ is the gradient of the flux density in the x direction.

18. Find the force on an electron when (a) its spin is oriented parallel and (b) anti-parallel to a non-uniform magnetic field having a gradient of flux density of -0.5 (weber/m²)/cm.

19. A silver atom in a non-uniform magnetic field having a gradient of flux density of 0.8 (weber/m²)/cm experiences what acceleration if the spin of its valence electron is parallel to the field?

20. Find the maximum separation of silver atoms in the Stern-Gerlach experiment under the following conditions. The atoms issue from a small heating furnace with speeds given by $\frac{1}{2} mv^2 = \frac{3}{2} kT$ where $T = 1300°K$. They pass through (at right angles) a non-uniform magnetic field which has a flux density gradient of 1.0 (weber/m²)/cm for a distance of 20 cm and are immediately deposited on the collector plate. (See problem 17.)

21. Show that the energy required to turn an electron 90° from the position where its magnetic moment is parallel to a magnetic field (of flux density B) is BM_B where M_B is the Bohr magneton.

22. Compute the wavelength of the K_α line of silver with the aid of Table 9-5.

23. Find the wavelength of the K_α line of gold with the aid of Table 9-5.

*24. Compute the separation in angstroms of adjacent lines of the three lines of the normal Zeeman effect for a $3D$ to a $2P$ transition if the flux density of the magnetic field is 2 weber/m².

25. Find the separation in eV of the magnetic sublevels for the normal Zeeman effect when the flux density of the magnetic field is 400 gauss.

*26. Show that the separation of the components of the normal Zeeman effect can be computed on the basis of classical theory. Assume the radiating electron moves in a circular orbit across a magnetic field and that the orbit is either increased or decreased in diameter depending on the direction of motion, thus changing the frequency.

Recommended Reading

Herzberg, G., *Atomic Spectra and Atomic Structure*. New York: Dover Publications Inc., 1944.

White, H. E., *Introduction to Atomic Spectra*. New York: McGraw-Hill Book Company, Inc., 1934.

Johnson, R. C., *Atomic Spectra*. London: Methuen & Co., Ltd., 1950.

Compton, A. H., and S. K. Allison, *X-Rays In Theory and Experiment*, 2nd ed. Princeton, N. J.: D. Van Nostrand Co., 1935.

Gamow, G., "The Exclusion Principle," *Scientific American*, Vol. 201, No. 1, p. 74 (July, 1959).

Early Work

Moseley, H. G. J., "The High Frequency Spectra of the Element," *Philosophical Magazine*, Vol. 26, p. 1024 (1913); Vol. 27, p. 703 (1914).

Stern, O., et al., *Zeit. f. Phys.*, Vol. 85, No. 4, p. 17 (1933).

Molecules; Molecular Spectra

10-1. Molecular Binding: Exchange Force

If two or more atoms are to form a stable molecule they must be held together by forces in what is called a *bound system*. To form a stable bound system the energy of the atoms must be less when they form the molecule than when they are separated. The amount of energy lost in bringing the atoms together to form the bound system is called the *binding energy* of the molecule. This is the amount of energy which must be supplied to the molecule if it is to be dissociated into its separate atoms.

In Fig. 10-1 the potential energy curve is given for a diatomic molecule. If one atom is located at the origin the other atom may be imagined to be brought toward it from the right. At large distances there is no appreciable attraction or repulsion. In the example shown in the region up to $r = r_A$ the potential energy curve rises slightly to A. This indicates some repulsion in this region though in many cases there might be none and the curve could be flat. Once inside this region the curve slopes downward as far as point B indicating attraction. At smaller distances of separation the curve rises rapidly indicating strong repulsion. At $r = r_0$ the forces of attraction and repulsion balance and this represents the stable point of separation of the two atoms. Evidently the atoms may vibrate back and forth about this equilibrium position. That they do so with quantized amounts of energy is to be explained in this chapter.

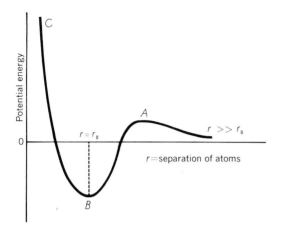

Fig. 10-1. The potential energy diagram for a molecule which absorbs energy when it dissociates.

The two chief kinds of binding between atoms to form a molecule are *ionic* or *heteropolar*, and *covalent* or *homopolar* binding. As an example of ionic binding consider the possible combination of a neutral sodium atom Na with a neutral chlorine atom Cl to form the molecule *NaCl*. Though these molecules may not form individually this type of molecular binding does occur in aggregates. The sodium atom has a weakly bound single $3s$ electron outside of a closed shell while the chlorine atom is lacking one electron to complete the $3p$ subshell. The sodium atom loses its weakly bound electron to the chlorine atom when binding occurs leaving each atom as an ion with a completed subshell. But now the chlorine atom is essentially a negative ion while the sodium is essentially a positive ion and the two ions attract each other. The stable distance of separation is $r_0 = 2.36$Å and the dissociation energy is 4.24 eV. The molecule with its displaced charge thus is a polar molecule with a permanent dipole electron moment, consequently the binding is often called heteropolar.

As an example of homopolar or covalent binding consider the example of how two neutral hydrogen atoms combine to form a hydrogen molecule. Since the two atoms are identical there can be no ionic attraction. Indeed before the advent of wave mechanics there was no satisfactory explanation of how such a combination could occur. Now we know that not only is the Pauli exclusion principle involved but also an entirely new quantum-mechanical phenomenon, the *exchange force*, which has no classical analogue and which can only be described in the non-picturable mathematical language of wave mechanics.

First it must be understood that when two hydrogen atoms are brought near enough that they attract one another, there is no possible way of distinguishing one electron from the other and neither one can be described as belonging to one nucleus more than the other. This is a fundamental characteristic of the exchange phenomenon. Indeed the mathematics involves terms which are unaffected by an exchange of electrons and these terms have been interpreted as representing a force of attraction. There are, however, two different ways in which two hydrogen atoms may be brought close together.

Wave-mechanical analysis indicates that if two hydrogen atoms are brought near, the potential energy increases indefinitely if their electron spins are parallel. This means there is no point at which forces of attraction balance forces of repulsion and no bound state can occur as required for a stable molecule (Fig. 10-2). Besides such a combination would violate the Pauli exclusion principle which requires that electrons in apparently the same state have opposite spins.

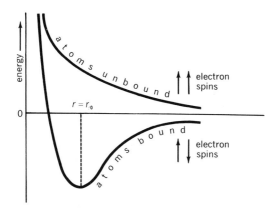

Fig. 10-2. Energy curves for two hydrogen atoms with electron spins parallel and antiparallel.

On the other hand when the electron spins are anti-parallel (Fig. 10-2) the potential energy curve falls to a minimum and the bound state can occur. Because the spins are anti-parallel the two electrons must exchange spins if they exchange positions and if the molecule is to be stable. This is a form of sharing of the two electrons by the two atomic nuclei and one way of looking at this sharing process is to say that each nucleus has an even chance of having its s subshell completed at least temporarily. Such a molecule has no permanent electric dipole moment and is therefore homopolar. In the hydrogen molecule $r_0 = 0.74\text{Å}$ and the dissociation energy is 4.48 eV.

10-2. Degrees of Freedom, Rotation, and Vibration

The simplest gas molecules are *monatomic*, i.e., consisting of one atom each, as for instance in the rare gases (He, Ne, A, Kr, Xe) and mercury vapor (Hg). Such molecules are said to have three degrees of freedom since they are free to move independently in any one of the three directions of space (Fig. 10-3), and there is no evidence that they are set in rotation by collisions; to be more precise, if they possess intrinsic rotation, there is no evidence that this rotation is changed by collisions.

Diatomic molecules such as hydrogen (H_2), oxygen (O_2), and nitrogen (N_2) each are composed of two atoms held together by mutual attraction. Molecules such as these, in which the forces holding the atoms together act between like atoms, are called homopolar molecules. The intermolecular forces between unlike atoms may be either homopolar or ionic in nature.

A diatomic molecule may be represented ideally as two spheres held together to form a kind of dumbbell arrangement (Fig. 10-4); there is good evidence that it may be set in rotation by collision. However, we must assume that a diatomic molecule cannot absorb energy of rotation about the axis joining the atomic centers any more than a single atom can about its axis. This leaves it free to rotate independently about either or both of the other two axes in space. Consequently it has three degrees of freedom of linear motion, plus two of rotation, or five degrees of freedom in all. That the degrees of freedom of a diatomic molecule are five instead of three was inferred from measurements of the energy absorbed by such a gas per degree change in temperature, namely, from measurement of specific heats.

When a molecule accepts more energy than can be accounted for by the degrees of freedom thus far described, it becomes necessary to infer more degrees of freedom, and there is unquestioned evidence that internal vibrations may occur in a molecule. In a diatomic molecule the atoms must be held in equilibrium positions relative to one another such that if the atoms are pushed closer together there is a net force outward, or if they are

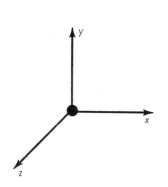

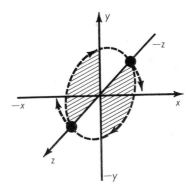

Fig. 10-3.   Degrees of freedom of atom. Atom can move rectilinearly in any of three directions of space but is not able to accept energy of rotation about any axis. Consequently, such an atom is said to possess three degrees of freedom.

Fig. 10-4.   Degrees of freedom of diatomic molecule. Molecule can move rectilinearly in any of three directions of space. It can also rotate about molecular axes x and y but not about atomic axis z. It can also vibrate.

pulled further apart there is a net force inward in agreement with Fig. 10-1. Such an arrangement would permit vibrations along the line of centers. In molecules of more than two atoms there are possibilities of other more complicated types of vibrations.

10-3. Quantum Theory of Molecular Heats of Gases

Many of the macroscopic or large-scale phenomena of gases such as the pressure of a gas may be described satisfactorily in terms of classical mechanics, supplemented by probability considerations involving a Maxwellian distribution of velocities (Chap. 11). However, not all molecular phenomena can be so easily described. In the study of specific heats of a gas at low temperatures classical methods lead to wrong results. Since we have witnessed the increased importance and application of the basic principles of the quantum theory, perhaps we should not be surprised to find that such considerations are now required and yield valid results.

The molecular heat, or specific-heat capacity per gram-molecular weight of a gas at constant volume (designated as C_v), is proportional to the average energy absorbed per molecule for a rise of temperature of 1 degree. It is commonly measured in joules or calories per gram-molecular weight per degree Kelvin.

When the molecules of a gas undergo an increase in energy this energy is divided between the different degrees of freedom according to the law of equipartition of energy. In a monatomic gas any increase of energy goes to increase the kinetic energy of translational motion. It is this energy which determines the temperature of a gas. In polyatomic molecules energy also goes into producing rotations and vibrations. Whatever the form, the total energy divided individually among the molecules of a gas is called the *internal energy* of the gas, but only the fraction represented by random translational motion determines the temperature.

The formula for the pressure of an ideal gas in terms of the number N of molecules per unit volume, the mass m of each molecule and the *rms* (root-mean-square) velocity (§11-3) of the molecules, is

$$P = \frac{1}{3} N m v^2_{\text{rms}} \qquad [10\text{--}1]$$

The general gas law for the pressure of a gas in terms of its volume and temperature (Kelvin) is given in elementary texts as

$$P = \frac{RT}{V} \qquad [10\text{--}2]$$

where R is called the gas constant. It has the particular value

$$R_0 = 8.314 \frac{\text{joules}}{°\text{K}} \text{ (per gram molecular wt)}$$

$$= 1.99 \text{ cal}/°\text{K}$$

Setting Eqs. 10–1 and 10–2 equal to each other we have

$$\frac{1}{3} N m v^2_{\text{rms}} V = R_0 T \qquad [10\text{–}3]$$

For $V = 22{,}415 \text{ cm}^3$, which is the volume of a mole (gram-molecular weight) of any gas, the total number of molecules NV is Avogadro's number N_0. Consequently, upon solving this equation for the average kinetic energy per gas molecule, we have

$$\frac{1}{2} m v^2_{\text{rms}} = \frac{3}{2} \frac{R_0}{N_0} T \qquad [10\text{–}4]$$

and

$$\frac{1}{2} m v^2_{\text{rms}} = \frac{3}{2} k T \qquad [10\text{–}4a]$$

where k is the *Boltzmann constant*. It is the gas constant per molecule, or

$$k = \frac{R_0}{N_0} = \frac{8.31}{6.025 \times 10^{23}} = 1.38 \times 10^{-23} \text{ joule}/°\text{K mol}$$
$$= 3.30 \times 10^{-24} \text{ cal}/°\text{K mol} \qquad [10\text{–}5]$$

From Avogadro's law that equal volumes of different gases at the same temperature and pressure contain the same numbers of molecules, and from Eq. 10–4a, it can be seen that the average kinetic energy of translational motion of the molecules should be the same for all gases at the same temperature since k is a constant.

According to the classical picture absolute zero would then be that temperature at which the molecules do not possess any kinetic energy of random motion. However, quantum considerations now require a certain minimum residual energy called *zero-point energy* at absolute zero, though at higher temperatures the classical relation still holds. At absolute zero the lowest energy states (next chapter) have all been filled, there can be no further change with change in temperature and consequently all specific heats drop to zero at that point.

From Eq. 10–4 it is seen that

$$N_0 \left(\frac{1}{2} m v^2 \right) = \frac{3}{2} R_0 T = \frac{3}{2} \left(\frac{1.99 \text{ cal}}{°\text{K}} \right) T \qquad [10\text{–}6]$$

where $(3/2)R_0$ is the kinetic energy per degree per gram-molecular weight for an ideal monatomic gas having three degrees of freedom. Consequently by the equipartition law each degree of freedom would require $(1/2)R_0$ or 0.99 calorie per gram-molecular weight. For a monatomic gas $3/2(1.99)$ gives for C_v 2.99 cal per °K per gram-molecular weight. For a diatomic molecule with five degrees of freedom the energy per gram-molecular weight per °K would be $5/2(1.99)$ or 4.98 cal. Measured values for real gases (Table 10-1) indicate that the agreement with theory is for the most part quite good at ordinary temperatures. However, at lower temperatures deviations occur that are in disagreement with classical theory. The most striking example is that of hydrogen, the specific heat of which becomes less as the temperature is reduced and finally reaches a lower level, indicating that the molecule has lost two degrees of freedom and now behaves like a monatomic molecule with only 3/5 the specific heat it had at normal temperatures. Other types of molecules show the effect to a lesser extent. Classical theory is helpless to explain these deviations, but quantum concepts offer the basis for a fairly simple explanation.

TABLE 10-1.   MOLECULAR HEATS AT 15° C

Molecule	C_v Experimental	C_v Theoretical	Degrees of Freedom
Helium (He) (monatomic)	2.98	2.99	3
Mercury (Hg) (monatomic)	2.98	2.99	3
Hydrogen (H_2) (diatomic)	4.83	4.98	5
Nitrogen (N_2) (diatomic)	4.94	4.98	5
Oxygen (O_2) (diatomic)	4.97	4.98	5

There are no restrictions on the free translational motion of a molecule in a straight line that would require quantization. The rotational motion of a molecule, however, like the orbital motion of an electron in an atom, is a repeated motion that forms a non-radiating stable state. Such states could be quantized by finding a suitable stationary pattern for the wave function, or what amounts to the same thing, simply permitting only those states for which the angular momentum is an integral multiple of $\hbar$ represented by $J\hbar$. This establishes a discrete set of quantized energy states for rotational motion in terms of the rotational quantum number J.

In each rotational state the energy is $\frac{1}{2}I\omega^2$ where I is the rotational inertia of the molecule and ω is the angular velocity. The latter then is determined by the rule that the angular momentum $I\omega = J\hbar$. Squaring both sides of this equation for the quantization of angular momentum and dividing by $2I$, it follows that the rotational energy E_{rot} of any state of rotational quantum number J_n is

$$\frac{1}{2}I\omega^2 = \frac{J_n{}^2 h^2}{8\pi^2 I} = \frac{J_n{}^2 \hbar^2}{2I} \qquad [10\text{--}7]$$

where J_n can be any integer including zero. From this we can find the energy required to raise a molecule from one rotational energy state J to the next or $J + 1$ state. This is the simple theory for what is called the *rigid rotator* in which the separation of the atoms in the molecule remains constant. Actually a small correction needs to be made for the effect of rotation on the separation but this need not concern us here. Wave-mechanical analysis confirms the relation (Eq. 10–7) in general but (as in earlier examples) substitutes for J the quantity $\sqrt{J(J + 1)}$. The energy of the nth rotational level now becomes

$$E_{\text{rot}} = J_n(J_n + 1)\frac{h^2}{8\pi^2 I} \qquad [10\text{--}8]$$

For molecules composed of light atoms the small rotational inertia I makes the energy a relatively large quantity even for the first state where n equals 1, and the angular velocity must likewise be large.

Although very small amounts of energy are required, at low temperatures the collisions of molecules may not be sufficiently energetic to excite even the first quantum state of rotation, and according to quantum theory either this degree of angular momentum is excited or none are. At a sufficiently high temperature higher quantum states of angular momentum may be excited, and these will consequently represent higher energy states. For instance, at room temperature an oxygen molecule may have 20 units of angular momentum, whereas a hydrogen molecule having about 1/40 the rotational inertia of an oxygen atom must spin far faster for the same amount of angular momentum and, on the average, at room temperature may have only 2 or 3 units of angular momentum.

As the temperature of a gas is reduced the probability of exciting rotational energy states becomes less, and for hydrogen a marked decrease is observed in the molecular heat, as indicated in Fig. 10-5. From the curve it is seen that below about 70° K no appreciable energy goes into rotational

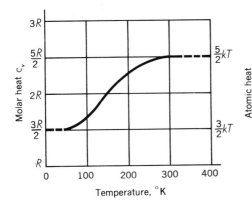

Fig. 10-5.   Specific heat of hydrogen at different temperatures.

states. The hydrogen molecule thus loses its two degrees of freedom representing rotations, and the diatomic hydrogen molecule then behaves like a single atom or monatomic molecule. For heavier molecules the effect is much less and is only detectable, if at all, at much lower temperatures than for hydrogen.

10-4. Quantum Theory of Molecular Spectra

For a long time after the discovery of spectra it was not understood why the spectra produced by molecules appeared to be broad bands, covering a considerable frequency range, whereas the spectra of atoms consist of separate and distinct lines. Progress was made when it was found by observation with instruments of higher resolving power that the broad bands, from which the name *band spectra* was derived, are in reality closely packed groups of individual lines.

A satisfactory explanation of the origin of the lines forming a band and of the bands themselves was not obtained until, with the aid of quantum theory, a scheme of possible energy levels was set up for an individual molecule. In an atom, energy absorption or emission occurs, as we have previously seen, by electron transitions by which the atom passes from one energy state to another. A molecule, however, has possibilities of absorbing energy by the excitation of rotational states and vibrational states, and also by electron transitions. The resultant energy state of a molecule depends on the total energy, and this may involve one, two, or all three types of excitation. Emission of energy occurs when the molecule undergoes a transition to a lower energy state, which again involves one or more of these factors.

A molecule may be excited to a higher rotational energy state and return to the next lower energy state by emission of a quantum of radiation $h\nu$. The selection rule is that J can change by ± 1 but not by zero.

$$\Delta J = \pm 1 \qquad \Delta J \neq 0$$

If n' represents $n + 1$, then the emitted quantum is given by the difference between the energies E'_{rot} and E_{rot} of the two corresponding states.

$$h\nu = E'_{rot} - E_{rot} = \frac{h^2}{8\pi^2 I} \qquad [10\text{--}9]$$

Absorption occurs when the transition is from the state of energy E to the state of next higher energy E'.

A set of energy levels for different values of n_r is represented in Fig. 10-6a. Since rotation spectra are usually studied by absorption methods the arrows for the transitions are directed from lower to higher energy states. The spectral lines corresponding to these transitions are shown in

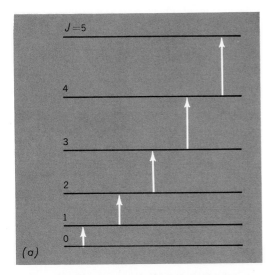

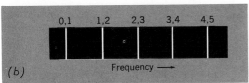

Fig. 10-6. a, Rotational energy levels of diatomic molecule; arrows represent transitions in which energy is absorbed; b, rotational spectrum showing absorption lines (equally spaced) for transitions shown in a.

Fig. 10-6b and are seen to be equally spaced, since each energy level represents the same increase in energy with respect to the preceding level.

Since these rotational states are excited at moderately low temperatures they represent small energy differences, and by the quantum relation $E_q = h\nu$ the lines will represent a small frequency difference and be close together. At such low temperatures there is not sufficient energy per collision to excite vibrational states or electronic transitions, and the spectra are called pure rotation spectra. Because of the low frequencies involved the lines occur in what is called the far infrared region of the spectrum, far beyond the long-wave limit of the visible spectrum. The lines are hard to detect, and not many successful studies have been made of such emission spectra, but such as have been made confirm the theory. A much greater advance has resulted from the more recent studies of absorption spectra by methods using microwaves (§10-6).

At higher temperatures vibrational energy states are excited in addition to rotational states. Whereas rotation spectra may be observed separately, vibration spectra cannot be so observed. Vibrational energy-level transitions always occur in connection with rotational energy-level changes, giving rise to what are called *rotation-vibration spectra*.

If ν is the frequency of vibration of the molecule in a given state we can write for the vibrational energy in any level where n_v is the number of the level, or the *vibrational quantum number*,

$$E_{\text{vib}} = n_v h \nu_v \qquad [10\text{--}10]$$

This type of quantization, however, belongs to the older quantum theory, and wave-mechanical theory predicts the energy to be

$$E_{\text{vib}} = \left(n_v + \frac{1}{2} \right) h \nu_v \qquad [10\text{--}11]$$

An interesting feature of the newer scheme is that it predicts a residual amount of energy for $n_v = 0$. This is a typical feature of wave mechanics, and the energy in any rotation-vibration state is then

$$E = E_{\text{vib}} + E_{\text{rot}} = \left(n_v + \frac{1}{2} \right) h \nu_v + J(J+1) \frac{h^2}{8\pi^2 I} \qquad [10\text{--}12]$$

The frequency ν of emitted (or absorbed) radiation in a transition from one level to another is then given by

$$h \nu = (E'_{\text{vib}} - E_{\text{vib}}) + (E'_{\text{rot}} - E_{\text{rot}}) \qquad [10\text{--}13]$$

where the primed quantities represent higher (or lower) energy states. Since vibrational levels represent much larger energy changes than rotational energy levels, there will be a series of rotational energy levels for each vibrational energy level. The energy-level scheme for a diatomic molecule such as HCl is shown in Fig. 10-7a, where sets of rotational levels for different vibrational levels are shown, together with the possible transitions leading to groups of lines in two branches, known as the P and R branches, Fig. 10-7b. Since J can change by only ± 1 the transition $0 \rightarrow 0$ is excluded and leads to a missing line characteristic of this type of spectra. This is the line that would be given for zero change in the rotational quantum number. Since it is not observed we conclude that the usual selection rule which excludes such a change is valid and that changes in vibrational energy are always accompanied by changes in rotational energy.

Rotation-vibration spectra are found in the near-infrared region, and intensities of lines can be measured by photometric methods, giving the type of curve represented in Fig. 10-8 where the position of the missing line is plainly evident.

If the available energy is sufficient to excite an electron transition as well as rotation-vibration states, the energy of the electron transition $h\nu_e$ must be added to that of the other transitions, giving generally for a rotation-vibration-electronic line in the spectrum,

$$h \nu = h \nu_e + (E'_{\text{vib}} - E_{\text{vib}}) + (E'_{\text{rot}} - E_{\text{rot}}) \qquad [10\text{--}14]$$

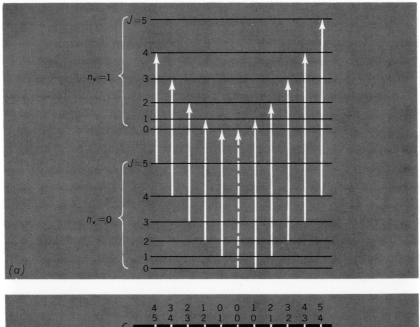

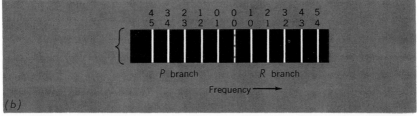

Fig. 10-7. a, Rotation-vibration energy levels of diatomic molecule such as HCl, showing transitions between rotational levels belonging to the first two vibrational levels; b, absorption lines of the rotation-vibration spectrum for the transitions shown in a.

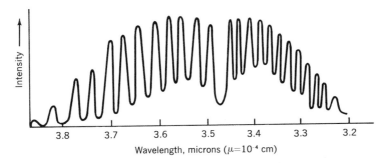

Fig. 10-8. Typical photometric measurement of intensities of rotation-vibration absorption spectrum of HCl. Note missing line for forbidden 0 → 0 transition.

From this the frequency of emitted (or absorbed) radiation is given by dividing both sides of the equation by h.

The effect of electronic transitions is to give groups of closely packed lines converging to a "head" on one side of the band, and this accounts for the common structure of molecular spectra in the visible region. Such spectra are called *rotation-vibration-electronic spectra*. An energy-level diagram involving all three types of levels, electronic, vibrational, and rotational, is shown in Fig. 10-9. For each electronic level there is a group of vibrational levels, and for each vibrational level there is a group of rotational levels. The transitions of the diagram are for electronic and rotational

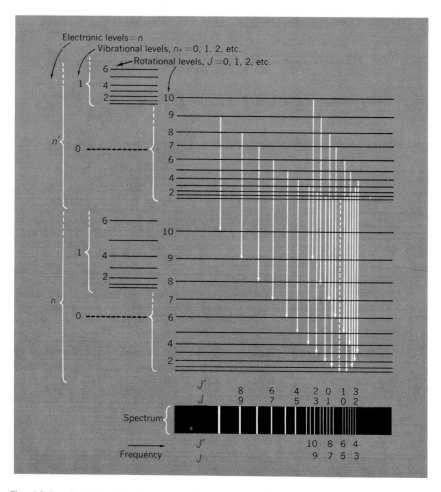

Fig. 10-9. Rotation-vibration-electronic energy levels, showing how transitions form typical "electronic" band with lines converging to a "head" at the high-frequency limit.

changes. The spacings of the rotational levels are different for the two electronic levels since electronic excitation may be expected to change the rotational inertia I of the molecule. Below the energy-level diagram the emitted (or absorbed) lines are indicated with a gap for the $0 \rightarrow 0$ transition for n_r and only those transitions are permitted for which J changes by ± 1. Transitions may also take place between various levels of different energy and between different electronic states, so that in a characteristic molecular spectrum many bands of lines may be observed, the lines always crowding in one direction toward a "head" for each band, as in Fig. 10-10.

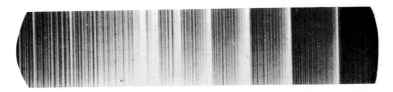

Fig. 10-10.   Typical molecular spectrum showing bands in the spectrum of cyanogen.

By way of summary it is convenient to represent the energy levels of a diatomic molecule superposed on the potential energy curves as in Fig. 10-11. Some of the quantized vibrational energy levels are indicated and any are possible up to the dissociation level. A few rotational energy levels are also indicated. They represent small energy changes with respect to the vibrational levels and are much more readily excited. The vibrational levels can only be excited under very much stronger excitation, and elec-

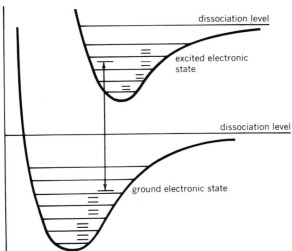

dissociation level

excited electronic state

dissociation level

ground electronic state

Fig. 10-11.   Energy-level diagram for a diatomic molecule indicating some of the rotational, vibrational and electronic levels.

tronic excitation requires a still more intense stimulus. As indicated in the diagram r'_0 for an excited state may be different from r_0 for the ground state. Dissociation energies may also be different.

From the figure it is evident that rotational energy levels may be excited at energies of excitation too small to excite vibrational levels. Such excitation results in the emission of pure rotational line spectra consisting of equally spaced lines very close together but far in the infrared. They extend even into the *microwave* region and they are difficult to observe. The detection and measurement of these lines, however, makes it possible to compute the rotational inertia of a diatomic molecule and in consequence the interatomic distance r_0. For polyatomic molecules there is more than one moment of inertia and the spectra are more complicated.

The separations of the vibrational energy levels of a diatomic molecule represent energy differences as much as a hundred times those for rotational spectra, but still the spectra are found in the infrared. When one or more vibrational states are excited many rotational states are possible and the rotation-vibration spectra consist of groups of lines, or rather a closely spaced group of rotational lines, appearing near the frequency for each vibrational transition. If electronic transitions are excited in the molecule still more energy of excitation is required and the number of possible transitions from one electronic level to another is much larger. But this also involves the possibilities of many vibrational and rotational transitions giving the full characteristic rotation-vibration-electronic spectrum of the molecule as previously described in more detail.

10-5. Raman Spectra

Certain additional faint lines on either side of an observed spectral line (Fig. 10-12) may be detected by special means when the observed light is scattered by suitable molecules. These Raman lines were first detected by Raman in India in 1928, for which he received the Nobel prize. The special method adopted was to make an extremely long exposure of the lines on a photographic film, greatly overexposing the primary lines.

The method of producing the Raman effect is to illuminate with an intense beam of light a molecular solution, the Raman spectrum of which

(a)

(b)

Fig. 10-12. Raman lines: a, incident light before scattering; b, scattered light shows Raman lines on each side of lines of incident light.

it is desired to study. The beam may be produced by a mercury arc, and the beam of light may be limited to a single wavelength (monochromatic). The light scattered in all directions by the solution is then passed through a spectrograph and focused on photographic film.

The explanation of the appearance of the extra lines involves the quantum theory. The lines of lower frequency than that of the incident photons are produced by scattering from molecules, which go into a higher energy state and take a small quantum of energy E_q from the incident photon of energy $h\nu_0$, thus, by the quantum hypothesis, lowering the energy of the photon and consequently lowering frequency to a new value ν given by the relation

$$h\nu = h\nu_0 - E_q$$

A similar relation holds for gain of energy in the scattering process:

$$h\nu = h\nu_0 + E_q$$

where the observed scattered frequency is higher than that of the incident light. At the moment of scattering the excited molecule contributes a small quantum of energy E_q to the incident photon, which then becomes a photon of higher frequency. Lines of higher frequency are usually less intense since they are due to scattering from molecules already in an excited state.

10-6. Microwave Spectroscopy: Maser; Laser

The subject of microwave spectroscopy has in recent years fairly leaped into prominence. Microwaves are electromagnetic waves less than a meter in length produced by electronic means. During World War II new methods of producing these waves by means of such devices as magnetron and klystron tubes were developed and have since been greatly improved. Where originally used for radar, they have now become very important in research in several fields.

Molecules often possess energy levels so closely spaced that the radiation frequencies are far below any detectable infrared radiation. They lie in a region continuous with the infrared, embracing wavelengths from a fraction of a centimeter to 15 or 20 cm in length. Successful techniques are now available for working with wavelengths shorter than 1 mm (the submillimeter region).

In *molecular gas spectroscopy* a beam of microwaves is sent through a gas. If the frequency of the microwave oscillator is varied, absorption of the microwaves occurs when the frequency is in resonance with possible rotational emission frequencies of the molecules. Absorption of a quantum of energy then causes the molecule to pass from one rotational energy state to the next higher one. Effects of external electric and magnetic fields upon the energy levels have thus been measured and even transitions representing hyperfine structure of the energy levels have been detected.

Whereas infrared spectroscopy would be unable to separate the observed emitted frequencies even if they could be detected, it is possible to separate them easily by means of electronic circuits. Since any emitted radiation at such frequencies would be masked by the ever-present thermal radiation of other bodies, microwave spectra are always absorption spectra and the frequencies detected are those removed from an incident beam by absorption.

By these methods molecular energy states may be studied and such properties as (a) distances between nuclei and the forces involved, (b) molecular potential energy functions, (c) molecular electric or magnetic moments, (d) nuclear spins (§14-14). Related to these are studies of the motions of electrons in solids in the presence of external magnetic fields known as *cyclotron resonance* and *electron-spin resonance*. In other areas microwaves have been used as a probe in studies of superconductivity (§12-11), and of dielectrics and plasmas. The development of "molecular clocks" and more recently the *maser* (*m*icrowave *a*mplification by *s*timulated *e*mission of *r*adiation) followed by the *laser* for light amplification have resulted from such molecular studies. In the *maser*, for instance, resonant absorption of microwave power raises ("pumps up") large numbers of molecules to higher energy states. A small input signal at the proper resonant frequency then stimulates the immediate return of these molecules to some lower state with emission of radiation of the same frequency as the input signal. This produces large-scale amplification of the input signal.

Masers and lasers are molecular quantum amplifiers which open up vast new fields of research and development. *Lasers* offer the first intense source of a narrow beam of *coherent* (in phase) light. In 1962 a powerful flash of light from a ruby laser was sent toward the moon and was observed to light up an area only 2 miles in diameter.

Problems

1. What is the average kinetic energy in eV of mercury atoms that escape into a room at 27°C? How does this compare with the average kinetic energy of the air molecules?

2. Find the rms speed of a nitrogen molecule at room temperature and pressure.

3. Compute the rms speed of an oxygen molecule at room temperature and pressure.

4. What energy in joules and in calories is required to raise the temperature of 1 mole (1 gm. mol. wt.) of helium from 0°C to 100°C if the gas is kept at constant volume?

5. Compute the potential energy in electron volts resulting from the repulsion of two protons if they are separated by a distance of 1.06 Å.

6. If all the human beings in the world could be turned into gas molecules of air, how much volume would they occupy at standard pressure and temperature? (Assume 3 billion inhabitants of the world.)

7. If there are 2.7×10^{19} molecules per cm^3 in a gas at standard pressure and 0°C, how many molecules per cm^3 would there be at the extremely high vacuum of 10^{-8} mm pressure of mercury? How far apart on the average would these molecules be?

8. Show that the molecular rotational inertia I of two nuclei about their common center of mass is

$$I = \frac{M_1 M_2}{M_1 + M_2} R_0^2$$

where R_0 is the intermolecular distance and M_1 and M_2 are the nuclear masses.

9. The rotational energy levels of a diatomic molecule are given by the Schrödinger equation as

$$E_j = \frac{h^2}{8\pi^2 I} J(J + 1)$$

where J is the rotational quantum number and it may have the values 0, 1, 2, ... By what increment of energy is the difference between adjacent rotational energy levels increased with increasing values of J?

*10. Compute the rotational inertia for the hydrogen molecule if the separation of the nuclei is 1.06 Å. Compute the energies in eV of the first three rotational levels. Compute the wavelengths of the allowed transitions from these levels. $\Delta J = \pm 1$.

*11. Compute the energies in eV of the first three rotational levels for the HD molecule and the wavelengths of the allowed transitions. $(D = {}_1 H^2)$ assuming the distance between nuclei is 1.06 Å.

*12. Compute the rotational inertia of the HCl^{35} molecule if the separation of the nuclei is 1.25 Å. Find the energies of the three lowest energy levels.

*13. In the simple theory the rotating molecule is assumed to be a *rigid rotator*, i.e. the intermolecular distance is constant regardless of the degree of rotation. In a more complete theory the effect of centripetal force is taken into consideration. Show what effect this would have on the energy levels.

14. Explain by means of the formula why the lines in a pure rotation spectrum are equally spaced although the energy levels are not equally spaced. If the energy levels were equally spaced, how many different spectral lines would be observed?

15. Why are pure vibrational spectra and electronic spectra of molecules not observed separately?

*16. In the rotational spectrum of the HCl molecule lines are observed in the far infrared for which the wave numbers are 81; 104; 124; and 145. Compute the rotational inertia of the molecule and the separation between the H^+ and Cl^- ions.

Recommended Reading

Richtmeyer, F. K., E. H. Kennard, and T. Lauritsen, *Introduction to Modern Physics.* New York: McGraw-Hill Book Company, Inc., 1955.

Kennard, E. H., *Kinetic Theory of Gases.* New York: McGraw-Hill Book Company, Inc., 1938.

Zemansky, M. W., *Heat and Thermodynamics*, 3rd ed. New York: McGraw-Hill Book Company, Inc., 1957.

Rice, F. O. and E. Teller, *The Structure of Matter.* New York: John Wiley and Sons, Inc., 1949.

Gordy, W., W. V. Smith and R. Trambarulo, *Microwave Spectroscopy.* New York: John Wiley & Sons Inc., 1953.

Quantum Statistics

It will be the object of this chapter to show (1) how classical statistical laws had to be revised in favor of *quantum statistics* to account for radiation phenomena; and (2) how such quantum statistics were further revised in order to apply to the electrons in a metal.

11-1. Black-Body Radiation and the Wien Displacement Law

Toward the close of the last century scientists were deeply concerned with their failure by means of classical theory to predict the shape of the thermal radiation curve (energy versus wavelength or frequency) for a hot body. Radiation from a perfect radiator or *ideal black body* in particular, and from any body in general, does not occur at a single frequency but covers a range of frequencies (or wavelengths) with a maximum rate of energy emission at a frequency which depends upon the temperature. Curves representing the energy radiated at each frequency (or wavelength) range are shown in Fig. 11-1. Such curves have been measured experimentally for a variety of conditions.

Solid bodies heated to 700° C begin to give off visible light although the radiation peak is far down in the infrared. As the temperature is increased the height of the curve is increased and the peak of the curve shifts toward shorter wavelengths (higher frequencies). For all ordinary

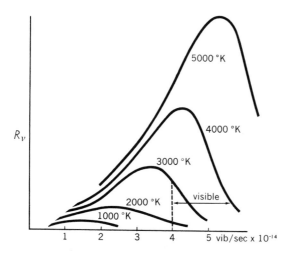

Fig. 11-1. Energy - distribution curves for different temperatures showing the energy R_ν radiated in unit frequency range at any frequency by an ideal black body.

sources of light the peak of the radiation curve lies considerably below the visible region. For the sun the peak of the curve comes near the middle of the visible region, but for the intensely hot blue-white stars it may be in the ultraviolet region.

Wien found that the frequency at which maximum energy is radiated per second is proportional to the absolute temperature. This is called *Wien's displacement law*, and the frequency of the maximum for any absolute temperature T is given by experiment and later checked by theory to be

$$\nu \ (\text{sec}^{-1}) = 1.04 \times 10^{10} \ T \ ^\circ\text{K} \qquad [11\text{--}1]$$

11-2. The Failure of the Classical Radiation Theory: Planck's Theory

THE WIEN RADIATION FORMULA

Wien attempted in 1896 to obtain the correct formula for the radiation curve by noting the similarity between the curve and Maxwell's distribution law for the speeds of molecules in a gas. By means of classical methods of computing the energy of a wave of given frequency he tried to distribute these energies just as the energies of the molecules of the gas are distributed. By this process he arrived at the formula for the rate of energy emission per unit area R_ν per unit frequency range at a given frequency in terms of the frequency ν, the absolute temperature T, the base of the natural system of logarithms ϵ, and constants c_1 and c_2.

$$R_\nu = c_1 \frac{\nu^3}{\epsilon^{c_2 \nu / kT}} \qquad [11\text{--}2]$$

The formula was successful in describing the shape of the curve except at the low-frequency end of the curve, where it was increasingly in error.

THE RAYLEIGH-JEANS FORMULA

Lord Rayleigh shortly afterward took up the search for the correct radiation formula, and the mathematics was further developed in 1905 by Jeans. The method is of great historical interest and importance, not because it gave the correct formula, which it failed to do, but because it foreshadowed events to come in quantum theory and wave mechanics. Instead of borrowing the Maxwellian distribution directly, Rayleigh borrowed the idea of the equal division of energy between degrees of freedom in a gas, applying it to the radiation in a perfectly black enclosure. To do this he applied classical methods to find just those wavelengths which could form standing waves in the enclosure, and he called each of these modes of vibration a "degree of freedom." Unfortunately for the theory there were too many possible short wavelengths and the energy represented tended toward infinity for which it was called the "Rayleigh-Jeans catastrophe."

However, although a total failure throughout most of the frequency range it did have some success far out toward the long wavelengths where the Wien formula failed. Thus, classical methods failed to yield a single formula that could completely describe the entire radiation curve. The dilemma was a serious one.

THE PLANCK RADIATION FORMULA

Max Planck in 1900 sought a formula that would fit the radiation curve from the shortest wavelength to the longest, and his mathematical search was successful with the development of the following formula for R_ν the rate of radiation of energy per unit area per unit frequency range at frequency ν and temperature T °K.

$$R_\nu = \frac{8\pi h}{c^3} \frac{\nu^3}{\epsilon^{h\nu/kT} - 1} \qquad [11\text{--}3]$$

h being the Planck constant and k the Boltzmann gas constant. This equation is of the same form as the Wien equation (Eq. 11–2) except for the -1 in the denominator. At high frequencies this term is negligible, but at low frequencies it is just what is needed to make the equation fit the experimental curve where the Wien equation fails.

Planck saw that the idea of a classical oscillator continuously radiating energy was wrong in principle because no atomic oscillator could have an unlimited supply of energy to radiate. By clever reasoning he hit upon the idea of quantizing the oscillators so as to limit the energy radiated or absorbed to separate units or quanta E_q where the unit of energy $E_q = h\nu$ is determined by the frequency ν and a constant h. As it turned out what

Planck at first thought was a mathematical artifice is now recognized as representing something basic to the nature of things. Today we may derive Planck's formula by a more general method based on quantum statistics but before showing how this can be done we must look at the methods of classical statistics.

11-3. The Classical Maxwell-Boltzmann Statistics

Maxwell and Boltzmann applied probability methods to the molecules of a gas in order to find just how the velocities of the particles could be affected by successive collisions and how many molecules could be expected to have a given velocity range at a given temperature when equilibrium was reached. Since some molecules gain velocity by collision and others lose velocity, equilibrium is that state in which in a given time interval the gains in velocity balance the losses in such a way that the total kinetic energy of random motion remains constant as long as the collisions are perfectly elastic. Maxwell derived his famous velocity distribution law from an application of what were considered to be the *laws of pure chance*. A more rigorous deduction was made later by Boltzmann, in which actual effects of collisions as determining the distribution of velocities in equilibrium were more explicitly involved. Consequently the law of distribution is often called the *Maxwell-Boltzmann law*.

From the viewpoint of the probabilities involved it is well to start with the idea of the random deviations of bullets aimed at a target (Fig. 11-2a).

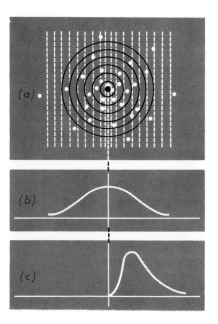

Fig. 11-2. *a,* Random distribution of shots at a target; *b,* lateral distribution curve; *c,* radial distribution curve.

Unless unknown factors are involved this is presumed to represent a chance distribution grouped about the center of the target. If the number of shots that deviate to the right or the left by a certain amount is plotted, that is, the numbers in the vertical spaces, the curve of Fig. 11-2b is obtained. This is quite closely described by the so-called Gauss curve of errors the mathematical form of which is

$$y = a\epsilon^{-b^2 x^2} \tag{11–4}$$

where a is the height of the curve for $x = 0$, and b^2 is a constant. However, let us now assume that it is desired to know how many shots miss the center of the target by a given amount regardless of direction. Very few if any hit the exact center, and very few if any miss the target by a large amount. The numbers to be plotted are the numbers in the concentric rings. The desired equation is obtained by multiplying the probability distribution function, Eq. 11-4, by the area of each ring surrounding the center. The product is the number of shots in each ring of the same width, and the values when plotted give the curve of Fig. 11-2c.

Let us transform the picture and apply it to the molecules of a gas. The points representing hits on the target (Fig. 11-3) may now be interpreted as velocity points in "velocity space," each point representing the velocity of a molecule. The direction of an arrow drawn from the center of the target to the point represents the direction of the velocity, and the length of the arrow represents the magnitude of the velocity. If v^2 is substituted in Eq. 11–4 for x^2, the distribution of points then represents a velocity distribution. However, the constant b needs to be evaluated and for the velocities of thermal agitation of gas molecules at temperature T, $b^2 = m/2kT$, where k is the Boltzmann constant and T is the Kelvin temperature. From this

$$y = n = a\epsilon^{-b^2 v^2} = a\epsilon^{-mv^2/2kT} \tag{11–5}$$

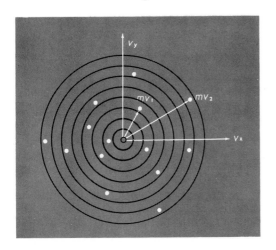

Fig. 11-3. Points representing a distribution in "velocity space" or "momentum space" of two dimensions.

This is really an energy distribution, since $\frac{1}{2}mv^2$ is the kinetic energy of the molecules and kT also represents energy, but from it the velocities may be found. The equation may equally well be applied to components of velocity in the x direction. The exponential term on the right-hand side of Eq. 11–5 is called the *Boltzmann probability distribution function*. This function is required in order to obtain the actual distribution equation for speeds of gas molecules in three-dimensional space and it has many uses.

As one example the ratio of the Boltzmann function for two different energy states E_1 and E_2 at a constant temperature T is $\epsilon^{-(E_2-E_1)/kT}$ and the ratio of the number n_2 in state 2 to the number n_1 in state 1 is

$$\frac{n_2}{n_1} = \epsilon^{-(E_2-E_1)/kT} \qquad [11\text{–}5\text{a}]$$

This formula may be applied to quantized states as well as to classical problems.

Early in the century in a historic experiment Perrin determined Avogadro's number by counting numbers of small particles (of gamboge) per cm^3 suspended in water at two different depths. The effect of gravity is to make the concentration of particles greater at greater depths. Similar considerations apply to the density of the air at different elevations. From Eq. 11–5a Perrin could determine kT but $k = R_0/N_0$ and since the gas constant R_0 is known, N_0 could be determined.

Since velocities may take any direction in space, we must now imagine the points in velocity space surrounding the center on all sides in three dimensions. The number of molecules having speeds between v and $v + \Delta v$ irrespective of direction is represented by the number of points in a thin shell surrounding the center of the coordinate system. The number of points in such a shell is proportional to the volume of the shell. Take the radius of any shell to be v for that shell. The volume of this shell is $4\pi v^2 \Delta v$ where Δv is the thickness of the shell (Fig. 11–4). Multiplying Eq. 11–5 by this, we have for the number of molecules Δn possessing speeds of a magnitude between v and $v + \Delta v$, regardless of direction

$$\Delta n = 4\pi a v^2 \epsilon^{-mv^2/2kT} \, \Delta v \qquad [11\text{–}6]$$

This is the Maxwell distribution equation for speeds, and it only remains to evaluate the constant a, a matter too lengthy for inclusion here, to obtain the complete form of the equation

$$\Delta n = 4N \sqrt{\frac{m^3}{8\pi k^3 T^3}} \, v^2 \epsilon^{-mv^2/2kT} \, \Delta v \qquad [11\text{–}7]$$

where N is the total number of molecules in the gas, k is the Boltzmann constant, ϵ is the base of the natural system of logarithms, and T is the absolute temperature. The graph of this distribution is given in Fig. 11–5,

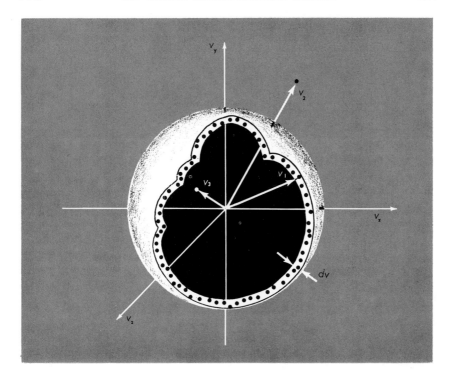

Fig. 11-4. Velocity space in three dimensions showing points such as v_1 lying within a spherical shell of thickness dv and volume $4\pi v^2 dv$. Points such as v_2, v_3, etc., lie outside the shell. This velocity space is readily converted to momentum space by multiplying each velocity by the mass of the particle it represents.

where the three speeds (most probable, average, and rms) are indicated. The summation of all the molecules represented by the curve is the total number of molecules in the gas.

We learn from this distribution law that only 1.61 per cent of the molecules of gas have speeds less than ¼ the average speed, and only 1.71 per cent have speeds as much as or more than twice the average. The chance that a molecule may gain a very high speed by successive collisions is extremely small, and less than one in a hundred million would have speeds more than 4 times the average.

Although in the derivation of Eq. 11–7 the directions of motion have been disregarded we can multiply the mass of each particle by its velocity, represented by a vector in velocity space, so that any point represents a particular momentum. We can then think of the array of points as existing in a new region called *momentum space*. The idea of representing the momenta of gas molecules by vectors measured to points in mathematical space called momentum space is of much importance in what follows.

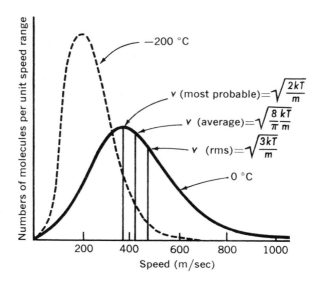

Fig. 11-5. The curves representing a Maxwell distribution of speeds at two different temperatures.

The validity of the Maxwellian distribution of speeds for gas molecules can be checked experimentally in several different ways and has recently been confirmed in great detail by Nobel prize winner Kusch. One of the most direct methods was initiated by Stern in 1920 and was carried further by Zartman in 1931. Atoms of a metal are evaporated from a vapor source (Fig. 11-6), and pass through a series of slits limiting the beam to a narrow width. A rotating cylinder above the slits has a slit at S. As the cylinder rotates, a group of atoms pass the slit S into the cylinder and continue to

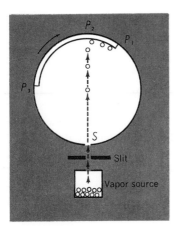

Fig. 11-6. Sketch of apparatus for determining distribution of atomic speeds. Atoms from vapor source (small furnace) enter rotating cylinder at slit S in a group moving vertically upward. Those with highest speeds hit recording plate first and are carried to P_1 by rotating cylinder. Slower atoms hit later at points such as P_2.

move in a straight line to the top of the cylinder where they are deposited on a curved plate P_1P_3. The atoms with highest speeds hit the plate at P_1. However, the cylinder is rotating at a known speed, and slower atoms reach the plate later, for instance, at P_2. The density of the deposited film at any position is proportional to the number of atoms having speeds enabling them to cross the diameter of the cylinder while the cylinder has turned through a known angle. The results of the experiment are found to be in agreement with Maxwell's theory within the limits of experimental error.

The many successes of the Maxwell distribution law have established its value as an accurate description of this aspect of molecular phenomena. We shall find, however, that other types of distribution law involving quantum concepts are now required in other fields, as for instance the Bose statistics which apply to radiation and the Fermi statistics which apply to the random speeds of free electrons in a metal.

The Maxwell distribution law can also be derived by starting with the classical definition of the *most probable state* of a given arrangement. Classical statistics defines the thermodynamic probability W of a given arrangement of particles as

$$W = \frac{N!}{N_1!\, N_2!\, N_3! \cdots N_m!} \qquad [11\text{--}8]$$

where N is the total number of molecules, N_1 is the number in a given group, and $N!$ is the factorial of N. The thermodynamic probability of a given state of an assemblage has values from 1 up and must be distinguished from the ordinary probability of an event represented by values from 0 to 1 where 1 stands for certainty.

The factorial of the number of particles such as N_1 in each group is divided into $N!$, the factorial of the total, because the particles in any group are assumed to be indistinguishable and any two in a group may change places without affecting the arrangement. If all the molecules were in one group we would have the value unity, and this would be the least probable arrangement. If all the molecules were divided as evenly as possible between all possible groups the value of the probability W would be a maximum, and this would be considered the most probable arrangement.

This definition, as it stands, applies directly to the distribution of molecules of a gas in space, as, for instance, the air in a room. Although statistical theories properly apply only to very large numbers, an example with small numbers may make things clearer. Figure 11-7 shows four boxes and four marbles. In distribution a they are all in one box, and the probability is 1. Since $0! = 1$ these are omitted.

$$W = \frac{4!}{4!} = 1 \qquad [11\text{--}9]$$

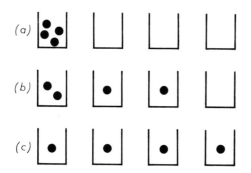

Fig. 11-7. Distributions of balls in boxes with different degrees of probability: a, least probable; b, intermediate; c, most probable according to classical statistics.

In b, where two are in one box and the other two are in separate boxes, the probability is

$$W = \frac{4!}{2!\,1!\,1!} = 12 \qquad\qquad [11\text{–}10]$$

In c, where the distribution is uniform, the probability is

$$W = \frac{4!}{1!\,1!\,1!\,1!} = 24 \qquad\qquad [11\text{–}11]$$

Consequently the first distribution is least probable and the last is most probable. From this we may say that it is far more probable that gas molecules will, on the average, be fairly evenly distributed about a room than that they will all be found on one side or in the middle of the room, since all parts of the room are equally probable.

If we try to apply such probability considerations to a velocity distribution, the boxes can represent velocity groups, but we know from the Maxwellian distribution curve (Fig. 11-5) that not all velocities are equally probable in a given volume of gas at constant temperature and that the velocities tend to cluster about a most probable value in a manner similar to rifle shots fired at a target. Consideration of this fact led to the introduction of the probability distribution factor $\epsilon^{-mv^2/2kT}$ (Eq. 11–5) into the final Maxwell formula. The derivation of Maxwell's equation by this method is not significant here, but it is important to notice how the classical definition of probability must now be changed in the realm of photons and electrons where quantum considerations arise, and classical methods fail.

11-4. Bose-Einstein Statistics

Twenty-four years after the origin of the quantum theory, Bose (1924) (in India) and Einstein independently developed a new system of statistics involving certain quantum restrictions, the new theory being applicable to radiation photons. This was called the Bose-Einstein statistics, now shortened to Bose. They noted, as had Rayleigh and others, that there was a strong resemblance between the shape of the energy-distribution curve for the radiation of different frequencies from a black body (Fig. 11-2) and the Maxwell distribution curve for the speeds of molecules in a gas at a given temperature (Fig. 11-5).

Since radiation quanta (photons) have particle-like characteristics it seemed that a space filled with photons could be treated as a "photon gas." But when the methods of the Maxwellian distribution were applied to determine the energy radiated at different frequencies by a black body the results were in complete disagreement with experiment. Instead of showing a curve for radiation similar to the Maxwell-Boltzmann distribution of speeds they obtained a curve showing continually increasing numbers of quanta of radiation at increasing frequencies.

Bose and Einstein set themselves the task of obtaining a form of quantum statistics which would describe a *photon gas* and yield the correct radiation formula which had been obtained earlier by Planck by other methods.

In order to have a distribution representing ideal black-body radiation at a temperature T, it is assumed that the radiation is inside an enclosure, the inner walls of which are perfectly black. Then, under equilibrium conditions the walls emit as much radiation as they absorb in unit time, and the radiation in the enclosure will be ideal black-body radiation.

It must be remembered that the photons in such an enclosure are different in important ways from gas molecules. Photons all travel in free space with the same speed regardless of frequency, and it is the frequencies (or energies) which are distributed. On the other hand, gas molecules have a distribution of speeds, though all have the same mass. A convenient connecting link between the two is the concept of momentum. Since the masses of all gas molecules in a simple ideal gas are the same, the velocity distribution is just as well described as being a momentum distribution. The relation to radiation photons now becomes apparent. Despite the constant speed of all photons there can be a momentum distribution since frequencies may vary and since the momentum of a photon (§5-6) is $h\nu/c$ or h/λ. Thus a momentum distribution for photons would mean a frequency (or wavelength) distribution, which is exactly what is observed.

The classical Maxwell-Boltzmann probability distribution function of Eq. 11-7 assumed without question that a gas molecule could have any available energy (quantization had not been invented) and there was nothing to forbid two or more molecules from having the same energy. It was also assumed that although the molecules of a gas were identical they could in theory be distinguished from one another as if they had been given names or numbers. Consequently in distributing molecules between energy states, those states with apparently the same numbers of molecules must be considered different and counted as possible arrangements if for example two molecules a and b have been interchanged between two different states.

Now it is a fundamental tenet of quantum physics that two or more identical particles can never be distinguished. There is no way to number them or give them names. This is one way in which quantum statistics differs from classical statistics. Consequently in counting possible energy or momentum distributions a different result is reached.

Bose altered the classical definition of probability in the following manner. He defined the probability W^* not in terms of particles (now photons) in a given state but in terms of the numbers of states having a given number of particles in them, and the states must be quantized.

$$W^* = \frac{Z!}{Z_0! \, Z_1! \, Z_2! \, Z_3! \, \cdots \, Z_m!} \tag{11-12}$$

where Z is the total number of states, Z_0 is the number of states having no particles in it, Z_1 the number having one particle, Z_2 the number having two, and so on. This is justified at least by the validity of the results. In terms of the previous example, with the provision that the boxes in Fig. 11-7 represent frequency states, we see that in a

$$W^* = \frac{4!}{3! \, 1!} = 4 \tag{11-13}$$

In b

$$W^* = \frac{4!}{1! \, 2! \, 1!} = 12 \tag{11-14}$$

In c

$$W^* = \frac{4!}{4!} = 1 \tag{11-15}$$

Thus, according to the new definition of probability, neither extreme is most probable, but the state b, in between, is.

Quantum statistics differs from classical statistics in that, in agreement with the uncertainty principle, the exact position of a point in momentum space cannot be specified when its exact position in ordinary space is specified. This may be expressed by resorting to a six-dimensional mathematical space which is called *phase space* composed of the three dimensions of ordinary space x, y, z, and three dimensions representing the three components of momentum p_x, p_y, p_z. An element of volume $dx\,dy\,dz\,dp_x\,dp_y\,dp_z$ in this mathematical space called *phase space* has the same physical dimensions as h^3, where h is the Planck constant. Quantum theory then states that a point in phase space representing the position and momentum of any particle can be no more precisely located than to say it lies somewhere within a small *cell* of volume h^3, and for mathematical purposes it may be assumed that in an element of volume $dx\,dy\,dz\,dp_x\,dp_y\,dp_z$ of phase space there may be a large number of these quantum cells of volume h^3. In passing then from one cell to another a quantized change takes place. Although only quantized values are possible as distinguished from classical statistics there is in Bose statistics no limitation on the number of particles which may occupy a given cell of phase space.

These considerations lead to a probability distribution function which differs in certain respects from the classical one. For the particular case of a photon gas in which the energy of a photon is $h\nu$, it may be written

$$n = \frac{1}{\epsilon^{-h\nu/kT} - 1}$$ [11–16]

where n is now the number of particles in a volume of phase space equal to h^3. Aside from the difference of interpretation of this function there is also the term -1 in the denominator which is important when the exponential term is not large compared to 1.

If we define n as the number of particles per unit cell of volume h^3 in phase space then n is equal to the total number N in an element of volume $dxdydzdp_xdp_ydp_z$ divided by the number of cells $(dxdydzdp_xdp_ydp_z)/h^3$. Eq. 11–16 can now be put in such a form that it can be integrated with respect to the ordinary space dimensions x,y,z leaving an equation in terms of three-dimensional momentum space. This is the desired probability distribution function and we may now follow the same procedure as in finding the Maxwellian distribution. The momentum distribution is symmetrical in momentum space and to find the number of momentum points in a thin spherical shell we multiply the probability distribution function by the volume of the shell $4\pi p^2 dp$. This gives us the actual distribution of momentum points. It is now desirable to shift from a momentum equation to a frequency equation by means of the relation

$$\frac{h}{p} = \lambda = \frac{c}{\nu}$$ [11–17]

The resulting equation can be readily put in the form to give the energy density dE, within a frequency range $d\nu$, of the radiation into an enclosed volume from an ideal black-body radiator, where

$$dE_\nu = \frac{8\pi h}{c^3} \frac{\nu^3}{\epsilon^{h\nu/kT} - 1} d\nu$$ [11–18]

This is the differential form of the famous Planck equation (Eq. 11–3).

Bose-Einstein statistics apply to an assemblage of identical particles which are indistinguishable from one another provided the particles have zero or integral spin. The name *bosons* has been given to such particles. The spin is a critical factor. Since electrons have half-integral spin they conform to the restrictions of the Pauli exclusion principle and an "electron gas" cannot be described by Bose statistics. These restrictions do not apply to similar molecules composed of an even number of particles and they are consequently bosons. On the other hand electrons, protons, and neutrons require Fermi-Dirac statistics and are called *fermions*. In terms of wave mechanics we would say that ψ, the wave function, is always symmetrical in coordinates and spins for similar nuclei if they are bosons. On the other hand, if they are fermions the wave function is antisymmetric, that is if two similar nuclei have their spatial coordinates interchanged the sign of ψ reverses.

The Bose-Einstein statistics were first applied to the study of photons. Since photons may be circularly polarized they are assumed to have spins, and correspondence with known facts is obtained if the spin is integral. Since the circular polarization may be either right or left-handed the number of momentum states is doubled and it was necessary to introduce a factor of 2 into the probability distribution function to obtain the correct Planck radiation formula.

Debye applied quantum statistics to the problem of specific heats of solids. The thermal vibrations of the atoms in a crystal are communicated to the crystal as a whole. The vibrational energy is conceived of as being quantized in units called *phonons* by analogy with *photons*. To obtain the frequency distribution of these phonons Debye assumed that they had zero spin and obeyed the Bose statistics. The results led to a satisfactory theory by means of which actual specific heats could be computed.

11-5. Fermi Statistics and Distribution of Speeds

Since the Bose statistics were found not to apply to the free electrons in a metal, Fermi and Dirac independently sought a different statistical theory which could apply. Bose and Einstein had introduced quantization into statistical theory but in dealing with a radiation gas consisting of photons they had found no need to limit the number of photons that could occupy the same momentum cell in momentum space thus having the same momentum. In other words the fact that one photon had a particular momentum did not exclude some other photon from having the same momentum.

However, for the electrons in an atom the Pauli exclusion principle forbids any two electrons to have the same quantum numbers and Fermi and Dirac decided to apply this idea to the momentum states of the free electrons in a metal. Whereas in the Bose theory any number of photons could occupy the same cell of volume h^3 in phase space, now only two electrons are permitted, one with spin quantum number $+\frac{1}{2}$ and the other with spin quantum number $-\frac{1}{2}$. Thus the electrons are paired with antiparallel spins in their momentum states and if their spins are parallel they cannot be paired in the same momentum state.

The general method of deriving the Fermi-Dirac distribution is similar to that for the Bose-Einstein statistics or for that matter for the Maxwell-Boltzmann statistics with the appropriate restrictions in each case. The method is to find the suitable probability distribution function in phase space (or to find it for the momentum or energy) and multiply it by the number of available states. The underlying assumptions are that the particles which make up the assemblage are identical and indistinguishable, that they have half-integral spins, and that the Pauli exclusion principle applies to them in such a way that no two particles can occur in the same state unless they have opposite spins.

This leads to the derivation of the following probability distribution function

$$n = \frac{1}{\epsilon^{(E_i - E_F)/kT} + 1} \qquad [11\text{--}19]$$

where n is the average number of particles in any given quantum state representing an energy E_i, T is the Kelvin temperature, k is the Boltzmann constant, and ϵ is the base of the natural system of logarithms. Comparing this with the Bose probability distribution function (Eq. 11–16) it is seen that the -1 in the denominator now becomes a $+1$ and that in the logarithmic term an energy E_F is subtracted from the energy of the given state. The energy E_F is called the *Fermi energy* or the energy of the *Fermi brim*. It is nearly constant for most temperatures, and it is the energy represented by a particle having the velocity v_0 in Fig. 11-8. Its physical significance will become more apparent shortly.

The Fermi probability function (Eq. 11–19) has a significant characteristic for the limiting value of $T = 0$. For energies $E_i < E_F$ the first term in the denominator is zero and the function has the value $n = 1$. This means that every quantum state is filled. For energies $E_i > E_F$ the first term in the denominator becomes infinite and the function has the value $n = 0$. This means that every such energy state is empty. The function for $T = 0$ is represented in Fig. 11-8.

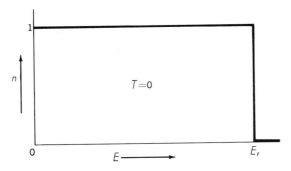

Fig. 11-8.   The graph of the Fermi probability function for different energies at $T = 0$. For energies below E_F all states are filled, all other states are empty.

To obtain the final Fermi-Dirac distribution equation the appropriate probability distribution function (Eq. 11–19) must be multiplied by a function representing the available states per unit energy range. This results in the following energy distribution law for the particles of a "Fermi gas."

$$N_E = \frac{8\pi n^3}{h^3} \frac{v^2}{\epsilon^{(E_i - E_F)/kT} + 1} \qquad [11\text{--}20]$$

where N_E is the number of particles of mass m having an energy E and speed v. Since $E_i = \frac{1}{2}mv_i^2$ the distribution of speeds can be readily obtained and is shown in Fig. 11-8.

According to the Maxwell-Boltzmann theory, if electrons were to behave like gas molecules they would all behave on the average very much the same. As the temperature of a block of metal is lowered, the kinetic energy of random motion should decrease steadily until at absolute zero such motion should cease, and all free electrons would then have reached the same zero energy state. According to the Fermi theory, however, a quite different situation exists. Momenta are quantized, and only two electrons (with opposite spins) can have a given amount. As the temperature is decreased, electrons would settle down by quantized steps to lower momentum values, that is, to cells in momentum space nearer the origin at which the momentum is zero, avoiding, of course, values of momentum (cells) pre-empted by other electrons.

At absolute zero they would be clustered as closely as possible about the origin of momentum space, filling all cells and leaving no vacant cells within the limits of the group. This irreducible amount of energy is called zero-point energy and is in direct contrast with the classical Maxwellian conception of zero energy at the absolute zero of temperature. The top energy level at this point is the Fermi level or brim.

Looking again at the probability distribution function Eq. 11–19 we see that if the energy of an electron $E_i = E_F$ then $n = \frac{1}{2}$. This means that the probability of the state being occupied at the Fermi brim is $\frac{1}{2}$. For higher energies the probability falls rapidly to zero and at sufficiently high temperatures approaches the Maxwellian probability function. At lower temperatures the exponential term approaches zero and the probability rises rapidly to 1 or certainty that the lower states will be filled. Since there are a very large number of free electrons in a metal, however, the outermost filled cells in momentum space, even at absolute zero, are a considerable distance from the origin and the Fermi brim represents a relatively large amount of energy. This is of importance in many phenomena.

The Fermi theory leads to an interesting and important result when we consider what happens with rising temperature. Since at absolute zero there are no unfilled momentum cells except on the outer edge of the group, where in our representation the electrons already have considerable amounts of momentum, the average electron, upon being offered extra momentum, has "no place to go" and cannot accept it unless the amount is sufficient to raise it to an unfilled cell. Consequently only the electrons of highest momentum, that is, those adjacent to unfilled cells, can respond to ordinary temperature changes and move across the Fermi brim to outer cells. This is the result of the quantum restriction, and the picture is changed quite completely from that of the Maxwellian theory.

The height of the Fermi brim has been computed on the basis of the free-electron model to be 7.0 eV for copper, 5.5 eV for gold and 3.1 eV for sodium. These correspond respectively to effective electron-gas temperatures T_F of 82,000° K, 64,000° K and 37,000° K. The fraction of the valence electrons that are near enough the Fermi level to be excited thermally to vacant levels can be shown to be of the order of magnitude of T/T_F where T is the temperature of the conductor and it is this number which takes part in thermal and electrical conduction.

Fig. 11-9 shows a comparison of the distribution of speeds of (*a*) particles in a Maxwell gas, and (*b*) particles in a Fermi gas. The solid line in

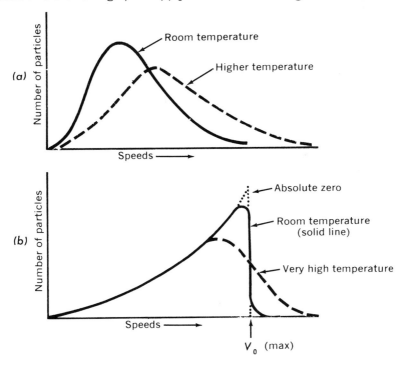

Fig. 11-9. Comparison of: *a,* Maxwellian, and *b,* Fermi distributions of speeds at different temperatures. Dotted line in *b* shows Fermi distribution for absolute zero, with the maximum speed for that temperature indicated. Dashed line in *b* shows how Fermi distribution approaches a Maxwellian one at sufficiently high temperatures.

(*b*) indicates the Fermi distribution of speeds at room temperature. The modification of this curve to show the speeds at absolute zero is indicated by the dotted lines, with the notably sharp cutoff where the curve drops perpendicularly to zero at the upper end of the range. The dashed line in each figure represents the distribution for a higher temperature. As the temperature is increased, the Fermi curve becomes more rounded, departing from the sharp upper limit of the distribution at absolute zero. This rounding of the curve represents the shift of some electrons to higher states. The Fermi statistics will have its most important application in the next chapter on metals and the solid state.

NOTE ON CONSERVATION OF STATISTICS

In the subsequent chapters on nuclear physics, reference will be made to Fermi and Bose statistics and their applications to atomic nuclei and to the particles of which those nuclei are composed. When the wave functions of nuclear particles are set up it is found that there are two different classes, if the spin of the particles is included in the equations. In one group the sign of the equation changes from plus to minus when the signs of the coordinates are changed. In the other group the sign does not change. The former equations are associated with Fermi statistics, and the latter are associated with Bose statistics. Nuclei composed of an even number of particles are described by Bose statistics; whereas nuclei composed of an odd number of particles are described by Fermi statistics. Electrons, protons, or neutrons are fermions and "obey" Fermi statistics. The statistics of any particles involved in a nuclear transformation are found to remain the same during any nuclear transformation. This invariance is called the *conservation of statistics* and the statistics of a particle or group of particles are just as important as other quantities such as mass, charge, and spin.

Problems

1. If the most probable speed of gas molecules is 356 m/sec, what is the average speed? What is the rms speed?

2. If the average speed of gas molecules is 250 m/sec, what is the most probable speed and what is the rms speed?

3. What is the most probable speed of nitrogen molecules in a gas at 0°C? (Take density of nitrogen to be 1.2 kg/m³.)

4. How can you justify the statement that the average value of the molecular velocities in a gas is zero?

5. Show that the volume of a cell in phase space equal to h^3 has the same dimensions as the element of volume of phase space $dx\,dy\,dz\,dp_x\,dp_y\,dp_z$.

6. An oxygen *molecule* (O_2) having a velocity of 465 m/sec hits head-on an oxygen *atom* momentarily at rest. What is the velocity of the molecule after collision? (Assume the simple laws of elastic collision.)

7. If 10^{10} hydrogen molecules escape into a room at 27°C, approximately how many of these would have speeds between 4000 and 4001 m/sec?

*8. In air at 27°C, how many oxygen molecules per unit speed range ($\Delta v = 1$ m/sec) have four times the most probable speed if there are a total of N molecules?

*9. Outline the steps to be followed in finding what fraction of the total number of molecules in a volume of gas have speeds $\frac{1}{2}$ the average speed or less?

10. Atmospheric pressure varies with altitude h according to the equation

$$P = P_0\,\epsilon^{-(mg/kT)h}$$

where P_0 is the pressure at the earth's surface and m is the mass of a molecule. Find the pressure at an elevation of 5 km. (Assume that air is chiefly nitrogen, the temperature is 300°K, and the pressure at the earth's surface is 76 cm of mercury.)

11. Using the Boltzmann distribution function, find the height above the surface of the earth at which the density of the air is $\frac{1}{2}$ what it is at the surface. Assume constant temperature of 300°K for simplicity and that air is mostly nitrogen. Then $E_2 - E_1 = mgh$ per molecule.

12. A molecule of mass m_1 moving with velocity v_1 hits head-on another molecule of mass m_2 having negligible velocity. What fraction of the energy of the first molecule is transferred to the second?

13. If potassium atoms are expelled horizontally from a furnace at a temperature of 900°K with energies equal to $\frac{3}{2}kT$, how far could an atom fall in a vacuum under the action of gravity if the horizontal length of path is one meter?

*14. In 1955 Miller and Kusch confirmed the Maxwellian distribution of speeds of thallium atoms evaporated from an oven at 900°K. Atoms of a particular speed would pass longitudinally through a helical slot in a rotating cylinder (Fig. 11-9) if the cylinder was rotating fast enough. The angle of the slot was 0.084 radians. Show that an atom with a speed of $v = \omega L/\theta$ will pass through the slot without deviating toward the sides where L is the length of the cylinder ($L = 20$ cm). At what angular speed in rps would the cylinder need to rotate to pass the largest number of thallium atoms per second through the slot?

15. Explain why if some copper sulfate is dissolved in the water and allowed to stand in a tall jar, the water at the bottom is bluer than at the top?

*16. Show that when the Boltzmann distribution function is put in terms of R_0 the gas constant, and Avogadro's number N_0 instead of k, it can be solved for Avogadro's number to give

$$N_0 = \frac{R_0 T\,\ln\!\left(\dfrac{n_1}{n_2}\right)}{mg(h_2 - h_1)}$$

Recommended Reading

Sproull, R. L., *Modern Physics*, 2nd ed. New York: John Wiley & Sons, Inc., 1963.

Sears, F. W., *Thermodynamics*. Reading, Mass.: Addison-Wesley Publishing Co., Inc., 1953.

Heitler, W., *The Quantum Theory of Radiation*, 3rd ed. Oxford: Clarendon Press, 1954.

Zemansky, M. W., *Heat and Thermodynamics*, 3rd ed. New York, McGraw-Hill Book Company, Inc., 1957.

Early Work

Fermi, E., "Quantum Theory of Radiation." *Reviews of Modern Physics*, Vol. 4 p. 87, (1932).

Planck, M., *Theory of Heat*. New York: The Macmillan Company, 1949.

Solid State Physics

12-1. Electrical Conduction in Solids

The problem of understanding how electricity flows through a conductor was long one of the puzzles of science. But at the beginning of the century Drude, followed by Lorentz, assumed that in a conductor of electricity there are a large number of so-called "free" electrons (the one or more valence electrons per atom) possessing a random motion similar to the molecules of a gas. The drift of this "electron gas" along a conductor under the influence of a difference of potential would then constitute an electric current. The free electrons would not need to drift at a high speed through the conductor in order to constitute a considerable electric current because there are so many of them. Drift speeds on the average might be only a small fraction of a centimeter per second. This theory, based entirely on the particle-like characteristics of the electron, had some considerable success despite its equally conspicuous failures.

Since it had been known for a long time that the best conductors of electricity are also the best conductors of heat, it was concluded that both kinds of conductivity are due primarily to the "free" electrons present in the conductor. A drift of the electron gas in one direction or another would constitute an electric current, and the transfer of any increase in the energy of random motion in any direction would be thermal conduction. This theory seemed at first to be in general agreement with the experimental results. However, the theory went into a state of collapse for years when it was noted that the free electrons apparently make little or no contribution to the specific heats of the metals concerned. Since they had just been proposed as the carriers of thermal energy like gas molecules, this seemed to be an utter contradiction. The impasse thus presented was only resolved by the development of quantum statistics, in particular the Fermi-Dirac statistics.

12-2. Specific Heats of Metals According to Fermi Statistics

According to the classical theory, the large number of free electrons able to participate in a rise in temperature by sharing the increased kinetic energy would make the energy increase considerable. Consequently, the specific heat of any conductor should be much larger, because of the presence of free electrons, than that of a substance not possessing such free electrons. With the Fermi distribution this is not true.

In Fig. 12-1 the Fermi distribution is plotted for energies instead of speeds as in Fig. 11-8. In Fig. 12-2 the curve is turned on end and left open at the top to represent various energy levels and how they are filled. Higher energy states now appear higher up on the diagram, and the horizontal lines represent a few of the many possible energy levels. At *a* the diagram shows how, for absolute zero, all energy levels are occupied up to a certain maximum. At *b* the diagram indicates how, for a much higher temperature, some electrons in the upper levels have been able to accept energy and move to still higher levels. Owing to the quantum restrictions most of the electrons have not been able to participate in the temperature rise. Their contribution to the specific heats of metals is then relatively small, since only about four or five in a thousand of the valence electrons in common metals take part at room temperature in either thermal or electrical conduction.

This is just what was required to clear up the difficulty with specific heats. If all the valence electrons belonging to an atom were free, and if all

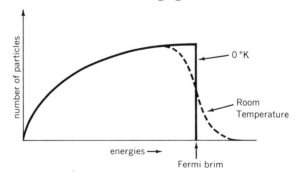

Fig. 12-1.   Fermi distribution of energies.

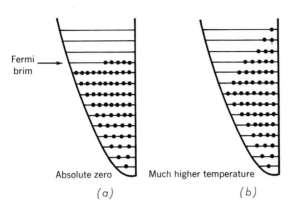

Fermi brim →

Absolute zero   Much higher temperature

(a)   (b)

Fig. 12-2. Representation of Fermi distribution: *a*, at absolute zero with all levels filled up to the maximum; *b*, an approximation of how some electrons move to higher energy states at a very much higher temperature.

such free electrons acted like gas molecules, it would be necessary according to classical theory to assign to them a heat capacity of $3k/2$ per electron per degree Kelvin. However, experiments indicated that the specific heats of most metals are quite close to the value assigned to the thermal agitation of the atoms themselves. Consequently it is impossible to explain experimental results on the assumption that electrons absorb the amount of thermal energy they would according to Maxwell-Boltzmann statistics. Now, by the Fermi theory, such absorption is seen to be negligible, and the theory is in close agreement with experiment.

12-3. Band Theory of Electric Conduction

The success of the Fermi theory in describing specific heats of metals would be one-sided indeed if the new theory ruined what had appeared to be a satisfactory explanation of electric conduction on the basis of an electron gas with a Maxwellian distribution of speeds.

Lorentz had based his original theory of electric conduction on what seemed to be a reasonable assumption that all valence electrons are free and that electron mean free paths in metals are of the order of magnitude of the spacing between atoms in the metallic crystal. The restriction on free motion by the Fermi theory to a small fraction of the valence electrons would now imply that mean free paths are of the order of a hundred times or more the distance between atoms.

Sommerfeld, applying Fermi statistics to the problem of electric conduction, arrived at an equation similar to that of Lorentz, but he had had to arbitrarily assume the existence of such long mean free paths. However, with this assumption the theory successfully described conductivity in metals. Though a fraction of the valence electrons were now seen to be free to move, it was only necessary to assume because of their long mean free paths that they would move at proportionately higher drift speeds. Even then the drift speeds are surprisingly low.

The long mean free paths seemed unreasonable, but here again the new wave mechanics came to the rescue. Instead of treating electrons as particles colliding with the atoms of the crystal lattice of a metal such as copper, Bloch and others pictured moving electrons in terms of de Broglie waves of wavelength $\lambda = h/mv$. The passage of such waves through a lattice of atoms could now be treated mathematically by methods like those used in describing the passage of light waves through a similar lattice.

In fact it turned out that under ideal conditions with a perfect crystal lattice the crystal might be "transparent" to the electron waves which could then pass through practically unimpeded. That electrons do not always do this is the result in part of the thermal agitation of the atoms of the crystal and in part of imperfections (§12-5) which occur in all crystals. Of course a copper wire is not a single crystal anyway but a conglomerate of crystal fragments. The wave picture does, however, provide for the possibility of much longer mean free paths and it is quite different from the picture of an electron as a particle bumping into the atoms in its path.

Aside from such obvious crystal defects as dislocations, fragmentations and slips along "slip planes" there are a number of common defects (§12-5) which might occur in an otherwise perfect crystal. Some of the most common are (1) an impurity atom taking the place of a regular atom on the lattice, (2) an interstitial impurity atom, that is one crowded in between the atoms on the lattice, (3) lattice vacancies, that is an atom missing from the lattice. Such imperfections would impede the motions of the electron (or electron waves) to a marked degree. From the wave picture all of these effects would involve scattering of waves and diffraction and a quite different mathematical treatment from that previously given to electrons as particles.

In the earlier theories of conduction of electricity by metals, it was thought that electrons moved inside the metal in a region of uniform field in which they were uniformly accelerated between collisions. This was soon recognized as only a crude approximation. From a large-scale viewpoint a conductor of finite length, on which an emf is impressed, does have a certain average fall of potential per unit length, but the electrons in the conductor belong distinctly to the atomic realm where there must evidently be variations of potential from atom to atom even without an impressed emf. A more exact theory of conduction would have to take these variations into consideration.

The simplest arrangement is the regularly spaced arrangement of atoms of a crystal lattice. To get from one atom to another an electron has to go up over a potential hill. In Fig. 12-3 the approximate variation of

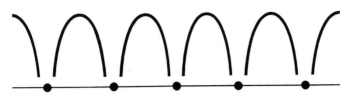

Fig. 12-3. Smoothed-over variation of potential energy along a one-dimensional crystal lattice for five atoms.

potential energy of an electron with distance is shown for a one-dimensional model crystal with no applied emf. If the Schrödinger wave equation is to be solved for this potential distribution, the complicated function representing variation of potential energy with distance must be put into the equation (Eq. 8–13a) instead of V. This makes the equation a very difficult one to solve, requiring intricate methods of approximation. By a more simple method of attack certain salient features may be revealed.

The kinetic energy $(E - V)$ in the Schrödinger equation may be set equal to $p^2/2m$ where p is the classical momentum. From the equation for the de Broglie wavelength $\lambda = h/mv$, the momentum mv is h/λ. From this the kinetic energy $p^2/2m$ is $h^2/2m\lambda^2$. If $1/\lambda$ is defined as the de Broglie wave number represented by $\tilde{\nu}$,

$$E - V = \frac{h^2}{2m}\,\tilde{\nu}^2 \qquad\qquad [12\text{--}2]$$

If V is constant throughout the metal, as was assumed in the Pauli-Sommerfeld theory, the total energy E varies as the square of $\tilde{\nu}$. If we include negative values of $\tilde{\nu}$ for convenience this leads to the parabola of Fig. 12-4a, showing how E varies continuously with $\tilde{\nu}$. However, if the potential energy V is assumed to vary as in Fig. 12-3, the energy E is no longer a continuous function of $\tilde{\nu}$.

Mathematical analysis of this situation by Strutt, More, Brillouin, and others has shown that in general the energy curve jumps discontinuously for particular values of the de Broglie wavelength, as shown in Fig. 12-4b at positions 1,1, 2,2, etc. This is interpreted as meaning that not all energies for an electron are possible. At each discontinuity a band of energies is forbidden. Between these are the allowable energy bands (shaded regions in b).

Those valence electrons free to move through the atomic lattice experience periodic variations of energy. Any one of these is more likely to be found between two atoms where it is repelled by electrons on either side, but it may pass from one of these regions to another. According to the solution of the wave equation, in so doing it can only have energies lying in certain allowed bands.

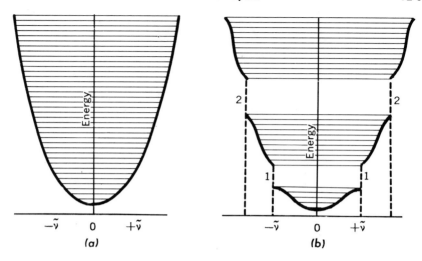

Fig. 12-4. Energy vs. wave number curve: *a*, not taking account of variation in potential between atoms; *b*, assuming a potential variation between atoms similar to Fig. 12-3.

Another way of considering the problem is to think of a block of conductor as a "giant molecule" which may contain as many as 10^{23} valence electrons per cm³. Just as each electron in a single atom is in a particular quantized state, according to the Pauli principle, so also all the electrons in a block of conductor are in quantized states. But no longer are these states sharply defined by narrow energy levels. Here the atoms are so close together that mutual interactions occur and fields overlap. What were quite sharp energy levels are now broadened into wide bands. In some substances these bands may overlap, and sometimes they are separated by forbidden energy regions.

Consider, for instance, how in a hydrogen atom the electron is bound to its nucleus in sharply defined quantized energy states. Similarly in more complex atoms the electrons exist in sharply defined quantized energy states, the energies between these states being forbidden. The outer or valence electrons of a metal belong for the most part to *s* or *p* subshells and are consequently said to be in *s* or *p* energy states or levels. For an individual atom unaffected by neighboring atoms these energy levels are sharp and may be represented by the lines in Fig. 12-5 at *a*.

But in a solid where the atoms are close together and affect one another the energy levels are quite different. It is possible to compute these levels for regular arrangements of atoms as found in crystals. Wavemechanical theory shows that when the fields of force of the atoms interact not only may each energy level be split into a series of levels (Fig. 12-5*b*) but the levels themselves may be broadened so as to lose their sharply

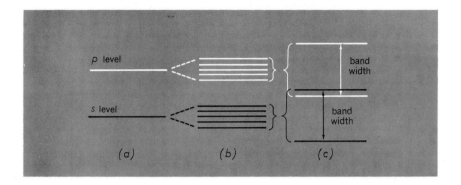

Fig. 12-5. Illustrating the band theory of conduction: *a,* narrow (sharp) energy levels of single atoms; *b,* levels split and broadened into bands when atoms are close together in a solid; *c,* bands broadened so as to overlap in a good conductor.

defined character and in effect become *allowed bands* with forbidden regions or bands in between. In good conductors the allowed bands overlap as indicated in the figure at *c.* Electrons then existing in what would normally be a "filled band" would be free to accept any available amount of energy and could move under the influence of a difference of potential in any given direction in the overlapping unfilled band.

In an insulator, however, according to quantum physics we would say that the electrons occupy a filled band which is separated from the nearest unfilled or conduction band by a large forbidden gap, and they cannot accept energy to move anywhere unless enough energy is furnished to enable them to cross the forbidden zone. In Fig. 12-6 three allowed bands *A, B* and *C* are illustrated for different kinds of conductors. The shaded regions represent the allowed bands; the unshaded regions are the forbidden energy regions. The black regions represent completely filled energy levels. At *a,* the lowest band is not completely filled, and electrons in the filled region (black) can accept energy, raising them as far as the highest level at the top of the *A* band. Such electrons are thereby free to move in this band under an impressed emf, and they then constitute an electric current; the diagram represents a fairly good conductor. At *b,* the allowed bands *A, B, C* overlap. There are no forbidden regions, electrons can accept a wide range of energies, and the diagram represents a metal, a very good conductor. At *c,* the allowed band *A* is completely filled. No electron in the band can accept energy unless the energy is sufficient to raise it to the next band. Since the forbidden range is wide and represents a large energy change, the diagram represents a good insulator. Only under an extremely high potential gradient could electrons be raised to the next allowed level *B,* and then the insulation would break down and a spark might occur.

12-4. Semiconductors

Another class of substances, semiconductors, is now acquiring increasing importance. It is represented at Fig. 12-6*d*, where the lowest band is filled, or nearly so, but the forbidden region is so narrow that a moderate applied emf or even thermal agitation may raise some electrons to the next allowed band where they are free to move with an applied field. The vacancies left in the filled band are called *holes*, and when these migrate they move in a direction opposite to the electrons, thus behaving like a flow of positive charge.

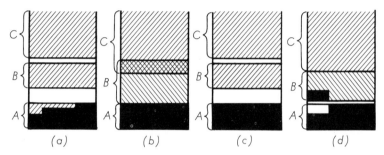

Fig. 12-6.   Conduction bands (shaded) for: *a*, a fair conductor (conduction band not filled); *b*, a good conductor; *c*, a good insulator (conduction band filled); *d*, a semiconductor (conduction band filled but small energy interval between bands).

Among the semiconductors of special interest are germanium and silicon because they are used in the making of *transistors*. Transistors now take the place of electron tubes in many applications. Their chief features are their small size and very low power consumption. Germanium and silicon atoms each have 4 valence electrons and form crystals in which the electrons represented by dashes (Fig. 12-7*a*) are paired. If an impurity atom called a *donor* with 5 valence electrons, such as aluminum, is introduced into the crystal and appears on the lattice as at *b*, an extra electron for each such atom is produced and may act as a free carrier of current. Such an impure crystal is called an *n*-type crystal. If an impurity atom called an *acceptor* is introduced with only 3 valence electrons, such as arsenic, as at *c*, a "hole" is produced, and it is free to act as a positive car-

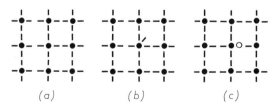

(a)   (b)   (c)

Fig. 12-7.   Lattice showing: *a*, arrangement of atoms in a crystal of silicon or germanium; *b*, the same lattice with a donor atom at the center having 5 valence electrons; *c*, the same lattice with an acceptor atom at the center having only 3 valence electrons.

rier. A crystal with such impurity atoms is called a *p*-type crystal. Both *n*-type and *p*-type crystals may now be prepared artificially.

The simplest application of *p*- and *n*-type crystals is in the crystal diode or rectifier. The rectifying action is represented in Fig. 12-8, where at *a* the electric field will pull electrons and holes back from the interface between two sections of crystal, one *p*-type and one *n*-type. At *b*, where the difference in potential is reversed, both holes and electrons are drawn across the interface, and current flows. The development of the three-contact transistor from the two-contact crystal rectifier won the Nobel prize in 1956 for Bardeen, Brattain, and Shockley.

A junction transistor consists of a very thin slice of *p*-type crystal between two small blocks of *n*-type, forming an *n-p-n*-type transistor, or a very thin slice of *n*-type crystal between two blocks of *p*-type, forming a *p-n-p*-type transistor. The thin slice in the middle controls the flow of electrons and holes in much the same way as the grid of a radio tube controls the flow of electrons in the tube. The point-contact transistor consists of a single crystal in which suitable *p*-type and *n*-type regions have been formed by local diffusion and to which contact is made by metal points.

Great improvements in electronics are now being made by the miniaturization of such circuit elements, but even more significant progress is taking place by doing away with individual circuit components and integrating circuit functions into thin wafers or solid blocks of material.

12-5. Lattice Defects, Electron Traps

The ideal arrangement of atoms in a crystalline solid would be that in which the atoms are arranged in perfectly regular geometrical order on the crystal lattice to which they belong. Such an ideal crystal would usually have different properties, such as electrical conductivity or tensile strength, for instance, in different directions. But the perfect regularity of such a crystal would enable many of its properties to be computed from the known constants of the crystal.

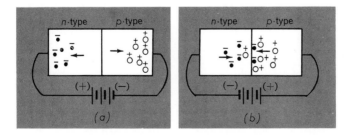

Fig. 12-8. Rectifying action at contact of *p*- and *n*-type crystals; *a*, direction of high resistance; *b*, direction of low resistance.

Usually any real crystal differs widely from the ideal, and precise computations are difficult if not impossible because of the many defects or imperfections of the crystal. One of the commonest of these is *impurities*. Impurity atoms may either take the place of normal atoms on the crystal lattice as illustrated in Fig. 12-9a or they may become interstitial and squeeze in between normal atoms as at *b* thus straining or deforming the crystal lattice.

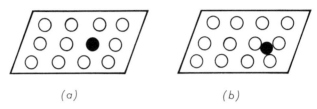

(a)   (b)

Fig. 12-9.   Impurity atoms in a crystal: *a*, an impurity atom substitutes for a normal atom; *b*, the impurity atom is interstitial.

Another type of defect is a *vacancy* on the lattice. For instance in an ionic crystal there might be a positive ion vacancy or a negative ion vacancy. In one type of vacancy the atom may have migrated to another position where it is "squeezed in" between atoms on the lattice. Other defects are a *dislocation* such as in Fig. 12-10a and a slip along a so-called *slip plane* as in Fig. 12-10b.

The properties of the solid are strongly affected by these defects. For instance consider electrical properties. All of these defects produce abnormalities in the uniform variation of electric potential in a perfect crystal. Potential troughs may occur in which wandering "holes" could be trapped for shorter or longer periods of time, and potential peaks would trap free electrons. In a negative ion vacancy the surrounding positive ions are in effect reaching out for a wandering electron and an electron thus trapped is called an *F-center*. These could strongly affect the electrical conductivity. In a photoconductor for example the energy of absorbed photons of light

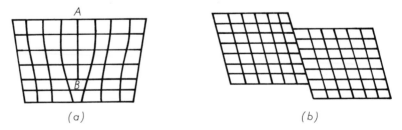

(a)   (b)

Fig. 12-10.   Crystal defects: *a*, the line **AB** represents the edge of a dislocation putting compression on the upper part of the crystal and tension on the lower part; *b*, a slip dislocation.

releases electrons from traps and raises them into a conduction band where they stay until trapped again. This is what makes the substance a better conductor under the influence of light. F-centers may explain the colors of certain crystals. If the .F-centers absorb a particular band of frequencies from the incident white light the color is affected. Measurements on the variation of color of crystals with temperature confirm the theory. Such things as these illustrate some of the lines of progress in the study of the solid state as well as some of the complications.

12-6. The Hall Effect

Classical theory predicts that an electric current in passing through a conductor should be deflected by a magnetic field just as moving charges in free space can be deflected although to a much less degree. This effect was discovered in 1879 by E. H. Hall and is called the *Hall effect*. It was one of the first experiments performed to give information about how the charges constituting an electric current move through a conductor and what these charges are.

If a slab of conducting material as shown in Fig. 12-11 is placed in a magnetic field and if the current I in the conductor (or the field $\mathcal{E}$) is at right angles to the magnetic field $\mathbf{B}$, then there will be a force tending to deflect the current in the third dimension of space. The force on a charge q moving with velocity v under the action of combined electric and magnetic fields is given by the Lorentz vector equation (§2-24)

$$\mathbf{F} = q\,[\mathcal{E} + \mathbf{v} \times \mathbf{B}] \qquad [12\text{--}3]$$

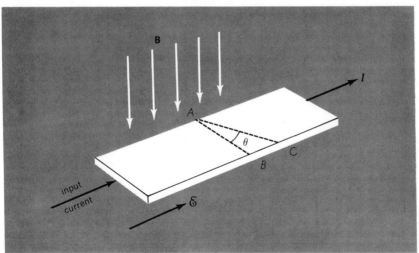

Fig. 12-11. Hall effect. Charge carriers in conducting slab are deflected by a transverse magnetic field B so that there is a difference of potential between A and B.

The second term of the equation shows that for a positive charge moving in the direction **E** there would be a force on the charge in the direction from *B* to *A* (Fig. 12-11). *A* should therefore be positive with respect to *B* and this can be tested experimentally. Without the magnetic field, *A* and *B* would be at the same potential. The difference in potential between the point *A* and *B* is sometimes called the *Hall voltage* and it is surprisingly small. The effect of the field may also be described as turning the equipotential line from *AB* to *AC* through an angle θ. The quantity θ/jB, in which j is the current density, gives a measure of the effect and is called the *Hall coefficient*.

When the experiment was tried with a copper conductor the point *A* was found to be negative to *B* and the Hall coefficient was negative. This was evidence (made before the discovery of the electron) that the moving charges were negative. They were similarly negative for a number of other metals including gold, silver, nickel and aluminum. But for certain other conductors, for instance iron, cadmium, and beryllium, the effect was reversed and the Hall coefficient was positive. This seemed to indicate that the carriers of charge were positive and raised questions which were not settled until the development of the quantum-mechanical band theory of conduction. On this basis it is noted that the conductors with positive Hall coefficients are among the poor conductors or semiconductors. This is interpreted to mean that the conduction bands are nearly filled with electrons so that it is not the electrons which seem to migrate but the vacancies or holes in the band which behave like positive charges and in effect migrate in the opposite direction when the electrons shift position.

That the Hall coefficient is surprisingly small means that the carriers of charge move slowly on the average. Of course the drift motion of the carriers under the action of a field is superposed upon the random thermal motion. The average drift speed in a field of unit intensity is called the *mobility*. Studies of the Hall effect give information about the mobilities of the carriers of charge and the numbers of carriers per unit volume, and are of particular value in the study of semiconductors.

12-7. Emission of Electrons from Metals

There are four common ways of getting electrons out of metals. These are thermionic emission, photoelectric emission, secondary emission, and field emission.

1. *Thermionic emission* is the emission of electrons from bodies at high temperatures by a process of evaporation.

2. *Photoelectric emission* is the ejection of electrons from a sensitive surface by the action of light (electromagnetic radiation) of the proper frequency falling on this surface. It was discussed in Chap. 5.

3. *Secondary electron emission* is the emission of electrons from a surface that is being bombarded by other high-speed electrons. In an electric discharge in a gas, electrons may also be liberated at the cathode by positive ion bombardment.

A practical application of this type of emission is the multiplier tube which is used for very high amplifications of very weak signals. In the form of a *photomultiplier* it is mentioned in connection with the scintillation counter (§13-20). One or more electrons emitted by light falling on the photosensitive cathode of a photomultiplier are drawn to the first anode (dynode) where they dislodge secondary electrons which are drawn to the next anode and this is repeated at each successive anode thereby enormously amplifying the initial signal.

4. *Field emission* is the emission of electrons from some portion of a surface by an applied electric field intense enough to enable the electrons to escape from the metal.

Of these types of emission we will only have space here to discuss thermionic emission in some detail.

12-8. Thermionic Emission

Early in the century Richardson developed a theory of thermionic emission based on the concept of an "electron gas." He conceived that in the random motions of free electrons in a metal if a given electron should happen to acquire enough velocity it might be expected to pass the reverse field (potential barrier) at the surface and escape from the metal. He then deduced the number of electrons that would be expected to escape per second from unit area of a hot filament as a function of temperature. The accepted form of this equation is

$$i = A T^2 \epsilon^{-(\varphi/kT)} = A T^2 \exp\left(-\frac{\varphi}{kT}\right) \qquad [12\text{–}4]$$

In the exponential term, φ is called the *work function* of the emitting surface, and k is the well-known Boltzmann constant. Both kT and φ must be measured in the same units of energy.

The work function φ of the surface is the average work required to enable an electron to escape from the emitter and it is a measure of the electric potential barrier which the emitted electrons have to pass at the surface of the emitter. Work functions are often expressed in electron volts, but in Eq. 12–4 they must be reduced to joules or ergs since the denominator of the exponent will also be in joules or ergs. Values of the work function are characteristic of the particular material used and for the most part vary between 2 and 6 electron volts (Table 5-1).

According to theory the constant A should be independent of the particular metal used and, for perfectly clean metals when the emitting surface area is 1 cm², should have a value of 120 amp/cm² °K. Experimental difficulties in measuring both the work function and the constant A for clean metallic surfaces are very great and the values of A found experimentally for several metals differ considerably but are usually nearer to 60 amp/cm² °K.

An experimental check of the general validity of the equation can be made by a plot of experimental values in the following manner. First, take natural logarithms of both sides of the equation.

$$\ln i = \ln A + \ln T^2 - \frac{\varphi}{kT} \qquad [12\text{--}5]$$

$$\ln \left(\frac{i}{T^2} \right) = \ln A - \left(\frac{\varphi}{k} \right) \frac{1}{T} \qquad [12\text{--}6]$$

If common logarithms are used the equation becomes

$$\log_{10} \frac{i}{T^2} = \log_{10} A - \left(\frac{0.434\varphi}{k} \right) \frac{1}{T} \qquad [12\text{--}7]$$

Equation 12–6 (or 12–7) is now of the form

$$y = b + mx$$

which is the equation of a straight line, and when values of $\ln (i/T^2)$ are plotted against $1/T$ the slope of the line is φ/k (or $-0.434\varphi/k$). From the known value of k, the thermionic work function φ may then be obtained. The fact that the plotted points actually lie on (or close to) a straight line indicates the validity of the equation.

EXAMPLE   Find the thermionic-emission current from the surface of a pure tungsten filament 0.1 mm in circumference and 1 cm long at a temperature of 2500° K.

$$\text{Assume } A = 60$$

Emission in amperes per cm² is given by Eq. 12–4.

$$\frac{\varphi}{kT} = \frac{4.52 \text{ eV} \times 1.6 \times 10^{-19} \text{ joule/eV}}{1.38 \times 10^{-23} \text{ joule/°K} \times 2500°\text{K}}$$

$$= 21$$

$$\exp(-21) = 7.58 \times 10^{-10}$$

$$i = 60 \times (2500)^2 \exp(-21) = 0.28 \text{ amp/cm}^2$$

$$I = \text{amp/cm}^2 \times \text{area}$$

$$= 0.28 \times 0.01 = 0.0028 \text{ amp} = 2.8 \text{ ma}$$

Careful measurements of the distribution of speeds of electrons emitted by hot filaments show that the speeds closely follow a Maxwellian distribution. It might at first be thought that, although these electrons possess a Fermi distribution of speeds inside the metal, they quickly acquire a Maxwellian distribution of speeds by collision with the gas molecules of the region into which they are ejected. However, it was found that even if the thermionic emission occurs in a very high vacuum, where the chance of hitting gas molecules is negligible, the electrons still apparently have a Maxwellian distribution of speeds. That such electrons belong to a Fermi distribution of speeds inside a metal and to a Maxwellian distribution outside the metal seemed at first contradictory, but further analysis shows that it is not so.

According to classical theory, any electron in the Maxwellian distribution may possibly gain enough energy to pass the potential barrier at the surface of the metal and escape when the temperature of the metal is raised. According to the Fermi distribution, only the electrons at the top of the filled energy levels are likely to accept energy and gain enough to escape. Theory indicates that enough of these electrons are available to account for experimentally measured emission currents. The number of electrons having speeds just sufficient to enable them to escape with small remaining velocities after having passed the surface barrier is large, but the probability that they will actually escape is small. For electrons of higher speeds the probability of emission is greater until maximum emission is reached, at which point the decreasing numbers of electrons of higher energies cause the curve to fall again. Thus the distribution of speeds of emitted electrons turns out to be essentially Maxwellian.

Although, according to the Fermi distribution, only the electrons at the higher energy limit of the group are relatively free to accept energy and move to higher energy levels, the distribution of the speeds of those electrons in a metal which move into energy states above the limiting value for absolute zero closely approximates a Maxwellian distribution in that part of the curve. Indeed, at extremely high temperatures, far beyond anything attainable in the laboratory, nearly all electrons would be shifted to higher energy states, and the whole curve would approach that of a Maxwellian distribution in its general characteristics. It thus becomes evident that the Maxwellian distribution is actually a limiting case of the Fermi distribution.

By purely theoretical procedure, involving wave mechanics and the Fermi distribution function, Dushman arrived at the same equation for thermionic emission as a function of temperature as that obtained much earlier by Richardson on the basis of classical theory (Eq. 12–4). Although wave-mechanical theory introduces the idea that some electrons with sufficient energy to escape may be reflected at the surface of the metal, there is also the possibility that some with less energy may penetrate the barrier (tunnel effect). This makes little appreciable change in the theoretical conclusions which generally present a successful theory.

12-9. Paramagnetism, Diamagnetism, and Ferromagnetism

Paramagnetism and diamagnetism are small-scale effects so feeble as to be difficult to detect usually, whereas ferromagnetism is a large-scale effect with many technical applications. Since all substances show some type of magnetism, all in a sense may be said to be magnetic. However, only three common elements, iron, nickel, and cobalt, are ferromagnetic, and of these iron is notably more strongly magnetic than the others. In addition, many alloys of iron are intensely ferromagnetic, and so also are some alloys of elements which are themselves only feebly magnetic.

PARAMAGNETISM AND DIAMAGNETISM

Paramagnetism is the weak magnetic effect possessed by some substances, in which there is sufficient orientation of magnetic moments in the direction of an applied magnetic field to give the substance a permeability greater than unity relative to empty space. The magnetic moment of an atom may result either from the orbital motion of an electron or from the spin of such an electron about its own axis. Whenever an electron is not paired with another of opposite spin or rotation, so that these effects cancel, there will be a net magnetic moment greater than zero.

It might be expected that in the presence of a magnetic field, if the atoms of a substance possess a magnetic moment, they would tend to align themselves with the direction of the field. However, as previously mentioned (§9-4), the direct effect of the field is not to align the magnetic moments but to produce a precession of the axis of the magnetic moment about the direction of the applied magnetic field. Indeed, the magnetic moments cannot turn into a position of greater alignment unless there are atomic collisions or other atomic interactions to enable them to do so. In most solids such interactions are very small, and the total effect makes the permeability of a paramagnetic substance relative to empty space only slightly larger than unity. For most purposes the difference is negligible, and the substances behave magnetically almost like empty space. However, the precession produces an exactly opposite effect called *diamagnetism*.

Diamagnetism is an effect in each atom that opposes the inducing field and reduces the permeability to less than that of empty space. According to classical theory, the orbit of a revolving electron becomes smaller or larger, if it crosses the field, depending on the direction of the applied magnetic field, and the consequent change in magnetic moment opposes the field. This is the same as an induced current which by Lenz's law opposes the action producing it. According to quantum theory, such a change is impossible, and the actual effect of the field is to produce a precession of the vector representing magnetic moment about the direction of the field, as just mentioned. This precession can only take place at certain permitted angles (space quantization) (§9-4). Yet whenever it occurs it is always in a direction to oppose the applied field and thus acts to reduce the permeability with respect to empty space, again in accordance with Lenz's law.

The result is that the relative permeability of a diamagnetic substance is slightly less than unity, but for most substances the difference is negligible for all practical purposes. Since the tendencies to produce orientation and precession are in competition with each other, the question of whether a substance is paramagnetic or diamagnetic depends upon which effect is greater. In any event the net effect is small, and the relative permeability usually differs from unity by a mere few parts in a million and only occasionally by as much as a few parts in a hundred.

FERROMAGNETISM AND ANTIFERROMAGNETISM

In ferromagnetism relative permeabilities are often hundreds or thousands of times that of empty space and may go as high as 10^6. Unlike the other types of magnetism a magnetic moment may remain after the inducing field is removed. Instead of being primarily an effect of individual atoms, it is a cooperative effect of groups of relatively large numbers of atoms acting in concert in what are called domains. Each iron atom has a considerable magnetic moment. When iron crystallizes these domains form, and all the magnetic moments of the atoms in a domain point in the same direction, thus the domains become spontaneously magnetized. When the specimen as a whole is unmagnetized these domains form small groups in which the net magnetization is zero and the object is said to be "unmagnetized" (Fig. 12-12a). In the presence of a magnetizing field the favorably located domains at first enlarge by a shift of boundaries to give a net magnetic moment (Fig. 12-12b) and as the magnetizing field is made more intense they swing toward alignment with the field (Fig. 12-12c) to give magnetic saturation.

The magnetic moment of an iron atom is largely due to the spin of four unpaired electrons in the $3d$ subshell. That magnetization is due to some

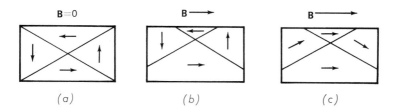

12-12.   Magnetic domains in ferromagnetic substance. a, No external field; effects of domains cancel; b, if external magnetic field is increased, favorably oriented domains grow at expense of others, at first reversibly and then irreversibly; c, in strong field magnetic moments of domains may rotate.

kind of *spin* was confirmed by Barnett who measured the magnetization of a bar of iron when it is set rotating about a longitudinal axis. The increase in magnetization resulting from this rotation enabled Barnett to compute the gyromagnetic ratio (§9-6) for the atoms in the bar. This turned out to be close to $g = 2$ as it should be if the magnetization is due to electron spin instead of $g = 1$ if the magnetization were due to orbital motion.

The cooperative action of atoms in any one domain is difficult to explain on a classical basis, as the electrons in different atoms are presumably too far apart to interact strongly. However, according to quantum mechanics there is *exchange* of electrons between atoms on the crystal lattice, and theory predicts that because of this the atoms are in a lower energy state when the spins of the unpaired electrons are all parallel. Since the atoms tend to assume the state of lowest energy the domains are thus self-magnetizing. The *exchange* is, of course, a strictly quantum-mechanical effect and has no classical counterpart.

The successful wave-mechanical theory of domains was first developed by Heisenberg and was based upon the assumption that the integral representing the exchange forces should have a positive sign indicating that the spins in any domain were parallel. If the negative sign were chosen, a quite different effect would result because this would indicate that neighboring spins were paired in antiparallel alignment. The name *antiferromagnetism* has been given to this type of magnetization (a very small effect) and it has been found to occur in a few substances such as manganese dioxide. Experimental evidence was obtained by Shull and Smart in 1949 by neutron diffraction which showed "extra" lines due to the rows of reversed spins on the crystal lattice. These subjects may be pursued further in more advanced texts.

12-10. Low-Temperature Physics

In recent years new studies at temperatures near absolute zero have become one of the most important fields of investigation. Two surprising discoveries have been made, that of the superconducting state of some metals and that of the superfluid state of liquid helium. To investigate phenomena at low temperatures, in the field now called *cryogenics*, low-temperature laboratories have been established at a number of universities and at the National Bureau of Standards.

This kind of low-temperature physics became possible after Kammerlingh Onnes at Leyden first liquefied helium in 1909 at -268.9 °C and later was able to freeze it at -272.2 °C and 26 atmospheres pressure. At lower pressure it does not solidify regardless of temperature. Such temperatures are very near to absolute zero which is -273.16 °C. By cooling bodies in liquid helium and then allowing the helium to evaporate, temperatures nearer absolute zero than these may be obtained, and by other special experimental procedures, in particular by magnetic cooling, still lower temperatures very close to absolute zero have been attained.

MAGNETIC COOLING

When a body is magnetized, work is done on it by the external field and it is then in a higher energy state, that is, the internal energy of the body has been increased. If such a magnetized body is cooled by liquid helium as much as possible and if the magnetizing field is then removed while the body is thermally isolated, the internal energy becomes less and a state of lower temperature is reached. By such means temperatures within a few hundredths of a degree of absolute zero have been reached.

12-11. Superconductivity

The phenomenon of superconductivity was discovered by Kammer- lingh Onnes in 1911. While experimenting with mercury at very low tem- peratures he found that the electric resistance began to drop very rapidly at 4.26 °K and that at 4.20 °K it had vanished completely. This was a startling discovery.

At ordinary temperatures electric current will exist in a closed circuit only so long as there is an emf to maintain it, such as, for instance, from an electric cell or an induced emf. Consider, for example, a solid conducting ring of metal, as in Fig. 12-13. At ordinary temperatures if a magnet is moved into the center of the ring or removed from the center, a momentary current will occur only so long as the magnetic flux through the conductor is changing. For a superconductor at low temperatures the situation is radically different. It is not too difficult, once the metal ring has been brought to a low temperature, to repeat this experiment. Pulling the magnet out of the ring produces an induced current in the ring as before, but now the strength of the current does not diminish after the magnet has been removed. At the end of a minute, or an hour, or a day, or even longer, it still

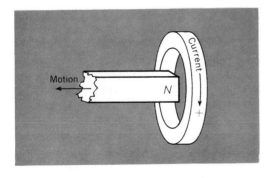

Fig. 12-13. Below the transi- tion temperature, when a mag- net is withdrawn from a ring of superconducting metal, the induced current persists inde- finitely.

has not diminished by a measurable amount. For as long a time as the ring can be maintained at the proper temperature no measurable decrease in the current can be detected. In a record-breaking time test at the Massachusetts Institute of Technology, a lead ring was said to have carried a current for over a year without appreciable change. Since sensitive methods are used, which could detect a decrease of as little as 0.001 of 1 per cent, it is concluded that the current experiences no resistance at all. This is the state of superconductivity, and it presents an intriguing but baffling problem.

The possibility of superconductivity had not been predicted by any theory. Bloch applied wave mechanics to the problem and arrived at the conclusion that electrons could perhaps pass through a crystal lattice without colliding with any atoms if the atoms did not possess thermal vibration. But quantum theory predicts a residual amount of energy at absolute zero, and some vibrations must still occur. Thus a new theory was needed which would explain not only why superconductivity occurs at all, but why it occurs at temperatures above absolute zero, and only in some metals. In 1957 Bardeen, Cooper, and Schrieffer assumed a different type of interacting between electrons and the vibrating atoms in which under certain conditions the vibrations may help instead of hinder the current. An idealized model formulated on this basis shows some of the chief properties of superconductivity and has permitted some exact computations to be made.

The following more or less common metals are now known to be superconducting at temperatures a few degrees above absolute zero: aluminum, lead, zinc, mercury, tin, cadmium, thallium, vanadium, indium, osmium, and at least twelve others which are less common. It is of interest that elements, the atoms of which have 3, 5 or 7 valence electrons outside of filled shells, become superconducting most readily, that is at higher temperatures. In addition to the elements a considerable number of alloys and compounds has been found to be superconducting. A compound of niobium (columbium) and tin becomes superconducting at the relatively high temperature of 18 °K and niobium nitride at 15 °K. Such substances give promise of important scientific and technical uses particularly in the handling of extremely small electric currents without loss.

Onnes also made the discovery that the superconducting state may be destroyed by the application of a sufficiently intense magnetic field, and it is now known that the lower the temperature is, the more intense must the field be. Even the magnetic field due to the current itself may destroy the superconducting state if the current is large enough. This condition put a limitation on those who hoped to use the superconducting state to produce intense magnetic fields by means of intense currents. Further study leads to the conclusion that in the superconducting state the magnetic permeability is also zero. In other words, in the superconducting state the substance is perfectly diamagnetic and is perfectly opaque to an external field.

Problems

1. How many "free" electrons are there per m³ of a block of silver? The density of silver is 1060 kg/m³. Assume one "free" electron per atom. Why, according to quantum theory, can only a fraction of these ordinarily participate in the conduction process?

2. What is the number of "free" electrons in the conduction band of sodium in a cube 1 cm on a side? The density of sodium is 970 kg/m³. Assume one "free" electron per atom and that 0.001 of these are in the conduction band.

3. There is a current of 10 amperes in a copper wire 1 mm in diameter. What is the average current density j in amperes/m²?

4. Assuming 1 free electron per atom and that 0.001 of these are in the conduction band, what is the average rate of drift of the electrons in a copper wire 1 mm in radius carrying 1 ampere. (Density of copper is 890 kg/m³.)

*5. Show that according to quantum ideas (Fermi distribution) less than 0.01 of the free electrons of a copper wire at room temperature are near enough the Fermi brim to be likely to take part in the conduction process.

*6. The number of filled quantum states N per unit volume in a metal at absolute zero can be obtained by integrating the function representing the available states (in terms of energies) up to the Fermi brim E_0. Since all states are filled, N also represents the number of valence electrons.

$$N = \frac{2^{9/2} m^{3/2} \pi}{3h^3} E_0^{3/2}$$

where E_0 is in joules. Compute the energy of the Fermi brim for copper in electron volts, assuming one "free" electron per atom.

7. Repeat problem 6 for sodium using the data of problem 2.

8. Solve the equation in problem 6 explicitly for the energy E_0 of the Fermi brim, and adjust it to give the result in electron volts.

9. From the tables of electrical conductivity (or resistivity) compute the ratio of conductivity of copper to that of glass. How do you explain the very great range?

10. Assuming an average atomic mass of 21 for a certain kind of glass and a resistivity of 10^{14} ohm cm, find the approximate number of atoms for each electron in the conduction band. Take density of glass to be 300 kg/m³. Compare with copper.

Note. For problems in thermionic emission assume that $A = 60$ amp/cm² °K.

11. How many electrons per second are emitted per cm² by a cathode at 3000 °K if the work function is 4 electron volts?

12. How much thermionic current is emitted by a tungsten ribbon 0.1 cm wide and 1 cm long if kept at a temperature of 2727 °C?

13. In a mercury arc in which an intensely hot spot on the surface of a pool of mercury is the cathode, what is the thermionic-emission current if the effective temperature of the spot is 2227 °C and if the effective area is 1 cm²? (Take work function to be 4.5 eV.)

Recommended Reading

Shamos, M. H., and G. M. Murphy, eds. *Recent Advances In Science.* New York: Science Editions, Inc., 1961.

Sproull, R. L., *Modern Physics*, 2nd ed. New York: John Wiley & Sons, Inc., 1963.

Dekker, A. J., *Solid State Physics.* Englewood Cliffs, N. J.: Prentice-Hall, Inc., 1957.

Kittel, C., *Introduction to Solid State Physics.* New York: John Wiley & Sons, Inc., 1956.

Seitz, F., *The Modern Theory of Solids.* New York: McGraw-Hill Book Company, Inc., 1940.

Shockley, W., *Electrons and Holes in Semiconductors.* Princeton, N. J.: D. Van Nostrand Co., Inc., 1950.

Bozorth, R. M., *Ferromagnetism.* Princeton, N. J.: D. Van Nostrand Co., Inc., 1951.

Mott, N. F., and R. W. Gurney, *Electronic Processes In Ionic Crystals*, 2nd ed., Oxford: Clarendon Press, 1948.

Smith, L. P., "Thermionic Emission" in *Handbook of Physics*, edited by Condon, E. U., and Odishaw, H. New York: McGraw-Hill Book Company, Inc., 1959.

Hachenberg, O., and W. Brauer, "Secondary Electron Emission From Solids" in *Advances in Electronics and Electron Physics*, Vol. 11. New York: Academic Press, Inc., 1959.

Matthias, B. T., "Superconductivity," *Scientific American*, Nov. 1957, p. 92.

Plate 1. Cloud-chamber tracks of alpha rays. It will be noted that there are two groups of different ranges representing widely different energies from a mixture of two different radioactive substances, Th B and Th C. Those of longer range show evidence of two sub-groups (fine structure). The long track downward to the left is that of a proton ejected from a nitrogen nucleus by an alpha particle. The O^{17} nucleus resulting from the disintegration recoils upward. The photograph was taken by P.M.S. Blackett, Imperial College of Science and Technology, London [Proc. Roy Soc. (London) 136, 325 (1932)] and is one of those reproduced in *An Atlas of Typical Expansion Chamber Photographs*, by Gentner, Maier-Leibnitz and Bothe; Pergamon Press.

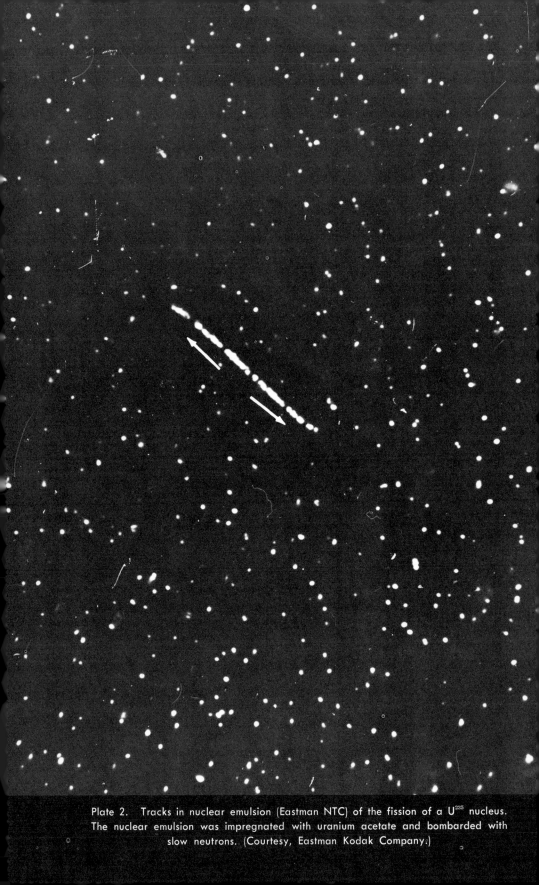

Plate 2. Tracks in nuclear emulsion (Eastman NTC) of the fission of a U^{235} nucleus. The nuclear emulsion was impregnated with uranium acetate and bombarded with slow neutrons. (Courtesy, Eastman Kodak Company.)

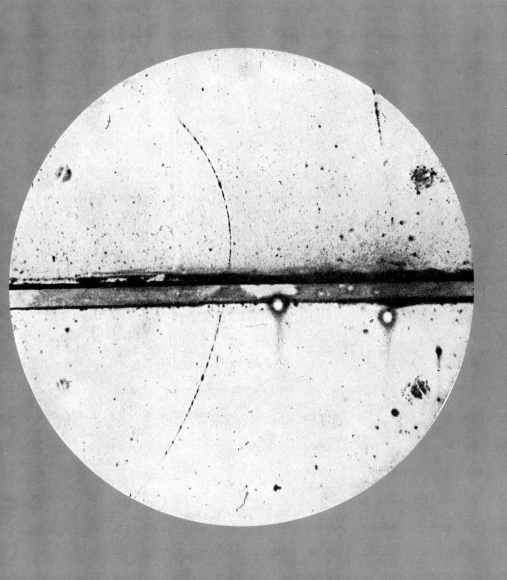

Plate 3. Historic cosmic-ray cloud-chamber photo by Carl D. Anderson, California Institute of Technology, in which the positron, the first antiparticle, was first identified. The track was evidently that of an electron but was curved by a magnetic field in the opposite direction to that of a negative electron. The particle passed upward through a 6 mm lead plate. Energy below plate was 63 meV; above plate, 23 meV. Phys. Rev. 43, 492 (1933). (Courtesy, C. D. Anderson.)

Plate 4. Giant shower of mesons from nuclear explosion. A massive nucleus (identified as iron) of extremely high energy comes in, at top of photo, from outer space and collides with a nucleus in the emulsion. From the disrupted nucleus comes a downward jet of about 40 pi mesons and some larger fragments ejected in different directions. The nuclear emulsion had been carried to an elevation of 106,000 ft by a Navy "Skyhook" balloon. Photo taken by AFCRL, Space Physics Laboratory, Bedford, Mass. (Courtesy, H. Yagoda and *Scientific American*.)

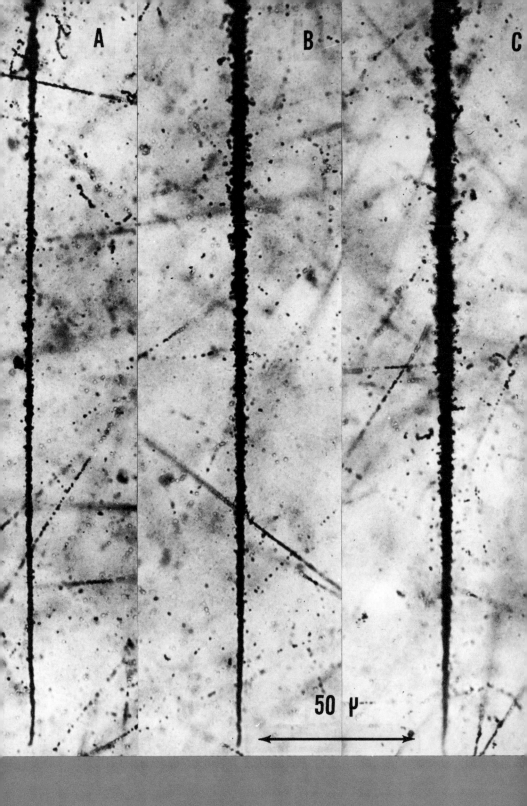

Plate 5. Tracks of three massive nuclei from outer space stopped in nuclear emul-
sions showing how ion density of tracks increases with increasing mass of particle.
The nuclei forming these tracks are identified as A, nitrogen; B, silicon; C, iron.
Photo courtesy of AFCRL, Space Physics Laboratory, Bedford, Mass.

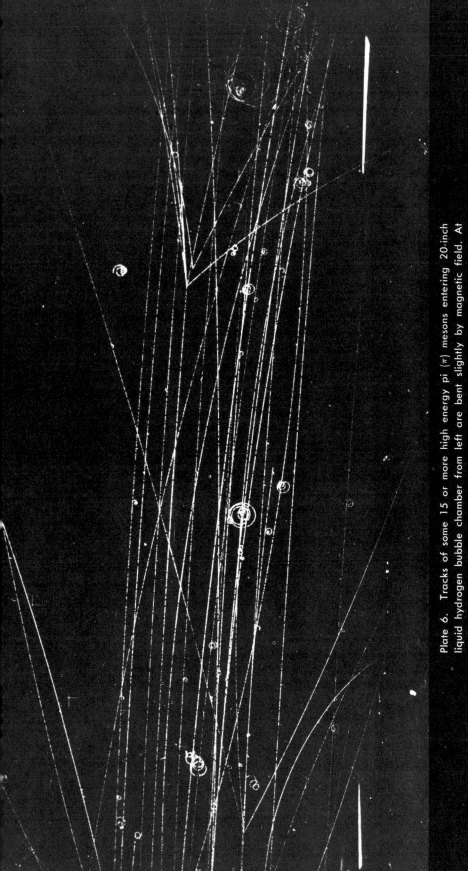

Plate 6. Tracks of some 15 or more high energy pi (π) mesons entering 20-inch liquid hydrogen bubble chamber from left are bent slightly by magnetic field. At right center a π meson hits a proton producing a small shower of particles. Typical events of this kind will be analyzed in successive plates. The tight spirals are dislodged electrons of low velocity slowing down. The pi mesons were produced by protons from the powerful alternating gradient synchrotron bombarding an aluminum target.

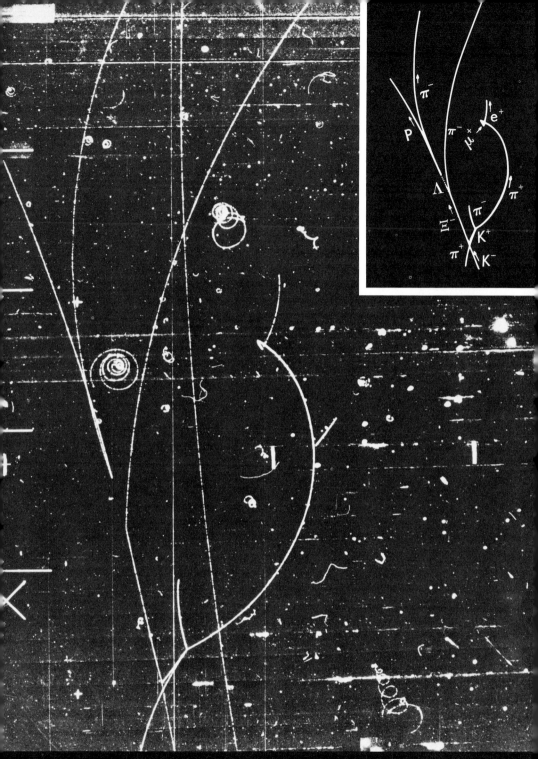

Plate 7. Bubble-chamber photo of production and decay of negative Xi hyperon. Note that the track on the right shows successive decays of a π^- meson to a μ^- (muon) and then to an e^- (positron). The K^+ meson formed in the first visible event decays to two π^+ and one π^- mesons. (Courtesy, Lawrence Radiation Laboratory, University of California.)

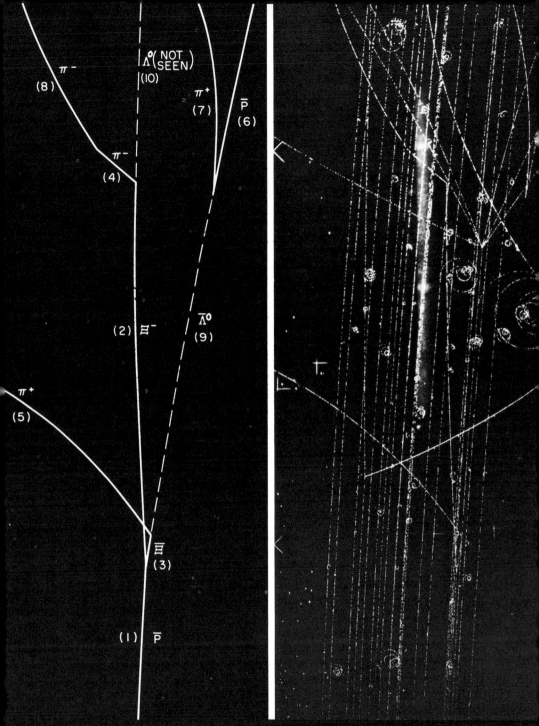

Plate 8.   Bubble-chamber tracks showing an incoming 3.3 beV antiproton ($\bar{p}$) (track 1) which collides with a proton to form a hyperon pair ($\bar{p} + p \rightarrow \Xi^- + \Xi^+$) of xi ($\Xi$) particles. The Ξ^- (track 2) decays to a π^- meson and a neutral lambda particle (Λ^0). The anti-Xi particle (track 3) decays to a π^+ and to an anti-neutral lambda particle ($\bar{\Lambda}^0$) whose track (9) is not seen but which in turn decays to an antiproton $\bar{p}$ and a π^+ meson (tracks 6 and 7). The photo is further confirmation of the existence of antiparticles.
(Courtesy, Brookhaven National Laboratory.)

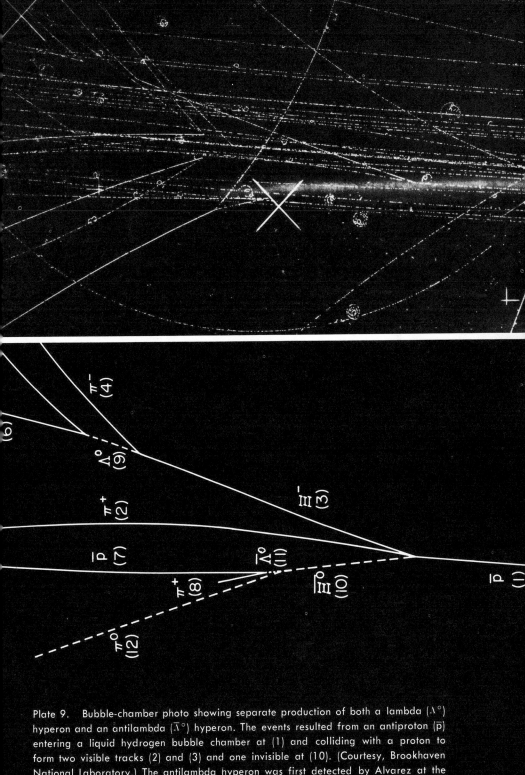

Plate 9.   Bubble-chamber photo showing separate production of both a lambda (Λ°) hyperon and an antilambda ($\overline{\Lambda}^{\circ}$) hyperon. The events resulted from an antiproton ($\overline{p}$) entering a liquid hydrogen bubble chamber at (1) and colliding with a proton to form two visible tracks (2) and (3) and one invisible at (10). (Courtesy, Brookhaven National Laboratory.) The antilambda hyperon was first detected by Alvarez at the Lawrence Radiation Laboratory and completes the list of common antiparticles.

Plate 10. Construction photo of tunnel for deflecting magnets and orbital tube in which particles are accelerated for the huge 33 beV alternating gradient synchrotron at Brookhaven. After completion the tunnel was buried under 10 feet of earth. Plan of accelerator now completed is shown in next plate. In the foreground is the Brookhaven nuclear reactor group showing stack from which cooling air of reactor is released. (Courtesy, Brookhaven National Laboratory.)

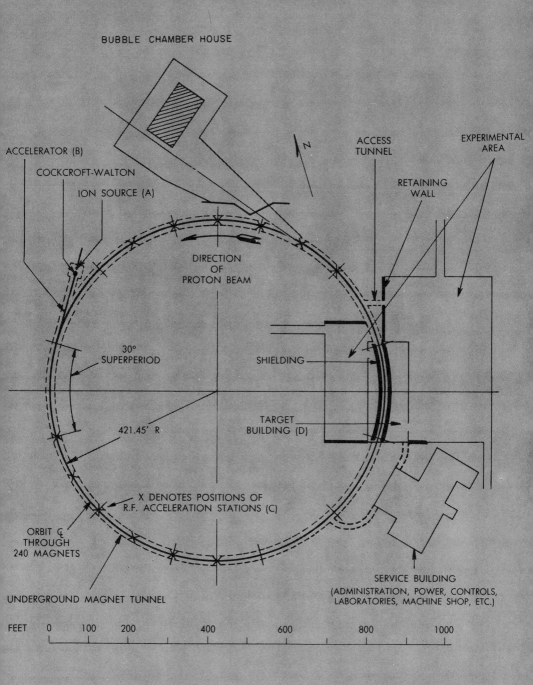

BUBBLE CHAMBER HOUSE

ACCELERATOR (B)

COCKCROFT-WALTON

ION SOURCE (A)

N

ACCESS
TUNNEL

EXPERIMENTAL
AREA

RETAINING
WALL

DIRECTION
OF
PROTON BEAM

30°
SUPERPERIOD

421.45' R

SHIELDING

TARGET
BUILDING (D)

X DENOTES POSITIONS OF
R.F. ACCELERATION STATIONS (C)

ORBIT ₵
THROUGH
240 MAGNETS

UNDERGROUND MAGNET TUNNEL

SERVICE BUILDING
(ADMINISTRATION, POWER, CONTROLS,
LABORATORIES, MACHINE SHOP, ETC.)

FEET   0   100   200   400   600   800   1000

Plate 11. Plan of Brookhaven synchrotron showing linear accelerator which injects
ions of 50-meV energy into orbit. Note bubble-chamber house, and location of experimental buildings. (Courtesy, Brookhaven National Laboratory.)

Plate 12.   Over-all view of linear accelerator (linac) looking from low energy end to high energy end where ions are injected into orbit of the giant Brookhaven alternating gradient synchrotron. (Courtesy, Brookhaven National Laboratory.)

Radioactivity: Detectors of High-Energy Rays

13-1. Radioactivity

The discovery of radioactivity was made by Henri Becquerel in February 1896 when he found that an unknown type of radiation from an ore containing uranium would affect a photographic plate wrapped in black paper.

In 1898 Marie Curie and her husband Pierre succeeded in extracting a very small amount of active substance from a ton or more of ore. The new substance was called *polonium* by Madame Curie in honor of her native land, Poland. Some months later she isolated another source of intense radiation and named it *radium*. In 1903 the Curies shared the Nobel prize with Becquerel for the discovery of radioactivity. For isolating radium which turned out to be a new element, and for measuring its atomic weight, Madame Curie herself received the Nobel prize in 1911. Soon a number of other active substances were isolated by the Curies and by other early workers in the field, among them Rutherford and Soddy. These substances were all found to be new elements and are now known to belong to one or more series of radioactive elements, the members of which are closely related.

During the first two decades after the discovery of radioactivity, it was found that the phenomenon of radioactivity was almost but not completely limited to atoms heavier than lead of mass number 206, atomic number 82. The earliest known exceptions were potassium and rubidium. Later other elements including carbon were found to be very feebly radioactive. Such radioactivity is now known to be due in each case to the presence of small amounts of a radioactive isotope mixed with the stable element. In carbon the activity is due to the rare isotope carbon 14, presumed to be formed in the atmosphere by the action of cosmic ray neutrons on nitrogen (§13-22).

13-2. Alpha, Beta, and Gamma Rays: Radiation Hazards

Natural radioactivity as found in nature must be distinguished from *artificial* or *induced radioactivity* (§15-2) produced in the laboratory. Three types of rays are emitted by natural radioactive substances, *alpha* (α), *beta* (β) and *gamma* (γ) rays. Measurements of the ratio of charge to mass of beta rays and their direction of deflection in a magnetic field soon led to their identification as electrons traveling at high speeds. In 1903 by somewhat similar methods Rutherford in England identified the alpha particle as a "doubly charged helium atom." That it was actually the same as the *nucleus* of a helium atom did not become clear until after the formulation of the concept of the nuclear atom.

In the meantime Rutherford had given a beautifully simple and conclusive demonstration that alpha particles actually are "charged helium atoms." The rays were allowed to pass through a thin window into an electric-discharge tube (Fig. 13-1) which had previously been evacuated. Then an electric discharge in the tube showed the characteristic spectral lines of helium where none had been observed before. The alpha particles entering the tube had collected outer electrons and had become helium atoms.

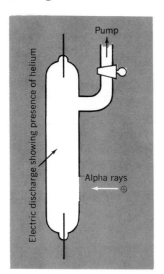

Fig. 13-1.   Simplified diagram of Rutherford's experiment which demonstrated that alpha particles are helium nuclei.

Since the nucleus of an atom is composed of protons and neutrons and since an alpha particle is a stable association of 2 protons and 2 neutrons it is clear that alpha particles can be formed in a heavy nucleus. How they are emitted is a more complicated problem that will be discussed in the next chapter. On the other hand the emission of beta rays (electrons) from a nucleus requires some explaining if only protons and neutrons are present. The latter is an oversimplification for in the nucleus, as we shall see later, a neutron may *decay* to a proton by the emission of a negative electron as in natural radioactivity, or a proton may decay to a neutron by the emission of a positive electron (positron) as in some instances of induced radio-activity (§15-2).

The gamma rays were discovered in 1900 by Villard. Because they were found to pass through the strongest magnetic fields undeflected it was not clear for some years whether they were uncharged particles or a form of wave motion. Now we recognize that gamma rays are electromagnetic waves of very short wavelength, even shorter than ordinary x-rays, and consequently have a very high penetrating power although like x-rays they may also have particle-like properties.

Whereas alpha rays can usually be stopped by a few sheets of paper and beta rays by a few millimeters of aluminum it may require several centimeters of lead or iron to reduce the gamma rays from a radioactive substance to a safe level. The even more penetrating radiations of various kinds from nuclear reactors and particle accelerators may require several feet of shielding. Since gamma rays are the most penetrating and the most dangerous, adequate protection from them must always be provided. This may be accomplished by means of shielding, or by the simple expedient of taking advantage of the inverse-square law and staying as far as possible from radioactive material in any appreciable quantity.

Among the earliest recognized properties of the different rays from a radioactive substance, in addition to penetration and the production of burns on the human body, were their capacity to

1. Ionize the molecules of a gas
2. Affect a photographic plate
3. Produce tiny flashes of light or scintillations in certain materials (especially alpha particles)
4. Release large amounts of energy with little decrease in intensity over long periods of time.

13-3. Absorption of Gamma Rays

The nature of the absorption process for gamma rays is essentially different from that of charged particles such as alpha and beta rays. The latter lose energy by inelastic collisions until they slow down and finally come to rest at the end of their range. A beam of gamma rays may lose energy but it does not "slow down." When gamma rays pass through matter the intensity of the beam decreases in a manner similar to x-rays, and the intensity for a narrow beam of rays of the same energy is given by the same equation as for x-rays (§4-5),

$$I = I_0 \epsilon^{-\mu x} \tag{13-1}$$

where μ, as before, is the absorption coefficient of the substance for the wavelengths in question and x is the thickness of the absorber. From this formula it is apparent that gamma rays have no definite range, as do alpha and beta rays. Just as x-ray photons possess particle-like quantum properties, so also do gamma-ray photons, and the decrease in intensity of a gamma-ray beam on passing through matter is chiefly due to three separate effects, photoelectric absorption, Compton scattering by electrons, and production of electron pairs. When the beam is attenuated by any or all of these processes it is said to be "absorbed."

In photoelectric absorption all the energy of the gamma-ray photon is transferred to an electron, and the gamma-ray photon ceases to exist. The ejected electron may escape from the absorber, or its energy may be used up in collisions. In Compton scattering of gamma rays, just as with x-rays (§5-6), the photon loses energy at any collision with an electron and its frequency is thereby reduced. Its direction is also changed so that it may be scattered out of the main beam. Such scattering is increasingly probable with a substance composed of atoms of higher atomic number since there are more electrons per atom that may be hit. In electron-pair production the energy of the gamma-ray photon goes to form a positive and negative electron.

At energies of 50 keV or less for aluminum, and 500 keV for lead, the loss of energy is chiefly the result of photoelectric absorption. At energies in the neighborhood of 1 meV in lead Compton scattering becomes pre-

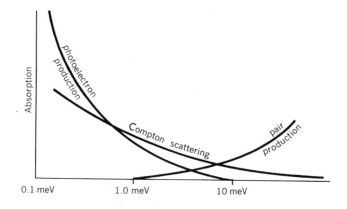

Fig. 13-2. Gamma-ray photon absorption processes in lead.

dominant (Fig. 13-2). At higher energies pair production becomes increasingly important and finally becomes the principal factor in absorption.

Intensities of radioactivity are commonly measured by the number of disintegrations per second. The common unit, the *curie*, is defined as 3.7×10^{10} disintegrations per second. This is approximately the activity of a gram of radium. The *millicurie* (mc) is then 37 million disintegrations per second. For weaker intensities a unit called the *rutherford* has been suggested. One rutherford is 10^6 disintegrations per second.

13-4. Energy Liberated by a Radioactive Substance

The surprising liberation of energy by a radioactive substance was contrary to expectation on any classical basis. The Newtonian conception that atoms are solid, everlasting and inert, was completely overthrown and this marks one of the greatest revolutions in physics. In some instances the atom appeared as an almost inexhaustible storehouse of energy. For instance measurements showed that every gram of radium liberates approximately 140 calories of heat per hour, enough energy to raise 1.4 grams of water from the freezing to the boiling point every hour. Furthermore, the decrease in the rate of emission is so little that, after 1600 years, the rate of energy release would only be reduced to one-half. Based on this fact, we say that the *half-life* of radium is 1600 years.

The energy evolved is actually the energy of the emitted rays. Radium itself emits high-energy alpha particles. Together with its decay products, some of which emit beta and gamma rays, 1 gram of radium releases

Alpha rays	124 cal/hr
Beta rays	6.3 cal/hr
Gamma rays	9.4 cal/hr
Total	139.7 cal/hr

That so much energy could be stored in atoms was not only a revolutionary idea, but one which was very difficult to understand until after 1905, when Einstein proposed that mass could be converted into energy. Though the diminution of mass in a given amount of radioactive material may be hardly noticeable, it is sufficient to account for the energy release.

13-5. Radioactive Decay and Half-Life

Many experimental measurements show that, wherever large numbers of atoms are dealt with, all radioactive substances follow the same general decay pattern. At the end of a certain length of time half the number of atoms present will have decayed. For one isotope this time period or *half-life* may be a fraction of a second, for another isotope it may be thousands of years or more. At the end of a second time interval equal to the first, half the atoms left of a given isotope of an element will decay, and in every succeeding similar interval half of those remaining will decay. Such points plotted on a graph give a logarithmic decay curve (Fig. 13-3), represented by the equation

$$N = N_0 \epsilon^{-\lambda t} \qquad [13\text{--}2]$$

where N is the number of atoms that have not yet decayed after time t, and N_0 is the number of atoms at $t = 0$. The quantity λ is called the *decay constant* and is characteristic of the particular atomic isotope undergoing decay. It is the fractional number of atoms of the substance that decays per second.

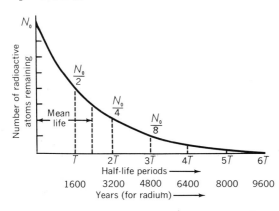

Fig. 13-3.   The decay of radium, a typical logarithmic decay curve, with the half-life intervals indicated. (T = half-life.)

The derivation of the decay equation [13–2] is as follows: If the number of atoms decaying in a small time interval Δt is ΔN, and if the number is proportional to the time Δt, then $-\Delta N \sim \Delta t$. The minus sign serves to indicate a decrease in total number. The number decaying is evidently proportional to the number N present at the beginning of the time interval, and λ is the proportionality constant needed to set up the equation. The definition of λ may be obtained directly from the equation, which now becomes

$$\Delta N = -\lambda N \, \Delta t \qquad [13\text{--}3]$$

In the limiting differential form,

$$dN = -\lambda N \, dt \qquad [13\text{--}4]$$

or

$$\frac{dN}{N} = -\lambda \, dt \qquad [13\text{--}5]$$

This may be readily solved by integration to give

$$\int \frac{dN}{N} = \ln N = -\lambda t + C \qquad [13\text{--}6]$$

When t is 0, the constant of integration $C = \ln N_0$ where N_0 is the number of atoms at $t = 0$. Therefore

$$\ln N - \ln N_0 = -\lambda t \qquad [13\text{–}7]$$

and

$$N = N_0 \epsilon^{-\lambda t} \qquad [13\text{–}2]$$

The decay constant may also be interpreted as the probability that a single atom will decay in one second. The larger lambda is, the more rapidly the element decays and the shorter will be its half-life. Evidently lambda and the half-life T of an element are closely related. To find this relation we put $N = N_0/2$. Then we solve the equation for $t = T$, the half-life. The equation then becomes

$$\frac{1}{2} = \epsilon^{-\lambda T}$$

$$\ln 2 = +\lambda T$$

and

$$T = \frac{\ln 2}{\lambda} = \frac{0.693}{\lambda} \qquad [13\text{–}8]$$

The *mean life* or average life expectancy of an atom is $1/\lambda$. This is not the half-life; it is greater than the half-life. The reason is that the last few atoms of a radioactive substance may last for a very long period of time, thus bringing the average to more than the half-life.

13-6. Statistical Nature of Radioactive Decay

There is no measurable quantity which can be called the life of a radioactive atom. The lives of human beings can be individually measured but there is no way of singling out a particular radioactive atom and measuring its life. Indeed, such a measurement would have no useful meaning, even if it were made, for it would apply to no other atom. Measurements of the rate of decay of a radioactive substance are purely statistical averages based on measurements made with very large numbers of atoms. An atom has no memory of past events. Nor does its life expectancy decrease with age, as it does with human beings. A particular atom may have a probability of decay of one in a million in a given length of time. After a thousand years or so, if it has not decayed it still has the same life expectancy or probability of decay. Quantum mechanics can predict the probability of decay of radioactive atoms, but it cannot tell us if the decay in a given atom is a result of favorable conditions that occur only at intervals in a way which we cannot foresee.

13-7. Radioactive Transformation and Series

When the nucleus of an atom emits an alpha or beta ray, sometimes accompanied by a gamma ray, the process is called *radioactive decay*, and the product nucleus is often found also to be radioactive. For instance, when an atom of radium undergoes decay and emits an alpha particle, the product nucleus is that of an atom of a different element, *emanation*, (formerly called *radon*). Emanation, it happens, is a gas at ordinary temperature and pressure, and is itself radioactive.

If radium is enclosed in a vessel the space around the radium becomes filled with this radioactive gas, which may be pumped off while the radium produces more. Emanation is an alpha-ray emitter and is found to have a half-life of only 3.8 days. This indicates that the decay goes on at a rate many thousand times as fast as the decay of radium itself. Careful study shows that the residue left by the decay of emanation likewise is radioactive, emitting alpha particles, and the residue or product atoms belong to still another element. Originally called radium A it is now known to be one of the isotopes of polonium. Thus radium and radium A are closely related. Radium A is said to be the daughter product of emanation, and is the daughter product of radium. However, radium is neither the beginning of this series, nor is radium A the end.

The three elements mentioned represent three stages near the center of a chain of 14 successive transformations, known as a radioactive series, in which the decaying atom winds up as a stable, nonradioactive atom of lead. This series begins with the element uranium and with the particular long-lived uranium atom of atomic number 92 and mass number 238. By successive emission of alpha or beta rays, sometimes accompanied by gamma rays, the decaying uranium atoms go through a series of transformations, as shown in Table 13-1.

TABLE 13-1.   URANIUM SERIES OF RADIOACTIVE ELEMENTS
(4n + 2 series)

Symbol (New)	Symbol (Old)	Element	Half-Life	Emitted Ray
$_{92}U^{238}$	UI	Uranium	4.5×10^9 yr	α
$_{90}Th^{234}$	UX_1	Thorium	24 days	$\beta\ (\gamma)$
$_{91}Pa^{234}$	UX_2	Protoactinium	1.14 min	$\beta\ (\gamma)$
$_{92}U^{234}$	UII	Uranium	3×10^5 yr	α
$_{90}Th^{230}$	Io	Thorium	83,000 yr	$\alpha\ (\gamma)$
$_{88}Ra^{226}$	Ra	Radium	1,600 yr	$\alpha\ (\gamma)$
$_{86}Em^{222}$	Rn	Emanation	3.8 days	α
$_{84}Po^{218}$	RaA	Polonium	3.05 min	α
$_{82}Pb^{214}$	RaB	Lead	26.8 min	$\beta\ (\gamma)$
$_{83}Bi^{214}$	RaC	Bismuth	19.7 min	$\beta\ (\gamma)$
$_{84}Po^{214}$	RaC'	Polonium (radium C')	10^{-5} sec	$\alpha\ (\gamma)$
$_{82}Pb^{210}$	RaD	Lead	22 yr	β
$_{83}Bi^{210}$	RaE	Bismuth	5 days	$\beta\ (\gamma)$
$_{84}Po^{210}$	RaF	Polonium	140 days	α
$_{82}Pb^{206}$	RaG	Lead	Stable	

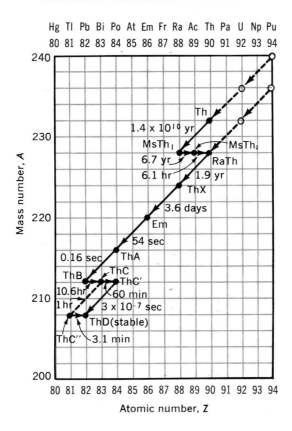

Fig. 13.4. The thorium or 4n series. The graph shows the main line of decay for the thorium series, named after its longest-lived member. It will be noticed that ThC may decay in one of two ways. Some earlier members of the series are shown dashed.

There are four chief radioactive series. Three normally begin with elements of atomic number 92 or less, common in nature, and all three series terminate with atoms that are isotopes of lead. These isotopes are stable and consequently end the series. In addition to the uranium-radium series given in Table 13-1, there are the thorium and actinium series represented in Figs. 13-4 and 13-5 by a different but convenient type of diagram. The fourth series (Fig. 13-6) begins with the more recently discovered "man-made" element plutonium, and the end of the series is a stable isotope of bismuth. Although the beginning of the series has now been traced back to plutonium, it is called the neptunium series after the long-lived isotope of neptunium (half-life $= 2.2 \times 10^6$ years), the most stable isotope in the series. Actually small amounts of neptunium and plutonium have been found to exist in some uranium ores.

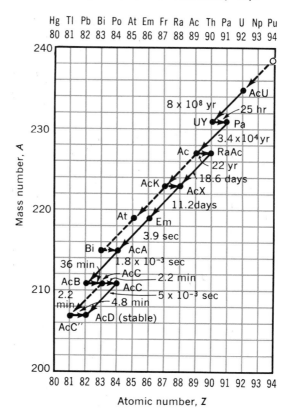

Fig. 13-5. The actinium or $4n + 3$ series. Some alternative modes of decay are indicated by dashed lines. The series may be traced backward beyond AcU (dashed line).

SYMBOLS AND TRANSFORMATIONS; MASS NUMBER

When an atom of an element such as radium emits an alpha particle the nucleus of the atom loses a particle of charge 2 and approximate mass 4. Its nuclear charge Z (atomic number) is thus reduced by 2 units, and its approximate mass or mass number is reduced by 4 units. The mass number, it will be remembered (§1-8), is the number of nuclear neutrons and protons of the isotope in question, represented by the symbol A. The symbol for the emitted alpha particle is $_2He^4$ where the subscript before the letters representing the element is the atomic number or nuclear charge, and the superscript following the letters is the mass number.

The symbol for the radium nucleus of nuclear charge 88 and mass number 226 is $_{88}Ra^{226}$, and by emission of an alpha particle this nucleus becomes transformed into a nucleus having 2 units less charge and 4 units

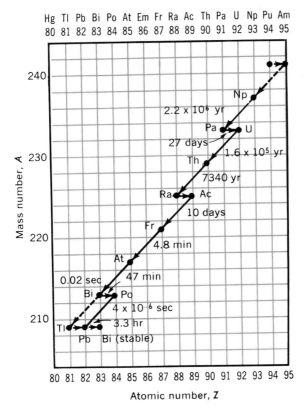

Fig. 13-6. The neptunium or $4n + 1$ series. The relatively short life of this series is the probable reason for the scarcity of its members, especially Np, in nature.

less mass, named emanation, the symbol for which is $_{86}Em^{222}$. The transformation accompanying alpha emission is described symbolically as follows:

$$_{88}Ra^{226} \rightarrow {}_{86}Em^{222} + {}_2He^4 \qquad\qquad [13\text{--}9]$$

The two sides of such a symbolic reaction must balance in total charge and in total mass number. Evidently the subscripts representing nuclear charge balance, since the 88 positive charges of the radium nucleus equals the 86 of the emanation nucleus plus the 2 of the alpha particle. Likewise the mass numbers (superscripts) on the right, 222 and 4, add up to the mass number 226 on the left. This is the characteristic manner of writing a nuclear transformation, and also the usual way of checking its validity, by balancing the two sides of the reaction as to both mass and nuclear charge.

An interesting relation between the four radioactive series may be observed if the mass numbers for the members of any one series are written in the form $4n + m$ (Table 13-2), where n is an integer and m takes the

TABLE 13-2.   FOUR HEAVY-ELEMENT DISINTEGRATION SERIES

(Relation of Mass Numbers)

Name of Series	Type	Start	End (stable)
Thorium	$4n + 0$	Th^{232}	Pb^{208}
Neptunium	$4n + 1$	Np^{237}	Bi^{209}
Uranium-radium	$4n + 2$	U^{238}	Pb^{206}
Actinium	$4n + 3$	U^{235}	Pb^{207}

values 0, 1, 2, and 3, respectively, for the four series. The three series with m having values 0, 2, and 3 had long been known, and the prospect that m might take the value 1 led to the discovery of the neptunium series.

RULES OF RADIOACTIVE DISPLACEMENT

The emission of an alpha particle by a radioactive nucleus means that the product atom has been shifted in the periodic table two steps in the direction of a lower atomic number (two steps to the left in Fig. 13-4) and four steps in the direction of a lower mass number. However, the emission of a negative beta particle by a radioactive atom, as for instance by $_{83}Bi^{210}$, represents a decrease in negative charge of the nucleus of 1 unit, which is equivalent to an increase in positive charge of 1 unit. This means that the atomic number is shifted one step in the direction of increasing atomic number (one step to the right in Fig. 13-4), and the mass number is unchanged since the electron has negligible mass. Therefore $_{83}Bi^{210}$ by emission of a beta particle becomes $_{84}Po^{210}$ and is now an isotope of polonium. These are called the rules of *radioactive displacement*.

Since many more radioactive particles were found than there were places for them in the atomic number series, it appeared that many must be isotopes of others.

13-8. Radioactive Growth and Decay

If a pure radioactive isotope is isolated at time $t = 0$, it does not remain pure. The decay products begin to form, and while any radioactive substance decays its products begin to grow. If a *daughter isotope* is stable the growth will continue until the *parent isotope* has all decayed. If a daughter isotope is also radioactive, equilibrium is reached when the daughter isotope decays as fast as it is being formed.

Radioactive growth and decay curves are represented in Fig. 13-7. The equation of growth is readily shown to be

$$N = N_0(1 - \epsilon^{-\lambda t})$$

[13-10]

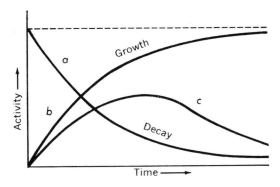

Fig. 13-7. Curves representing: a, decay of a radioactive substance; b, growth of the daughter element, assuming it to be a stable element with a long-lived parent; c, growth and decay of a daughter element which is itself unstable.

Curve a represents decay of an isotope, curve b, the growth of the daughter isotope assuming that the latter is stable and does not itself decay.

If the daughter isotope also decays, the total number of daughter atoms may be increasing or decreasing at any given moment, and the rate of change in number of the atoms N_2 of the daughter substance is

$$\frac{dN_2}{dt} = \lambda_1 N_1 - \lambda_2 N_2 \qquad [13\text{–}11]$$

when λ_1 and λ_2 are the decay constants of parent and daughter, respectively, and N_1 is the number of atoms of the parent. Then $\lambda_1 N_1$ is the gain in number of daughter atoms per unit time by decay of the parent, and $\lambda_2 N_2$ is the loss per unit time in number of daughter atoms owing to its own decay. Let $N_1 = N_{01} \epsilon^{-\lambda_1 t}$ where N_{01} is the number of parent atoms at time $t = 0$. Then

$$\frac{dN_2}{dt} + \lambda_2 N_2 = \lambda_1 N_{01} \epsilon^{-\lambda_1 t} \qquad [13\text{–}12]$$

By integrating this equation and putting the number of daughter atoms $N_{02} = 0$ for $t = 0$, the number of daughter atoms at any time t is given by

$$N_2 = \frac{\lambda_1}{\lambda_2 - \lambda_1} N_{01} (\epsilon^{-\lambda_1 t} - \epsilon^{-\lambda_2 t}) \qquad [13\text{–}13]$$

If the parent substance is so very long-lived that the daughter element may be assumed to be produced at a constant rate, this equation reduces to

$$\lambda_1 N_1 = \lambda_2 N_2 \qquad [13\text{–}14]$$

and is called *secular equilibrium*. For a series of several product isotopes in equilibrium

$$\lambda_1 N_1 = \lambda_2 N_2 = \lambda_3 N_3 \cdots \qquad [13\text{–}15]$$

where N_1, N_2, N_3 need only be numbers proportional to the numbers of each type of atom present.

13-9. Determinations of Extremely Long and Short Half-Lives

Half-lives of the more common radioactive substances cover an extraordinary range of time, from billions of years to a few microseconds. Some of the more recently discovered unstable particles have half-lives very much less. Whereas the half-lives of many of these may be determined by direct measurements made in the laboratory over periods ranging from minutes to months, half-lives that are extremely long or short must be determined by less direct methods. However, for any substance having a very long half-life there is a quite simple method.

If a milligram of uranium is found by laboratory measurement to emit 12.2 alpha particles per second, this is at a rate of 12200 alpha particles per gram per second. If this is put into Eq. 13-3 as ΔN, then Δt becomes 1 sec. From Avogadro's number and the atomic weight, it can easily be determined that there are 2.51×10^{21} atoms in 1 gm of uranium. This is N in the equation, which then becomes

$$12200 = \lambda \times 2.51 \times 10^{21} \times 1$$

from which

$$\lambda = 4.86 \times 10^{-18} \sec^{-1}$$

and by Eq. 13-8, since 1 year equals 3.156×10^7 sec, the half-life is

$$T = 4.5 \times 10^9 \text{ years}$$

Because the end product of the uranium series is lead, the relative amount of lead found in uranium ore in proportion to the uranium present affords a method of computing the age of the ore, assuming that it contained uranium only at the start. This period of time is often spoken of as the "age of the earth," but it is more accurate to call it the age of the earth's crust. Measurements indicate that it may be 5 or even 10 billion years.

Extremely short half-lives are more difficult to determine and sometimes are only approximate estimates. An estimate of both long and short half-lives for alpha decay may be obtained from measured ranges of the rays and application of the relation between range and decay constant, known as the Geiger-Nuttall rule (next section).

13-10. Alpha Rays: Range; Ionization; Absorption

A number of the first radioactive elements to be isolated are alpha-ray emitters. Among them are radium, emanation, and polonium. One of the isotopes of polonium ($_{84}Po^{214}$), originally called radium C', emits alpha rays of the highest energy (7.7 meV) of any isotope in the uranium-radium series. In the three natural series the most energetic alpha rays of all

(8.8 meV) are emitted by thorium C′, another isotope of polonium ($_{84}PO^{212}$). The alpha-ray emitters giving the highest energy rays have the shortest half-lives, measured in thousandths of a second or even millionths. Those alpha-ray emitters with the longest half-lives, uranium 238 and thorium 232, emit the least energetic alpha rays, both of them close to 4 meV.

The distance a particle travels in any substance is called its range in that substance. The alpha particles from any one isotope are all emitted with approximately the same energy and have a well-defined range characteristic of that isotope. Although most alpha particles may be stopped by a sheet or two of paper they may travel several centimeters in air at normal pressure. A cloud chamber (§13–15) is a useful tool with which to study the ranges of alpha particles. It is found that for most alpha-particle emitters the ranges are between 2.7 and 8 cm in air. For instance, for alpha particles from uranium the range in air is 2.7 cm; for radium it is 3.3 cm. The substance with the shortest half-life (164 microseconds) in the uranium series, and the most intense activity as just mentioned is radium C′. The alpha particles from radium C′ have a range in air of 6.9 cm, and their speed is nearly 1/15 that of light. See Plate 1, following Chapter 12.

A few alpha-ray emitters, in particular thorium C′ and radium C′, are found to emit rays of unusually long range occasionally. These are ascribed to emission from the parent nucleus when it is in an excited state. Thus the alpha ray carries off not only its normal energy but the excess energy of excitation of the parent nucleus.

Early in this century a surprising empirical relation was found between the half-life of an alpha-ray emitter and the range of the alpha ray. In fact, a single formula was found to fit all the alpha-ray emitters belonging to a particular decay series. This relation is known as the *Geiger-Nuttall rule* and is usually written in terms of the decay constant λ instead of the half-life, as follows:

$$\log \lambda = A \log R + B \qquad [13\text{–}16]$$

where R is the range and A and B are constants for a given decay series. In terms of the variables $\log \lambda$ and $\log R$ this is seen to be the equation of a straight line with slope A and intercept B. When the experimental values are plotted they determine a separate straight line for each of the natural decay series. For a long time there was no sound basis in theory for the unique relations involved in the rule, but it was later derived by means of quantum mechanics (§14-3), the constants were evaluated, and what was once purely empirical now has a theoretical basis.

ABSORPTION AND IONIZATION LOSSES

Alpha particles are stopped in passing through a material medium such as air because of loss of energy by collisions with the atoms of the medium. In a gas the energy-loss by collision is chiefly the result of the inelastic collisions that produce ionization of the atoms or molecules. At the start of its path 20 to 30 thousand ion pairs per cm of air may be formed by the passage of an alpha particle through it, and the probability of ionization rises as the speed of the alpha particle decreases until a maximum is reached of as much as 70,000 ion pairs per centimeter. The variation of ionization with distance along the path is shown in Fig. 13-8, where the ionization is seen to rise to a maximum and fall sharply as the alpha particle comes near the end of its range. Beta rays, on the other hand, being less massive produce something like 1/100 as many ions per centimeter.

ENERGY SPECTRUM AND FINE STRUCTURE

If observed in a cloud chamber, all the alpha particles from a given isotope seem to have the same range and consequently the same energy. However, closer study with more refined methods proved this not to be true, with a few exceptions. Rosenblum in 1929 found, by magnetic analysis, that alpha particles often fall into two or more groups which are close together in energy but have definite and fixed energy differences, as if different groups came from different energy levels within the nucleus. For

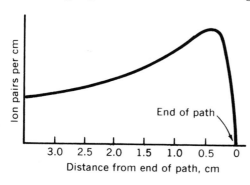

Fig. 13-8. Ionization vs range for alpha particles in air.

instance, alpha rays from thorium C are found to be composed of five groups having a maximum energy difference between groups of less than 0.5 meV. These sharply defined energy groups represent what is called the *fine structure* of the alpha-ray energy distribution. See Plate 1.

ALPHA-RAY SPECTROMETER

In order to determine more accurately the energies of various groups of alpha rays these energies may be measured by the method of magnetic deflection by means of an *alpha-ray spectrometer*. The method is similar to that of the mass spectrometer except that since all alpha particles have essentially the same mass the spectrometer is arranged so that particles of different velocity are focussed at different points (Fig. 13-9). In such a device magnetic field intensities of the order of 10,000 gauss are needed but because the method requires quite intense sources of alpha rays less accurate methods must sometimes be resorted to.

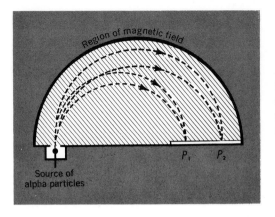

Fig. 13-9. Alpha-ray magnetic spectrometer with uniform magnetic field, showing focusing of rays of different energies at points P_1 and P_2.

NUCLEAR ENERGY LEVELS; DECAY SCHEMES; ORIGIN OF GAMMA RAYS

The discovery of the fine structure of alpha rays marks the real beginning of the analysis of nuclear structure. It furnished the clue that there may be different energy levels in the nucleus, that is, that the nucleus generally may exist in one or more higher energy states (*excited states*) above the lowest or ground state. The energy differences between groups do not, as was first thought, represent energy-level differences belonging to states of the parent atom; instead they belong to the daughter atom. The existence of these excited states also explains the origin of gamma rays from a radioactive substance. For a long time it was not known under what conditions gamma rays are emitted by a radioactive substance, but by 1925 proof was given that if gamma rays are emitted the emission follows closely that of alpha or beta rays at intervals of time ordinarily too short to measure.

The gamma rays from a particular radioactive isotope have wavelengths characteristic of that isotope. They are now known to be emitted when a nucleus returns from a higher energy state (excited state) to the normal or ground state. In a naturally radioactive substance gamma radiation follows the emission of an alpha or beta ray when the emission leaves the resultant nucleus with more than normal energy. With the emission of one or more gamma rays the nucleus then passes to the normal state. If it returns to the normal state in a single transition a single gamma-ray photon is emitted. If it returns by a series of transitions, "falling down the stairsteps" so to speak, a series of gamma-ray photons is emitted in what is called cascade emission (Fig. 13-10). Many measurements have been made of the energies of the gamma rays produced when a nucleus returns to the

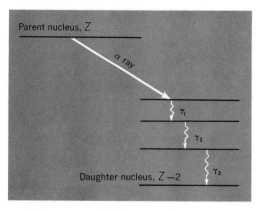

Fig. 13-10. Decay scheme, representing successive emission of a series of gamma rays (cascade emission) following alpha decay.

ground state, and these again serve to locate the energy levels for the various excited states of a nucleus.

In Fig. 13-11 the decay of radium to emanation is represented. Here, only two different energy groups of alpha particles are found, with energies, respectively, of 4.80 meV and 4.61 meV, but accompanying them gamma rays of 0.19 meV are also detected. When an alpha ray (α_1), belonging to the higher energy group, is emitted from the parent nucleus it is known that it is not accompanied by emission of a gamma ray. That is to say, the daughter element, emanation, is formed at once in its lowest or ground state (Fig. 13-11). On this basis it is a simple matter to explain the origin of the observed gamma ray by assuming that the emanation nucleus is not formed in the ground state by the emission of an alpha ray of the lower energy group, but that it is formed in an excited state, from which it passes to the ground state by emitting a gamma ray of energy 4.80 − 4.61 = 0.19 meV. Figures such as 13-11 are known as *decay schemes* for alpha-ray emission. Similarly when thorium C decays to thorium C″ five groups of alpha particles are

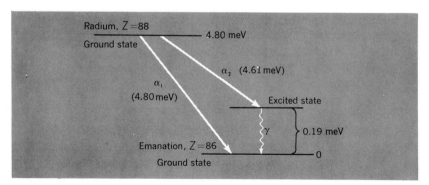

Fig. 13-11. Decay scheme for radium. Radium is transformed to emanation by emission of an alpha particle. Two groups of slightly different energy are present. The less energetic alpha emission is followed by gamma emission.

observed, and the existence of four excited states of thorium C″ above the ground state is inferred.

13-11. Beta Decay; The Neutrino

In beta decay a radioactive nucleus can gain or lose one unit of electric charge without changing the number of nucleons (the mass number). For a number of years the only known beta-emitters were the naturally radioactive substances which decayed by emission of a negative electron ($_-e^0$). The nuclear charge Z would then increase to $Z + 1$. However, many unstable (§15-2) atoms are now known to decay by positron ($_+e^0$) emission and the nuclear charge Z is changed to $Z - 1$. Still another method of beta decay is by *electron capture*. Instead of emitting a positron the unstable nucleus may capture an orbital electron. This would most probably be an innermost or K electron. If it captures an electron from the K shell of the atom this is called K *capture*. Capture of a negative electron results in the same change of nuclear charge Z as the expulsion of a positive electron. Since there is no emitted particle the decay must be detected by some other method.

When the nucleus of an atom captures a K electron a vacancy is created in the K shell. If this vacancy is filled by an L electron the transition produces the first line of the K series of characteristic x-rays of the newly formed element. Filling of the K vacancy produces another vacancy to be filled and another line in the series of characteristic x-rays. Such characteristic x-rays have been detected and indicate the occurrence of K capture. For example K-electron capture in cadmium ($_{48}Cd^{107}$) to form silver ($_{47}Ag^{107}$) was confirmed when Pool, Edwards, and Blake in 1945 detected the K lines of silver emitted in the process. Although usually not so frequent a mode of radioactive decay as the direct-emission process, it is still an important mode of decay.

Among radioactive substances there are more beta-ray emitters of all kinds than there are alpha-ray emitters. In contrast with alpha-ray emission, beta rays from a beta emitter have a wide distribution of energies. The beta rays from most naturally radioactive substances have maximum energies of less than 3 meV, and for a given substance the beta rays are found to have a continuous distribution of energies from the maximum or *end-point energy* down to nearly zero. Because of the small mass of the electron, beta rays have maximum speeds much higher than alpha rays of the same energy, and a 3-meV beta ray would have a speed 99/100 that of light. Beta rays frequently travel distances of as much as 1 to 10 meters in air though they may be stopped by a few millimeters of thickness of aluminum. The maximum energy of a group of beta rays may be indicated approximately by stating the maximum thickness of aluminum that can be penetrated.

ENERGY SPECTRUM; BETA-RAY SPECTROMETER

A more accurate method of measuring particular beta-ray energies than by absorption in aluminum is by means of a magnetic spectrometer especially designed for that purpose (Fig. 13-12). In this way the whole energy-distribution curve (*energy spectrum*) may be obtained. The paths of beta rays from the sample S are bent by means of a magnetic field so that they focus on a collector C. The magnetic field is produced by an electric current in a coil surrounding the case. Because the rays start off at an angle with the magnetic field they are in general deflected so as to follow spiral paths making one complete turn before they reach the collector. Suitable screens (baffles) A and B are so located that only rays of a particular speed can reach the collector. As the magnetic field is varied, groups with different momenta will be collected, thus permitting measurements of numbers of rays having different speeds. When these numbers are plotted a curve is obtained representing the distribution of speeds. More commonly the distribution of energies is plotted. A typical energy-distribution curve is shown

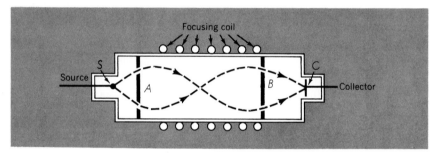

Fig. 13-12.   Beta-ray spectrometer. Beta rays of only a particular energy from the radioactive sample S are focused on the collector electrode and can reach it.

in Fig. 13-13, where it is seen that most rays have energies considerably below the maximum.

THE NEUTRINO

The continuous distribution of beta-ray energies presented a problem. It had seemed reasonable to expect that beta particles would always be expelled from a given type of radioactive nucleus with a fixed amount of energy just as alpha particles are. That a beta ray could actually have any amount of energy for a particular transformation was extremely puzzling. If the end-point energy represented the transition of the parent nucleus to the ground state of the daughter nucleus, what happened to the rest of the energy when the transition to the ground state occurred with lesser beta-ray energies?

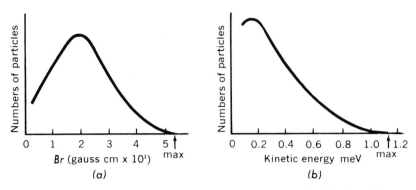

Fig. 13-13.   a, Momentum distribution of beta rays from radium E, plotted in terms of Br; b, energy spectrum for the same rays.

To avoid violation of the law of conservation of energy it was necessary to assume that the missing energy went somewhere. There was also a discrepancy in the angular momentum of the nucleus before and after beta emission. The beta particle being an electron must carry away a spin momentum $\hbar/2$ but the nucleus was usually found to have lost an amount $\hbar$ or 0. This was an intolerable dilemma and recourse was had to a "mysterious stranger," a method not without precedent in human as well as scientific affairs.

The possibility of the existence of a tiny neutral particle or *neutrino* was first suggested by Pauli and it was woven into a complete theory of beta decay by Fermi in 1934. To be successful the Fermi theory not only had to uphold the conservation of mass, charge, linear momentum, angular momentum, and energy but it had to account for the shape of the energy-distribution curve (energy spectrum), and it had to properly relate end-point energies, decay constants, and average energies. The success of the theory is only one of the great achievements of Fermi which put him in the first rank of scientists both as an experimentalist and as a theorist.

Since the radioactive nucleus undergoing beta decay suffers no change in charge other than that due to the loss of the beta particle, the charge of the neutrino was assumed to be zero. Since the nucleus suffers no appreciable loss in mass other than that due to the loss of the beta particle, the rest mass of the neutrino was assumed to be either zero or extremely small and experiments to measure the rest mass of the neutrino have not succeeded in detecting appreciable mass. In order to have conservation of angular momentum the neutrino must be assumed to have a spin of $\hbar/2$. It must also have the capacity to carry away energy and linear momentum. If its rest mass is actually zero, it must travel with the speed of light. With these characteristics (summarized below) the dilemmas of beta decay can be completely resolved.

Neutrino
_____

electric charge $= 0$
rest mass $= 0$
intrinsic spin $= \hbar/2$
linear momentum $= p$
relativistic energy $= pc$
speed $= c$

DETECTION OF NEUTRINO

For some time the existence of the neutrino was in doubt. Its interactions with matter are so feeble as to make it an almost indetectable quantity. According to one estimate something like 10^{14} neutrinos from the sun pass through each of us every second and few of them hit anything or are absorbed. In fact most of them pass completely through the earth.

The theorists had felt sure that it existed, but the experimentalists could not find it. Various attempts were made to detect the neutrino by such means as studying the recoil of the nucleus at the moment of beta emission. If the angle between the beta-ray path and the direction of recoil of the nucleus could be determined, together with the respective momenta, the angle of emission of the neutrino could be determined. Such experiments were always more or less inconclusive.

However, the efforts continued and in 1956 a research team consisting of Cowan, Reines, Harrison, Kruse, and McGuire, working at the Los Alamos laboratory, allowed an intense beam of neutrons from a nuclear reactor to fall upon a large tank containing cadmium chloride $CdCl_2$ and water. The tank was surrounded by a large number of photomultiplier tubes (Fig. 13-14). A proton absorbs a neutrino and decays by positron emission to become a neutron. The neutron, after a measurable time delay, encounters a cadmium nucleus and is captured, after which a number of gamma rays are emitted in cascade and may be detected by one of the photomultiplier tubes. Meanwhile the positive electron has combined with a negative electron (annihilation) to produce two gamma rays, which also can be detected by photomultiplier tubes. The reactions involved are represented as follows:

$$_1H^1 + \bar{\nu} \rightarrow {}_0n^1 + {}_{+1}e^0$$

$$_{+}e^0 + {}_{-}e^0 = 2\gamma$$

$$Cd^{113} + {}_0n^1 \rightarrow Cd^{114} + \gamma$$

where $\bar{\nu}$ is the symbol for the *antineutrino* (which we now know it to be), $_0n^1$ is the symbol for the neutron, γ represents a gamma ray, and e^0 is the electron. The detection of the almost simultaneous gamma rays from these two events even though at a rate of only a few per hour, confirmed the occurrences of the processes involved and the existence of the neutrino

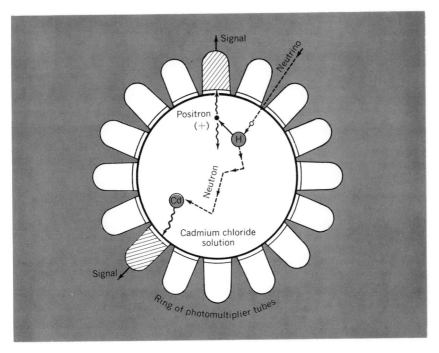

Fig. 13-14. Experimental detection of the neutrino (see text).

(actually the antineutrino). More recently similar experiments have been carried on at other laboratories.

13-12. Energy Relations in Beta Decay

In order that mass-energy be conserved in beta decay the mass-energy of the product nucleus plus the mass-energy of the emitted particles (including kinetic energy) must equal the mass-energy of the parent nucleus. Since in alpha decay there is no other particle emitted the alpha particle and the product nucleus must move in opposite directions with momenta of equal magnitude, and because of the large mass of the alpha particle the recoil nucleus may carry off considerable energy. But in beta decay the beta particle can be emitted at any angle with the recoil track of the product nucleus so long as the neutrino is emitted with proper energy and momentum to conserve both quantities. And because of the small mass of the beta particle the energy of recoil of the product nucleus can be neglected for most purposes. This means that the vector sum of the momenta of the beta particle, the neutrino, and the product nucleus must equal zero and the neutrino must carry off the difference between the end-point energy for the particular reaction and the actual energy of the electron.

Since an electron cannot exist as such in the nucleus it must be "created" at the time of emission just as a gamma-ray photon is "created" at the time it is emitted. If the decay is by electron ($_-e^0$) emission a neutron becomes a proton and an antineutrino (§17-6) is also emitted.

$$n \rightarrow p + {}_-e^0 + \nu \qquad\qquad [13\text{--}17]$$

If the decay is by positron ($_+e^0$) emission a proton becomes a neutron and a neutrino is also emitted.

$$p \rightarrow n + {}_+e^0 + \nu \qquad\qquad [13\text{--}18]$$

The neutron decay [13–17] can occur in free space because the mass of the neutron is greater than the mass of the proton. The decay of the proton [13–18] can only occur for a bound proton inside a nucleus since the mass on the left-hand side of the reaction is less than on the right-hand side and the reaction by itself is energetically impossible.

Beta decay by positron emission usually occurs when the radioactive nucleus is positive with respect to its nearest *isobar*. An isobar is any nucleus having the same mass number A but a different charge Z. Beta decay by electron emission will usually occur when the radioactive nucleus is negative with respect to its nearest isobar. Some radioactive nuclei have more than one neighboring isobar and may decay either way. For instance Cu^{64} may decay by electron emission to Zn^{64} or by positron emission to Ni^{64}.

DECAY SCHEMES

Just as the study of alpha-ray emission furnishes information about the nuclear energy levels of alpha-ray emitters, so also beta-ray maximum energies give similar information about the energy levels of beta-emitting nuclei. Sometimes a particular isotope which emits beta rays may emit more than one group of beta rays. Each group then has its distinctive end-point or maximum energy, and in each group the energies are distributed from zero to the maximum. In Fig. 13-15 the decay scheme is given for a

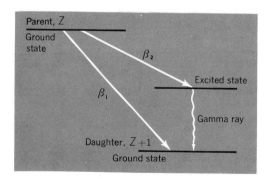

Fig. 13-15. Decay scheme for a nuclide of atomic number Z which emits two groups of beta rays.

nuclide of atomic number Z which emits two groups of beta rays. The daughter nucleus will then have an atomic number $Z + 1$. The rays of one group β_1 carry off enough energy to leave the daughter atom in the ground state. The rays of group β_2 do not carry off so much energy and leave the daughter atom in an excited state, from which it proceeds to the ground state by gamma-ray emission.

13-13. Internal-Conversion Electrons

A somewhat different process by which electrons may be emitted by a radioactive atom is the production of what are called internal-conversion electrons. It was suspected for some time that, in beta-ray emission from a radioactive substance, not all the electrons come from the nucleus, and finally it became apparent that certain electrons come from the outer electronic structure of the atom. These are easily distinguished from ordinary beta rays, since all of any one group have the same fixed amount of energy and, instead of giving a continuous energy spectrum, they give a "line" superposed on the customary continuous distribution.

The sharply defined energies of these conversion electrons indicates that they are associated with gamma-ray emission from the nucleus. At first it was thought that this was a kind of internal photoelectric effect in which a gamma ray from the nucleus ejected one of the atomic electrons surrounding the nucleus. Quantum considerations have shown that this is a highly improbable event, and it is more probable that transfer of energy to the electron takes place in a direct interaction of the nucleus and one of the surrounding electrons, occurring while the electron is very near the nucleus or perhaps even momentarily inside it. Such emission by internal conversion takes place without change of nuclear charge, and the study of conversion electrons and their energies gives additional information of value concerning the nucleus.

13-14. Instruments for Detecting High-Energy Rays

The methods used to detect various types of penetrating rays whether they originate from radioactive substances, nuclear reactors, particle accelerators or the rays we call *cosmic rays* which continually bombard the earth from outer space, are essentially the same. The most common types of high-speed ionizing particles, or rays, that can be detected are electrons (beta rays), positrons, protons, alpha rays, x-rays, gamma rays, deuterons and mesons (§17-3). Whereas any pronounced characteristic of a particular type of ray may serve to permit its detection, the most useful properties are the capacity to produce ions, the capacity to produce *scintillations* or flashes of light, and the ability to produce tracks in special types of photographic emulsions called *nuclear emulsions*.

One of the earliest detectors of radioactivity was a simple electroscope. If the electroscope was charged the rate of collapse of the leaves would be proportional to the number of ions formed per second by a sample of radioactive substance and, consequently, this was a measure of the activity of the sample. Before the advent of rockets delicate and sensitive electroscopes were devised so that they could be carried to high altitudes by small balloons to measure cosmic rays.

The most common instruments in use today are the Wilson cloud chamber, the bubble chamber, nuclear emulsions, the Geiger-Müller (G-M) tube, the semiconductor detector, scintillation detectors, the Čerenkov detector, the spark chamber, and the ionization chamber. Ionization chambers and electroscopes, despite their utility for many purposes, do not enable individual rays to be detected since they give average effects of a considerable number of rays. The other methods enable single events to be studied or at least counted. The detection of non-ionizing rays such as neutrons and neutrinos requires special methods (§16-2 and §13-11). The Čerenkov detector is explained in §17-5.

13-15. Cloud Chambers and Bubble Chambers

The *cloud chamber* was invented by C. T. R. Wilson in Cambridge, England in 1907 under the stimulus of J. J. Thomson. A common type of cloud chamber consists of an enclosed volume of air or gas saturated with water vapor and arranged so that by means of a piston or bellows or other method the pressure may be suddenly reduced, producing an adiabatic expansion of the air or gas. This cools the water vapor which then tends to condense in the form of tiny droplets. Such condensation, as is well known, tends to occur about dust particles and gas ions. If dust has been carefully excluded from the cloud chamber the expansion produces a supersaturated vapor and the ions formed by the passage of a high-speed particle will then act as centers of condensation about which droplets will form showing clearly the path of the particle. A piston type of cloud chamber suitable for use in the vertical position to study cosmic rays more readily is represented in Fig. 13-16.

Different kinds of particles passing through the cloud chamber may often be distinguished by the type of track produced if their energies are not too high. Because of its small size a high-speed electron passing through a gas or vapor may make no more than a few hundred ionizing collisions per centimeter. Consequently the track is a long and thin one. A high-speed proton or alpha particle, on the other hand, usually makes many more ionizing collisions per centimeter and forms a shorter, heavier cloud track (Fig. 13-17). To illustrate the great power and versatility of the cloud

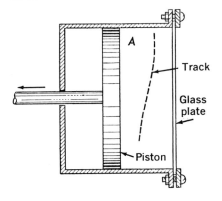

Fig. 13-16. Piston-type cloud chamber. When piston is moved rapidly to the left an expansion is produced in region A, where cloud tracks then form on ions and may be observed directly or photographed.

Fig. 13-17. Typical cloud-chamber tracks bent by a magnetic field, direction of which is indicated at *H*. Short heavy track is the kind left by an alpha particle or a proton; the thin tracks are of the kind left by electrons of different energy.

chamber some of the leading types of phenomena observed by means of it are listed.

    Ranges of rays
    Absorption of rays by various substances
    Ionization densities of tracks
    Collision phenomena
    Discovery of new particles
    Transmutations
    Pair production
    Fission products
    Decay processes
    Cosmic-ray particles
    Cosmic-ray showers

Cloud chambers are particularly valuable in studying collisions of nuclear particles. Since the paths before and after collision can be observed, the angles can be measured, and the momenta and energies studied.

The cloud chamber is often used in a magnetic field of known intensity to enable the direction of curvature of the path of a charged particle to be determined and consequently the sign of the charge. Measurement of the amount of curvature then enables the momentum to be calculated since the momentum $p = mv = qBr$ (Eq. 2-27). The quantity Br is sometimes called the *magnetic rigidity*.

Cloud chambers are often combined with G-M tubes (§13-17) for many purposes. The tubes may be arranged to select rays to be observed under various conditions, or to detect the results of a particular type of nuclear event, or to control the time of expansion of the cloud chamber so that only desired events will be observed and useless expansions are avoided.

The cloud chamber can only remain in the sensitive state for perhaps a tenth of a second after expansion and then if any ions or tracks occur these ions must be removed by an applied electric field before another expansion can detect another event. When studying cosmic rays in 1933 Blackett and Occhialini were the first to put a cloud chamber between two G-M tubes connected electrically, so that a switch would be operated only when an ionizing ray passed through both tubes and the cloud chamber between them. Closing the switch then produced an expansion. Thus a cosmic ray would in effect notify the apparatus when it was time to take its own picture, or rather the picture of its own track.

Recently a simplified type of cloud chamber called the *diffusion cloud chamber* requiring little apparatus has been developed and is widely used for demonstrations and qualitative studies. In its simplest form it consists of a glass jar with some liquid that vaporizes readily when it is set on a piece of "dry ice" or is otherwise cooled so that there is a strong temperature gradient from the surface of the liquid upward. When the warmer vapor descends it becomes cooled and supersaturated and then forms a continuously sensitive region in which tracks may be observed with the aid of good illumination.

In 1952 D. A. Glaser invented the *bubble chamber*. It is almost the exact inverse of a cloud chamber. Instead of droplets of liquid forming in a vapor region, bubbles of vapor form in a liquid. Instead of a supersaturated vapor in the cloud chamber the liquid must be in a *superheated* state. Various liquids have been tried such as liquid propane and liquid hydrogen. The liquid is cooled to a few degrees above its boiling point and is held in the liquid state by keeping the pressure higher than normal. The liquid then becomes superheated at the moment when the pressure is suddenly reduced and bubbles can readily form about any centers of agitation. An ionizing particle passing through the liquid leaves a trail of ions behind it and these acting as centers form a track of bubbles. Such bubble tracks can be readily photographed and studied (Fig. 13-18). Neutrons (and neutrinos) do not leave visible tracks in a cloud chamber or bubble chamber. But if a neutron hits a nucleus head-on it may produce a "knock-on" particle that will leave a track.

There are several definite advantages of bubble chambers compared to cloud chambers. In a cloud chamber the highest energy particles are likely to pass through the contained gas without hitting anything. If tracks form they are likely not to be completed and the particle stopped in the chamber. To have the same stopping power as the far denser liquid in a bubble chamber a cloud chamber would have to be unreasonably large. This is particularly evident now that bubble chambers have been made of several cubic feet capacity.

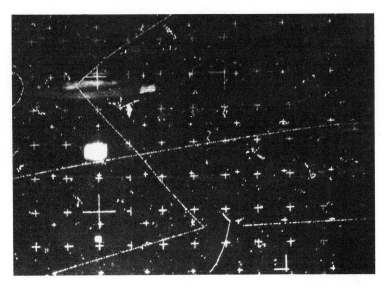

Fig. 13-18. Interesting bubble chamber tracks photographed by D. A. Glaser, inventor of bubble chamber. These tracks were formed in bubble-chamber 12″ diam. containing nearly $250,000 of liquid xenon. High density of xenon makes mean free paths for various events relatively short compared to liquid hydrogen. In this photo a pi meson (1.1 beV energy) enters from right and hits a proton in a xenon nucleus, $\pi + p = \Lambda^0 + K^0$. Neither of these particles leaves a visible track but the lambda (Λ^0) particle decays to a negative pi meson and a proton (small "V tracks") followed by the decay of the K^0 to a pi meson pair (large "V tracks"). One of the pi mesons makes a close encounter with a nucleus and is deflected 90°. These tracks were identified by the known properties of the particles (Chap. 17). Crosses are scale marks.

13-16. Nuclear Emulsions

A photographic emulsion particularly designed to detect nuclear particles is called a nuclear emulsion. It is made thicker than normal and when ionizing rays hit a grain of silver bromide in the emulsion it becomes "exposed" and forms a grain of silver upon development. Ionizing particles lose energy gradually and leave *tracks* before coming to rest. In a sense a nuclear emulsion forms a kind of "frozen cloud chamber." Many types of charged particles such as beta rays, proton rays, alpha rays and some of the new particles (Chap. 17) can thus be detected. However, it must be remembered that because of the density of the emulsions the tracks are relatively short, at best a few millimeters in length and they must be studied under a microscope or after enlargement (Fig. 13-19). Many important studies of cosmic rays and nuclear particles have been made with the aid of nuclear emulsions.

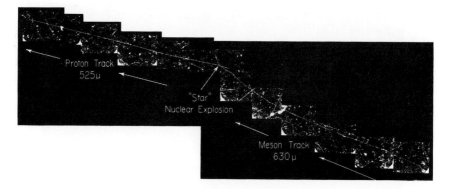

Figure 13.19.   Emulsion tracks of nuclear particles showing how the whole picture is built up of separate microphotos. The total length of tracks in the emulsion is less than 1.2 mm ($1\mu = 1$ micron $= 10^{-3}$ mm). (Courtesy, Kodak Research Laboratories and Department of Physics, University of Rochester.)

13-17. Gas-Filled Detectors

THE GEIGER-MÜLLER TUBE

Detectors which depend upon the electric pulse of current produced when ions are formed between two electrodes maintained at a sufficient potential difference are sometimes called *gas-filled detectors*. Chief of these are the Geiger-Müller (G-M) tube, the proportional counter and the ionization chamber. The Geiger-Müller tube in its simplest form consists of a metal cylinder, frequently enclosed in glass, with a fine tungsten wire stretched along the axis of the cylinder (Fig. 13-20). The tube contains a little gas at a few centimeters of mercury pressure. A potential difference of several hundred to a thousand volts is applied between the wire and the cylinder with the wire made positive. When a single ionizing ray passes through the glass or metal wall into the inside of the cylinder it needs only to produce a few gas ions in order to start a momentary discharge between cylinder and wire. This produces an electric pulse in the external circuit which is led to an amplifier and from there to more or less complicated electronic counting and recording devices.

As the potential difference between electrodes of a G-M tube is increased a point is reached where ionizing rays passing through the tube produce detectable pulses of current. When the voltage is sufficiently high such as V_2 (Fig. 13-21), the tube operates on a plateau along which for a considerable change in applied voltage the detectable pulses are essentially of the same magnitude independent of the number of ions formed in the tube by the ionizing ray. This is the normal operating region of a G-M tube and if these normal voltages are exceeded the current rises rapidly as at CD

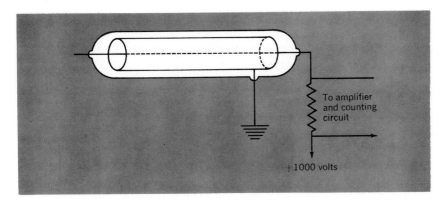

Fig. 13-20.   Geiger-Müller (G-M) tube, for detecting and counting rays capable of
penetrating to region between cylinder and central wire.

on the curve. The tube may then go into a continuous discharge and
be ruined.

To prevent the discharge in the G-M tube from spreading along the
wire and forming a glow in the normal operating range some method of
quenching the discharge is required. In the earlier type of air-filled tubes a
high resistance in series with the tube produced a voltage drop, when the
discharge occurred, sufficient to reduce the voltage on the tube below the
critical value to sustain the discharge. However, the common type of G-M
tube today is called a *self-quenching tube*. It may be filled with argon gas,
to which 10 per cent of alcohol or of some other organic vapor is added, or
it could contain helium to which some isobutane has been added. The
organic molecules absorb the radiation which tends to spread the discharge,
and they may become dissociated by it, but in the process the discharge is

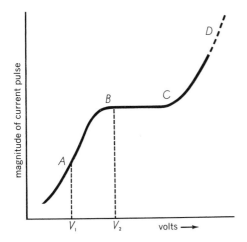

Fig. 13-21. The current voltage
characteristics of a G-M type tube.
B to C represents the Geiger-Müller
"plateau." A to B represents the
"proportional" region (see text).

automatically quenched. Elaborate circuits have been devised for rapid quenching so that the counting rate of the tube can be increased, but quenching and deionization in conventional counter tubes usually require as much as 100 microseconds.

A useful type of G-M tube is the end-window counter (Fig. 13-22). Instead of the wire extending through the cylinder it terminates in a point, the end of the cylinder consisting of a thin diaphragm which acts as a window for the rays and may even be thin enough to let alpha particles enter.

The G-M tube with a suitable circuit for registering counts is an extremely versatile instrument and serves many purposes, particularly when a large number of tubes is involved.

Two G-M tubes are said to be connected in *coincidence* when the circuit is so arranged that there is no response unless the ray goes through both tubes. Two tubes arranged in coincidence as in Fig. 13-23, may serve to form what is called a *cosmic-ray telescope*. A ray passing through one tube only is not counted. Incident rays coming within the angle θ pass through both tubes and are counted. With this kind of device it has been possible to scan the sky to try to find directions of greater or lesser intensity.

Another important method of connecting tubes is called *anticoincidence*. For instance, two tubes may be connected in such a way that counts are registered only when a cosmic ray goes through one tube or the other but not through both. The circuit is so arranged that when a cosmic ray goes through two tubes in anticoincidence the separate pulses cancel and no count is registered. An example is shown in Fig. 13-24, where the method of counting radioactive rays from a feeble source is illustrated.

If an attempt were made to count the radioactive rays from a feeble source with a single G-M tube the counts due to cosmic rays would also be registered. It would then be next to impossible to separate the counts produced by the feeble radioactive source from the even larger background of cosmic rays. In the figure a ring of overlapping G-M tubes surrounds the weak radioactive source, near which are placed one or more other counting tubes. The surrounding ring of guard tubes is connected in anticoincidence with the counting tubes that are near the source. A cosmic ray passing

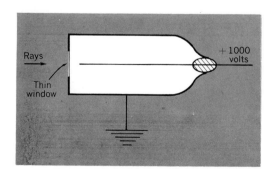

Fig. 13-22. End-on or end-window type of G-M tube with thin window useful for counting less penetrating rays such as beta and even alpha particles.

through one of the counting tubes would not be counted because it would first have to pass through one of the anticoincident guard tubes. Thus the only rays to which the counting tubes would respond would be those from the weakly radioactive source that pass only through a counting tube. This is the method used in carbon dating of archaeological specimens (§13-22).

PROPORTIONAL COUNTER

When a tube of the G-M type is designed to operate at some voltage such as V_1 in the AB region (Fig. 13-21) pulses are formed the intensities of which are proportional to the number of ions formed by the ionizing ray. If these pulses are viewed on an oscilloscope screen the pulse heights give a measure of the energies of the rays. This information is often of critical importance in the study of nuclear disintegrations, and various ways of discriminating between pulses of different heights and counting pulses of a particular height have been devised. It is a simple matter thus to distinguish between alpha and beta rays since they differ so much in ionizing capacity.

13-18. Ionization Chamber

In an ionization chamber (Fig. 13-25) the rays enter through a thin window and produce ions inside. These ions are attracted to opposite electrodes which are held at a difference of potential by means of a battery or other source of emf and they are collected directly by the electrodes without

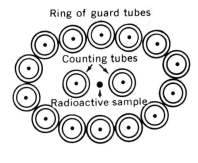

Fig. 13-23. Two G-M tubes connected in coincidence form a directional detector or "telescope." Any ray falling within the angle θ will pass through both G-M tubes and be recorded.

Fig. 13-24. Simplified arrangement of G-M tubes for counting rays from a weak source. Guard tubes are connected in anticoincidence, so that rays from outside passing through a guard tube are not counted.

any actual discharge taking place. One of the electrodes may be a metal lining of the chamber. A very sensitive electrometer tube or other device is used to determine the ion current. Such ionization chambers serve many purposes in detecting ionizing rays and are often used to measure cosmic-ray intensities (Chap. 17).

13-19. Spark Chamber

An increasingly popular type of detector which can be made to cover large areas is the *spark chamber*. A series of metal plates are alternately held at high positive and negative potentials with a gas at suitable pressure between the oppositely charged plates. An ionizing ray passing through the chamber leaves a string of ions behind it and causes a momentary series of sparks to form along the path of the ray. These tracks may be readily photographed as represented in Fig. 13-26.

13-20. Scintillation Counters

The use of a fluorescent screen to detect x-rays and the scintillations produced by alpha rays goes back to the earliest days of such study, but no great improvement was made in such detectors for many years. Since 1947, however, very efficient types of scintillation counters have been developed. For example a large crystal of one of several substances such as anthracene or naphthalene has been found to give scintillations. Not all scintillators

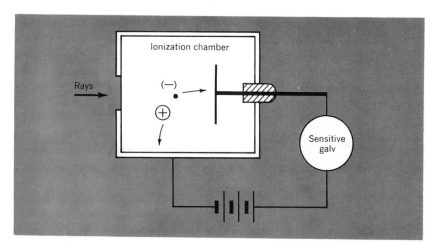

Fig. 13-25.   Ionization chamber. When rays form ions in chamber, a current to the electrodes can be detected.

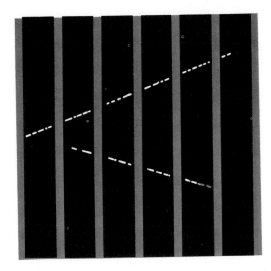

Fig. 13-26. Spark chamber. An ionizing ray causes spark to occur between oppositely charged metal plates.

are crystalline, and liquid scintillators are often used. One chief advantage is the great stopping power of solids and liquids and their high speed.

One type of scintillation counter is illustrated in Fig. 13-27. A suitable crystal is fitted closely to the end of a photomultiplier tube and shielded from all stray light. When an incident ray enters the phosphor and produces a tiny "flash" of light or scintillation some of the photons of this flash fall on the photosensitive coating on the inside surface at the end of the photomultiplier tube. They in turn eject one or more photoelectrons. The electrons are pulled by a potential of perhaps 100 volts to the first electrode (dynode) where a number of secondaries for each primary electron are emitted; these in turn are pulled to the next dynode where the process is

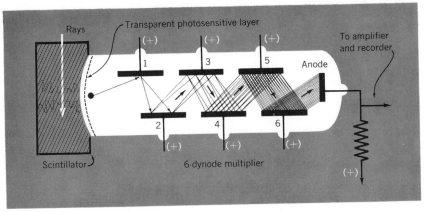

Fig. 13-27. Scintillation counter, consisting of scintillator close-coupled to transparent photosensitive surface of photomultiplier tube.

repeated thereby increasing the magnitude of the pulse. After this process is repeated at as many as 10 or 12 dynodes, each of which amplifies the pulse by secondary electron emission, the signal finally emerges at the anode amplified a million or more times where it may be further amplified and counted.

The entire process may take only a fraction of a microsecond, so that very high counting rates may be attained. Such a counter is of special value in counting gamma rays. Because of the high penetration of gamma rays the probability of ionizing a gas molecule in a G-M tube is very small; the efficiency for gamma rays is usually less than 1 per cent whereas in a solid or liquid phosphor it is much greater and may be 20 per cent or more.

13-21. Other Detectors: Crystal, Junction and Barrier Types

The development of newer, simpler and more useful types of detectors goes on and on. Non-metallic crystals such as diamond or silicon have been placed between electrodes held at a fairly high potential, like a kind of "solid ionization chamber." Since diamond is an insulator the valence electrons occupy filled bands separated widely from the conduction band. If an ionizing ray leaves a trail of ions behind and the liberated electrons are raised to the conduction band, these form mobile carriers leaving "holes" behind, both of which move to one or other of the electrodes forming a pulse of electric current which can be measured. Such crystals though not very efficient can perform fast counting, their recovery times being as short as a few microseconds.

More efficient modifications of the crystal counter have supplanted the simpler types and these may have recovery times as short as a few nanoseconds (1 nanosecond = 10^{-9} sec). Two of these are semiconductor detectors. In one type the junction between n-type and p-type layers (§12-4) plays the basic role. For instance in the junction rectifier of Fig. 12-8 the depletion region, that is the region near the interface from which charges have been removed, is sensitive to ionizing rays. If an ionizing ray penetrates the region and leaves a string of mobile charges by raising electrons across the relatively small forbidden gap of a semiconductor into the conductor band, then a measurable pulse of current will result.

In the surface barrier detector a charge at the surface of a semiconductor may form a depletion layer beneath the surface which can be equally sensitive and these later types of detectors have become increasingly useful.

13-22. Carbon Dating

The method described in §13-17 (and Fig. 13-24) for counting weak radiation is applied in measuring the weak radiation from historic and prehistoric organic remains. When radioactive carbon is measured it is called carbon dating. It is well known now that living objects absorb from their surroundings, and from foods, a certain number of carbon 14 atoms which exist in small numbers in the air. Carbon 14 is a rare isotope of ordinary carbon produced in the air by the indirect action of cosmic rays. In the upper air neutrons are liberated in considerable numbers from the nuclei of air molecules. If one of these is captured by the nucleus of a nitrogen 14 atom a proton is ejected, leaving carbon 14, as follows:

$$_7N^{14} + _0n^1 \rightarrow _6C^{14} + _1H^1 \qquad [13\text{--}19]$$

Carbon 14 is a beta-ray emitter, decaying to nitrogen 14.

$$_6C^{14} \rightarrow _7N^{14} + _{-1}e^0 \qquad [13\text{--}20]$$

with a half-life of 5600 years.

If, for instance, a piece of organic material from archaeological remains of 1000 or more years ago is studied, it is found still to possess some radio-activity due to carbon 14. The amount of this radioactivity per gram gives a means of measuring the time that has elapsed since the object was part of a living organism. When the organism died it stopped absorbing carbon 14. Such measurements are the most accurate method of dating archaeo-logical specimens, and the error may be as little as a few decades for speci-mens that are not too old. Unfortunately the increasingly wide dispersal of radioactive material from atomic explosions threatens to provide a back-ground of radioactivity which will in time cover up the effects of carbon 14 or other similar elements.

Problems

1. The half-life of Al^{28} is 2.30 minutes and the half-life of Na^{24} is 15.0 hours. If a source initially contains 1000 times as many aluminum as sodium atoms, what will be the ratio of the number of aluminum to sodium atoms remaining after 10 minutes? After 20 minutes?

2. What is the probability that 10 emanation (radon) atoms would last 5.5 days without any one of them decaying? (Average or mean life is the time for which the probability of decay is $\frac{1}{2}$ and equals half-life divided by 0.693.)

3. If the decay constant of a radioactive substance is 2×10^{-6} sec^{-1}, what is the half-life and what is the average life?

4. The half-lives of emanation and radium are 3.8 days and 1600 years, respectively. Find their decay constants and their average lives.

5. If 3.7×10^{10} alpha particles are emitted per second per gram of radium ($_{88}R^{226}$), compute the half-life of radium in years.

6. The decay constant for $_{82}Pb^{210}$ is 1.00×10^{-9} sec^{-1}. How long will it take $\frac{2}{3}$ of a given large number of atoms to disintegrate?

7. The half-life of emanation is 3.8 days. After how many days will only $\frac{1}{16}$ of the original atoms remain? What fraction of a given large number of emanation atoms will disintegrate in one day?

8. Find the ratio of numbers of emanation atoms to radium atoms when they are in equilibrium.

*9. What volume of helium gas in cm^3 at 76 cm mercury pressure and 0 °C could be produced by 1 gram of uranium ($_{92}U^{238}$) during a period of 3 billion years? (Since the half-lives of all daughter products are relatively short the alpha particles of all decay products may be counted.)

10. An alpha particle is ejected from a free emanation ($_{86}Em^{222}$) atom with a velocity of 10^8 cm/sec. What is the velocity of the recoil of the resultant atom?

11. If one-millionth of a gram-atomic weight of radium is found to be in equilibrium with its products emanation ($_{86}Em^{222}$) and polonium ($_{84}Po^{218}$), find the number of atoms of each present.

12. If 0.338 microgram of radium is in equilibrium with 1 gram of uranium ($_{92}U^{238}$), compute the half-life of the uranium from the known half-life of radium.

13. How long will it take for a sample of $_{84}Po^{210}$ (polonium) of half-life 140 days to decay to $\frac{1}{10}$ its original strength?

14. How much thickness of lead is required to reduce the intensity of gamma rays from thorium C to $\frac{1}{10}$ if the linear absorption coefficient is $\mu = 0.46$ cm^{-1}?

15. Gamma rays from RaB are passed through lead. If the linear absorption coefficient for these rays is 1.5 cm^{-1}, by what per cent will the intensity be reduced by a thickness of 1 cm?

16. A radioactive compound emits beta and gamma rays. It is desired to count gamma-ray photons. What thickness of aluminum of linear absorption coefficient 12 cm^{-1} for beta rays will reduce the beta-ray count to 1 in 100?

17. If the mass of a radium atom is 226.1031 amu, what is the kinetic energy of the alpha ray emitted if the mass of the product atom of emanation (radon) is 222.0940 amu and the mass of a helium atom is 4.003873?

*18. Suppose a counter which is 40 per cent efficient in counting beta rays subtends a solid angle of 0.2 steradians around a radioactive sample containing $_{90}Th^{234}$ of half-life equal to 24 days. If the counter registers 2 counts per second, how many thorium atoms are present in the sample at that time?

19. An alpha particle travels 5 cm in an ionization chamber and forms on the average 30,000 ion pairs per cm. If all the ions of one sign are collected at an electrode of 5 micromicrofarads ($\mu\mu f$) capacitance, what is the charge in coulombs and what is the change of potential of the electrode?

*20. A free emanation atom $_{86}Em^{222}$ emits an alpha particle of energy 5.6 meV and becomes the daughter atom $_{84}Po^{218}$. Compute the recoil velocity, momentum and kinetic energy of the daughter atom.

Recommended Reading

Kaplan, I., *Nuclear Physics*. Reading, Mass.: Addison-Wesley Publishing Co., Inc., 1955.

Evans, R. D., *The Atomic Nucleus*. New York: McGraw-Hill Book Company, Inc., 1955.

Segré, E. ed., *Experimental Nuclear Physics*, Vol. I. New York: John Wiley & Sons, Inc., 1953.

Price, W. J., *Nuclear Radiation Detection*. New York: McGraw-Hill Book Company, Inc., 1958.

Morrison, P., "The Neutrino." *Scientific American*, Vol. 194, No. 1, p. 58 (1956).

Allen, J. S., *The Neutrino*. Princeton, N. J.: Princeton University Press, 1958.

Early Work and Historical

Rutherford, E., J. Chadwick and C. D. Ellis, *Radiations From Radioactive Substances*. New York: The Macmillan Company, 1930.

Jauncy, G. E. M., "Early Years of Radioactivity," *American Journal of Physics*, 14, 226 (1946).

Nuclear Structure and Nuclear Forces

14-1. The Proton-Neutron Model of the Nucleus

The fundamental problem of nuclear physics is that of investigating the structure of the nucleus, the nature of the particles of which it is composed and the forces that hold the nucleons (nuclear particles) together. The name *nucleon* is given to either a proton or neutron in the nucleus and a *nuclide* is any particular type of nucleus. Some information about the nuclear forces can be obtained from a study of binding energies of the nucleus and from experiments on the interaction of particles, as, for instance, the particles of a proton beam colliding with protons in a solid or liquid target, or the particles of a neutron beam making similar collisions.

When Chadwick discovered the neutron in 1932 (§16-1) the importance of the new discovery was quickly recognized. The new particle appeared to be a fundamental constituent of matter, and Heisenberg suggested that all nuclei can most simply be represented as being composed of neutrons and protons. On this assumption the charge on any nucleus is determined by the number of protons in it, and the mass of the nucleus is determined by the number of both protons and neutrons. Since the number of charges on a nucleus is represented by the atomic number Z, and since A is the mass number of the nucleus, there must then be in any nucleus Z protons and $A - Z$ neutrons. The total number of nucleons is therefore

$$\begin{pmatrix} \text{Number of nucleons} \\ \text{in nucleus} \end{pmatrix} = Z \text{ protons} + (A - Z) \text{ neutrons} \quad [14\text{--}1]$$

The nucleus of a helium atom (an alpha particle) is then composed of 2 protons and 2 neutrons, giving it a charge 2 and a mass number 4. Uranium 238 ($_{92}U^{238}$) would be composed of 92 protons and $238 - 92 = 146$ neutrons.

The advantages of the new scheme were quickly recognized. The mass and charge of the nucleus were readily explained and previous difficulties with the magnitudes of spin and magnetic moment of nuclei were overcome. Indeed it can be said that the *proton-neutron model* of the nucleus is not inconsistent with any known facts. There are, of course, the problems of what protons and neutrons really are, what the forces are within the nucleus, and whether or not the nuclear particles are organized into a system or not organized. There is also the problem of fitting the many new kinds of sub-atomic particles (Chap. 17) into the scheme of things.

Before 1932 the nucleus of an atom was thought to be composed of protons and electrons. The mass of the nucleus was accounted for by assuming it contained a sufficient number of protons. The charge of the nucleus was accounted for by assuming it also contained enough electrons to reduce the net charge to the proper value. The attraction between positive protons and negative electrons was supposed to hold the nucleus together. This *proton-electron model* of the nucleus failed because of many inherent contradictions.

An electron, owing to its intrinsic spin, has a magnetic moment of 1 Bohr magneton, and where there is an odd number of electrons the odd electron should contribute this amount of magnetic moment to the nucleus. Yet the magnetic moments of nuclei are very much less than this, and so the electron as such can hardly be present even though it is often emitted as a beta particle. From the viewpoint of the wave picture, it appeared that for an electron to exist inside the nucleus it should have a wavelength given by the de Broglie formula $\lambda = h/mv$ at least of the order of magnitude of the diameter of the nucleus. To have so short a wavelength, however, the velocity, and consequently the energy, of the electron would have to be so large that it could not be expected to remain inside the nucleus. An even more serious difficulty arose from a consideration of the spins of nuclear particles and of nuclei themselves.

NUCLEAR SPINS

One of the chief characteristics of the common nuclear particles is that they possess angular momentum which apparently results from spin about their own axes. Inside the nucleus the spin of a particle may contribute to the angular momentum (spin) of the nucleus as a whole. For the proton, neutron, and electron, spin is as much an intrinsic property of these particles as charge and mass. It was first ascribed to the electron in order to explain the doublet structure of the alkali metal spectra (§9-1) by means of *spin-orbit interaction*. Later, with instruments of higher resolving power a new feature of the spectra of some elements was discovered and was called *hyperfine structure*. In 1924 Pauli suggested that this might be explained by assuming that the atomic nuclei also possess angular momentum of spin together with an associated magnetic moment.

In the study of molecular spectra the intensities of the lines can be explained by the assumption of nuclear spin. Study of these types of spectra, with the inclusion also of microwave spectroscopy, now furnishes methods of determining the amount of spin that a given type of nucleus possesses. The spin of a nucleus is the resultant of the spins of its component particles, and as it turns out, the spins of protons and neutrons, as well as of electrons, are all represented by the same quantum number $\frac{1}{2}$. The projections of the spins in a preferred direction determined by some field will then be $\pm\frac{1}{2}\hbar$.

One of the most serious objections to the proton-electron model of the nucleus arose over the matter of spins. On that model the total spin sometimes appeared to be half-integral when it should actually come out zero or integral. This occurs with light nuclei of even mass number A and odd atomic number Z. On the proton-neutron model, however, the spin always comes out exactly as it should. For instance, consider the nucleus of beryllium ($_4\text{Be}^9$). Since it has a mass number $A = 9$ and a charge number $Z = 4$, on the proton-electron model it should be composed of 9 protons and 5 electrons. The total number of particles is $9 + 5 = 14$. This is an even number, and the resultant spin should be integral or zero, but the spin is found actually to be odd, 3/2. On the proton-neutron model the nucleus is composed of 4 protons and 5 neutrons, the sum of which is odd, giving as it should half-integral spin or some odd multiple of it depending on how many nucleons are paired. We conclude then that the electron as a separate particle does not exist in the nucleus of an atom.

14-2. The Potential Barrier of the Nucleus

When a positively charged atomic "projectile" is "shot" at a positively charged atomic nucleus it is repelled. The closer the bombarding particle comes, the greater is the repelling force acting upon it. Indeed the early experiments of Rutherford on scattering of alpha particles (§7-1) indicated that the Coulomb inverse square law was obeyed up to something like 10^{-12} cm. The nearest approach that a positively charged atomic projectile can make to the center of the nucleus of an atom, before repulsion turns to attraction and the particle is captured, defines the radius of the nucleus. If the particle passes this point it enters a region of attraction instead of repulsion. It is then "inside the nucleus."

It was suggested by Gamow that, instead of plotting the electric field, the curve representing the potential at different distances from the nucleus could be drawn, and this is called the *potential barrier*. The potential drops very rapidly inside the nucleus and forms a kind of *potential well* into which particles may *fall* if they succeed in passing the barrier. Since barriers are lower for light nuclei those were the first to be surmounted experimentally by positively charged atomic "projectiles."

The potential V at any distance r from a charge Ze is

$$V(\text{volts}) = k \frac{Ze}{r} \qquad [14\text{--}2]$$

where k is 9×10^9 in mks units, r is in meters and e is in coulombs.

The potential energy Vne of a particle of charge ne approaching a nucleus of charge Ze is at any distance r

$$Vne = k \frac{Zne^2}{r} \qquad [14\text{--}2a]$$

When a positively charged particle approaches a charged nucleus with a particular initial kinetic energy it gradually loses kinetic energy and the loss becomes potential energy. The maximum amount of energy required to allow the particle to reach the boundary of the nucleus is the measure of the "top" of the *potential barrier* for that particle, and the approaching particle must possess this much kinetic energy in order to "surmount" the barrier and enter the nucleus.

An idealized form of potential well, called the *rectangular potential well* is shown in Fig. 14-1. The curved line outside the well is the potential barrier

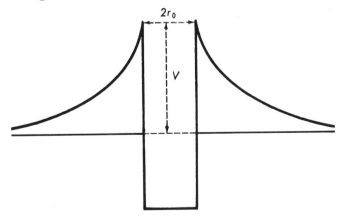

Fig. 14-1. Potential barrier with idealized rectangular well. Diameter of nucleus is $2r_0$ and height of barrier is V volts.

representing Coulomb repulsion. Distance $2r_0$ represents the diameter of the nucleus. The height V is the height of the barrier that must be passed by an incident particle if it is to enter the nucleus. The depth of the potential well is not uniquely determined. For most atoms the height of the barrier V is several million electron volts (meV). This would be the barrier which an approaching proton "sees." Since an alpha particle possesses two charges of electronic magnitude the Coulomb repulsion will be 2 times larger and it will "see" a potential barrier twice as high (Fig. 14-2). On the other hand a neutron with no measurable net charge will see zero barrier as indicated in the same figure.

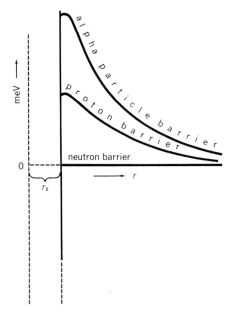

Fig. 14-2. Outside the nucleus the potential barriers for particles of different charge. Inside the nucleus the potential "well."

The type of potential well shown in Fig. 14-1 is an idealized form useful for mathematical purposes. The actual form of the barrier may be more nearly like Fig. 14-3 with sloping sides and a rounded top. The diameter of the nucleus is now not so sharply defined as in the more idealized diagram. The sloping sides of the well indicate a more continuous rather than discontinuous transition from outside to inside.

According to *classical theory* an incident positive particle must have sufficient kinetic energy to surmount the top of the barrier. If it does not possess the required energy it is slowed down to zero speed, and its motion is then reversed. The analogy is sometimes made to a peculiar type of cup on a golf green where the green slopes upward sharply to the cup. A ball lacking sufficient kinetic energy could not go over the top. The application of simple classical theory to the problem of the atomic nucleus, however, failed to explain observed phenomena.

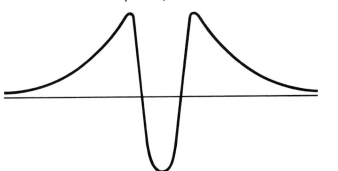

Fig. 14-3.   Modified barrier presumed more nearly to represent the actual barrier.

For example, consider the heaviest natural atom, uranium 238 (U^{238}). Rutherford showed that alpha particles of about 8.6-meV energy from thorium C′ were unable to pass over the top of the potential barrier of a uranium nucleus (U^{238}) and were scattered elastically by the opposing Coulomb field. Therefore the barrier for alpha particles is higher than this. But by classical theory, for an alpha particle in the nucleus to be emitted, it must somehow reach the top of the barrier, then like a ball rolling down hill it should gain energy equal to that required to reach the top of the barrier. However the alpha rays from U^{238} only have energies of 4.2 meV. The dilemma was a baffling one until in 1928 Gamow, and also Gurney and Condon, showed that, by wave-mechanical theory, barrier penetration might occur.

14-3. Theory of Alpha Emission

An explanation was given in Chap. 8 of how, according to wave mechanics, a particle within a barrier may sometimes pass that barrier without surmounting it. If the distance across the barrier is not too large, an appreciable probability always exists that a particle may penetrate the barrier (tunnel effect) and escape. Where classical theory is helpless quantum mechanics enables us to formulate why U^{238} decays by alpha emission so slowly that its half-life is 4.5 billion years. Apparently the barrier is very high compared to the average energy that an alpha particle on the inside of the nucleus can have. Since the barrier is high, perhaps as much as 28 meV, the alpha particle must penetrate the barrier where it is quite wide in order to have energy of only 4.2 meV when it escapes. The probability of passing through this barrier is extremely small, and consequently the half-life is very long. In a very intensely radioactive substance with a short half-life the barrier is either lower or is crossed nearer the top, or both.

With the aid of the idealized rectangular well Gamow determined theoretically the probability of escape of alpha particles, based on the idea that the particles in the nucleus possess random motion and collide incessantly with the barrier. It is assumed that the minimum possible velocity of a particle in the nucleus is such that its de Broglie wavelength h/mv is of the order of magnitude of the radius r of the nucleus. The number of collisions per second is then roughly

$$f = \frac{v}{2r} = \frac{h}{2mr^2} \qquad [14\text{--}3]$$

Since the decay constant is the probability of escape per second, it must therefore be equal to the probability P of escape each time the alpha particle hits the barrier, multiplied by the number of hits per second, or λ, the decay constant, is

$$\lambda = \frac{h}{2mr^2} P \qquad [14\text{--}3a]$$

where P can be computed by wave-mechanical methods and depends on the energy of the particle. All this assumes that an alpha particle before emission has some sort of individual existence in the nucleus, at least for a brief time. What Gamow achieved, after assuming reasonable values for r, was a complicated equation which reduces to the same form as the Geiger-Nuttall rule (Eq. 13–16). Thus the Geiger-Nuttall rule, applying to all the natural alpha emitters, is no longer purely empirical but represents fundamental relations based on wave-mechanical analysis.

NUCLEAR ENERGY LEVELS

In the discussion of alpha-ray fine structure (§13-10) it was pointed out that the various energy groups were believed to represent various energy states of the nucleus. To more nearly complete the representation of the nucleus in terms of a potential well, we must now add energy levels to the well, representing energy levels in the nucleus (Fig. 14-4). The energy of the escaping alpha particle then depends upon the energy level from

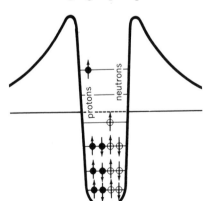

Fig. 14-4. Potential well of nucleus representing energy levels; neutrons in pairs and protons in pairs in lower levels, and one proton in a higher or excitation level. Arrows indicate opposite spins for paired particles.

which it comes in the nucleus. Since alpha rays have sharply defined energies, the indicated energy levels must also be unique and represent sharply defined energy states of the nucleus. Presumably, in a nucleus in the lowest energy state (ground state), the lower energy levels are mostly filled. When a nuclear particle (nucleon) is raised to a higher energy level the nucleus is then in an *excited state*.

14-4. Nuclear Structure

The name *nucleon* for a nuclear particle was adopted after the suggestion by Heisenberg that the forces binding a proton in the nucleus to a neutron in the nucleus might arise from *exchange of charge* such that the proton momentarily becomes a neutron and the neutron momentarily becomes a proton and the two may scarcely be said to lead independent lives. Indeed from one viewpoint the neutron and proton may be thought of as different energy states of the same particle. Experimental evidence to support these views has been obtained from collision experiments between neutrons and protons.

When fast neutrons collide with protons most of the neutrons appear to make a kind of grazing contact in which they are deflected very little but move on with about the same speed. However, in about half the cases the particle moving on is found to be a proton leaving the neutron behind. Since such high-speed particles are difficult to deflect the logical explanation is that in passing each other they exchange charge. That only half the particles exchanged charge for a given angle of deflection has been taken to indicate the presence of a repulsive force between the nucleon cores such that they cannot be "squeezed" much closer together. This would seem to imply that the core of a nucleus may have a fairly constant density of nuclear matter (See Hofstadter's experiments §14-13).

On the other hand experimental evidence points to the fact that there are forces binding two neutrons together of essentially the same amount as those between the proton and the neutron. If some type of *exchange force* binds a neutron to a neutron it is not the *net charge* that is exchanged but something else since the neutron does not have any appreciable net charge.

The lightest nuclide with more than one nucleon is that of heavy hydrogen H^2 (deuterium). The nucleus is composed of 1 proton and 1 neutron, indicating that there is some force acting between a proton and a neutron to bind them together. There is no nuclide consisting of 2 protons. The next stable nucleus is that of the extremely rare *helium 3*, consisting of 2 protons and 1 neutron. Next comes the ordinary helium nucleus which has 2 protons; it also has 2 neutrons, and it is a very stable combination. If the stability and abundance of ordinary helium were taken to indicate a tendency for the nucleons in a nucleus to form such groups it might be expected that stable nuclei would be composed of equal or fairly equal numbers of protons and neutrons, and perhaps even numbers of each. For the lighter elements up to about $Z = 30$, it turns out that few common stable nuclides have more neutrons than protons, and some of the most common nuclides such as helium 4, carbon 12, oxygen 16, and neon 20 are composed of even numbers of each and the same numbers of each. On the other hand, the common nitrogen nuclide has 7 of each, and beryllium 8 with 4 of each is violently unstable, breaking up to form 2 alpha particles.

Nearly six-tenths of all stable nuclides have even numbers of both neutrons and protons (Table 14-1). The remainder are nearly equally divided between those having an even number of one or the other, with the exception of four only, which have odd numbers of both. These are all light nuclides, H^2, Li^6, B^{10}, N^{14}. With increasing mass, as will be seen from the chart (Fig. 14-5), the proportion of neutrons to protons increases considerably. This may be taken as evidence that more binding force is required for nuclei of higher nuclear charge to balance the forces of repulsion between protons and that the extra neutrons supply what is needed.

TABLE 14-1.   NUCLIDES CLASSIFIED BY ODD-EVEN
NUMBERS OF PROTONS-NEUTRONS

Class	Mass Number, A	Proton Number, Z	Neutron Number, $N = Z - A$	Known Number of Stable Nuclides	Spins
I	Odd	Odd	Even	50	Half-integral
II	Odd	Even	Odd	51	Half-integral
III	Even	Odd	Odd	4	Integral
IV	Even	Even	Even	165	Zero

A lithium 7 nucleus has 3 protons and 4 neutrons; a beryllium 9 nucleus, the only stable beryllium nuclide, has 4 protons and 5 neutrons; carbon 12 has 6 of each, nitrogen 14 has 7 of each, and oxygen 16 has 8 of each. On the other hand, the heaviest natural element, uranium 92, has a mass number $A = 238$ and must then have $Z = 92$ protons, and $A - Z = 238 - 92 = 146$ neutrons, an excess of 54 neutrons over protons. Evidently stability requires an increasing ratio of mass to charge as the mass increases. When the nucleus of an atom captures one or more neutrons, its ratio of mass to charge increases. If in any transformation it loses neutrons its ratio of mass to charge decreases. If such a resultant nucleus is unstable it is presumed to have too much charge for its mass or too much mass for its charge. If there is too much charge for the mass it can achieve stability, or approach it, by emission of a positron, thus losing a unit of charge and increasing its ratio of mass to charge. If it has too much mass for its charge it can approach stability by emitting an electron, thus decreasing its ratio of mass to charge.

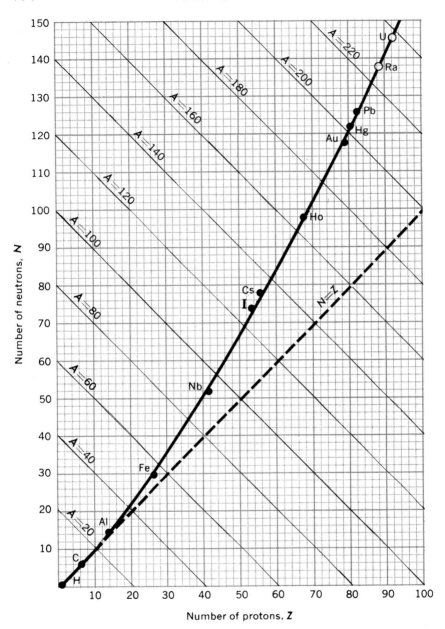

Fig. 14-5. Curve showing proton-neutron composition of a few typical stable nuclei (and two unstable ones). All stable nuclei would be located close to this curve, and all unstable nuclei cluster nearby. The increasing departure of the curve from the $N = Z$ line with increasing atomic number shows that the ratio of neutrons to protons also increases.

The fact that all the more massive nuclei have an excess of neutrons over protons (Fig. 14-5) indicates that more neutrons are required to make up in some way for the Coulomb repulsion between protons.

14-5. Stability of Nuclei and Binding Energies

Stable nuclei are those in which the mass of the nucleus is less than the sum of the masses of its component nucleons no matter how they are grouped. The loss in mass when the nucleus is formed is released in the form of equivalent energy, according to the Einstein energy-mass relation. The larger the *energy-mass deficit* is, the more stable the nucleus is.

The alpha particle is a particularly stable nuclide because it has a large mass deficit. For instance, the alpha particle is composed of two protons and two neutrons. The sum of the masses involved is as follows:

Mass of 2 protons $= 2 \times 1.007593 = 2.015186$
Mass of 2 neutrons $= 2 \times 1.008982 = 2.017964$
_____

Total   4.033150 atomic mass units

Subtracting from this sum the mass of the alpha particle, which is 4.002775 atomic mass units, gives

$$4.033150 - 4.002775 = 0.030375 \text{ amu}$$

or approximately 0.03 amu for the mass deficit. Reducing this to electron volts, and remembering that by the energy-mass relation

$$1 \text{ amu} = 931 \text{ meV}$$

the energy-mass deficit then

$$= 0.030375 \times 931.1$$

$$= 28.3 \text{ meV}$$

This is the amount of energy that would have to be supplied to an alpha particle to separate it into its component parts, and consequently it is the *binding energy* of the helium nucleus. It is also the energy that a bombarding particle must impart to disrupt the nucleus completely. The bombarding particle would actually need more than this in order to conserve momentum. This large energy-mass deficit explains why the alpha particle is such a stable particle. It also explains why the mass of a nucleus containing several (or many) nucleons is not the sum of the masses of the separate nucleons.

The strong tendency for two neutrons and two protons to form an alpha particle may be taken to indicate that binding forces between nucleons are most effective when only a few nucleons are involved. There is evidence that in the nucleus any one nucleon does not act on an unlimited number of other nucleons but only on a relatively few nearest to it. This gives what is called *saturation* of the forces.

Nuclei of a given type are characterized as possessing a fixed amount of binding energy, meaning that the same amount of energy would always be required to take the nucleus completely apart, that is, to pull all the nucleons so far apart that there would be no appreciable force between them. This amount of energy divided by the number of nucleons in the nucleus is the *average binding energy per nucleon.*

If a nucleus contains Z-protons their combined mass is $Z(1.00813)$ atomic mass units. If it also contains $A - Z$ neutrons their combined mass is $(A - Z)(1.00894)$ amu. The total mass of the separate nucleons is the sum of these masses. Subtracting from this sum the actual mass M of the product nucleus gives the mass deficit ΔM in amu.

$$\Delta M = Z(1.00813) + (A - Z)1.00894 - M$$

Then the average binding energy E_B per nucleon is,

$$E_B = \frac{\Delta M c^2}{A} = \frac{[Z(1.00813) + (A - Z)1.00894 - M]}{A} kc^2 \qquad [14\text{--}4]$$

E_B is the average binding energy in joules if k is the number of kilograms in 1 amu and c is the velocity of light, 3×10^8 m/sec. E_B may then readily be reduced to meV.

It is often more convenient to reduce a mass in amu directly to its energy equivalent in eV as in the preceding example, and the number of eV per amu is readily derived.

Since 1 amu $= 1.66 \times 10^{-27}$ kg and $E = mc^2$

$$E = \frac{(1.66 \times 10^{-27} \text{ kg})(3.00 \times 10^8 \text{ m/sec})^2}{(1.6 \times 10^{-19} \text{ joule/eV})}$$

$$= 931 \times 10^6 \text{ eV}$$

$$1 \text{ amu} = 931 \text{ meV}$$

The curve representing the average binding energy per nucleon in meV is given in Fig. 14-6 with the location of a few of the more important elements indicated. From the figure it is seen that the binding energy per nucleon rises rapidly to a broad maximum for elements in the middle of the periodic table and that it then decreases only slowly for isotopes of increasing atomic mass up to the end of the series of elements. Consequently it is evident that elements in the middle of the periodic table are most stable since they have the largest average binding energy per nucleon, a value in the neighborhood of 8.5 meV. Maximum stability is reached in the neighborhood of mass number 50, a little below iron in the atomic series.

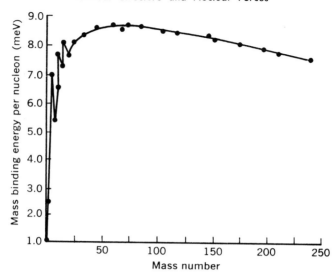

Fig. 14-6. Average binding energies per nucleon for the nuclei of the most stable elements.

From computations based on experimental data it is possible to find the energy required to remove a given type of particle from a given nucleus, and we now have considerable knowledge of the binding energies of individual nucleons. Although usually the separation energy is approximately equal to the average binding energy, in many cases there are considerable deviations. For example in a reaction in which a neutron is knocked out of a potassium 41 (K^{41}) nucleus the required energy is found to be 10.19 meV although the average binding energy per nucleon is 8.56 meV. However, to remove a neutron similarly from oxygen 17, for which the average binding energy per nucleon is 7.71 meV, requires only 4.13 meV. To remove a proton from magnesium 24 requires an energy of 11.00 meV whereas to remove a proton from helium 3 requires 5.44 meV.

Nuclei on either side of the maximum in Fig. 14-6 are less stable because they have not given up as much binding energy per nucleon, on the average. A study of the curve shows that, if the very light nuclei could be combined (fusion) to form heavier nuclei or nuclei nearer the maximum of the curve, energy must be released. On the other hand, if the very heavy nuclei could be split (fission) to form atoms nearer the top of the curve, energy must also be released. These processes of fission and fusion will be discussed in Chaps. 15 and 16.

14-6. Nuclear Forces; The Forces of Nature

The forces in the nucleus which bind neutrons to protons, protons to protons, and neutrons to neutrons are *strong forces* represented as *n-p*, *p-p*, and *n-n* forces. Experimental evidence indicates that these are essentially the same in magnitude. Since they do not seem to depend on the charge of the particle they are called *charge independent*. Since they only operate over the extremely short distances inside the nucleus they are nothing like inverse-square-law forces such as the Coulomb forces between electric charges. Since we do not know the nature of the *binding force* (or forces) that hold the nuclear particles together so strongly it is referred to in general as *the strong force*. This distinguishes it from an equally unknown but weaker force to be mentioned in what follows.

When an approaching particle comes within a distance r_0 (Fig. 14-1) of the center of a nucleus it is captured by the strong binding force and in effect it "falls" into the potential well of the nucleus. Nuclear distances are sometimes measured in a unit called the *fermi* (1 fermi $= 10^{-13}$ cm). When nucleons are more than a few fermis apart the short-range forces are inoperative. Experiments indicate that the most massive nuclei are not much more than 15 or so fermis in diameter. Of course it seems necessary to assume that to keep nucleons from getting too close together the force of attraction must turn to repulsion at short enough distances.

In addition to the strong binding force, which must be far larger than the Coulomb force of repulsion between charged particles, experimental evidence indicates that there is a third force, a short-range force far weaker than the nucleon binding force. For want of a better name it is called the *weak interaction*. For instance in the beta-decay of a radioactive substance the relatively long half-lifes of most substances indicates that there is only a weak interaction and particles so bound do not have energies that enable them to escape readily. Estimates indicate that this weak force may be as little as only 10^{-14} the magnitude of the strong nuclear force. This cannot be gravitational force either as gravitational force is something like 10^{-40} of the magnitude of the strong interaction.

It is of interest to note that the weaker the force the larger must be the system for it to become an important factor. Whereas the strong interaction holds the nucleons together, and the electromagnetic force holds together the far larger systems we know as atoms and molecules, the force of gravitation does not become the critical factor until we reach the astronomical magnitudes of the solar system and the stellar galaxies.

To summarize, the four chief forces of nature are as follows:

(1) The *strong nuclear force* which is a very short-range force and for which the quantized units involved are most probably mesons of one type or another (§14-8).

(2) The *electromagnetic force* which in its broadest sense may involve not only Coulomb interactions but the magnetic effects of spin. Classical theory does not quantize the electromagnetic field, but in the atom classical theory does not apply and the field itself is assumed to be quantized with the fundamental unit being the photon.

(3) The *weak force* is involved typically in emission of beta particles in radio-active decay and in the decay of all elementary particles except the relatively heavy neutral sigma (Σ^0) particles and the neutral pi (π^0) mesons (Chap. 17).
(4) The *gravitational force* is insignificant in the microscopic world.

14-7. Proton-Neutron and Proton-Proton Interactions

In the attempt to investigate forces between protons and protons, and also forces between protons and neutrons, studies have been made of the most uncomplicated examples of these forces. The deuteron is the simplest nucleus of all which possesses more than one particle, since it is composed of only one proton and one neutron. In the deuteron only the proton-neutron binding force is present, entirely uncomplicated by other forces. Thus the deuteron becomes a particle of extraordinary interest in the study of nuclear forces.

Much of present information comes from a study of the angles of scattering of neutrons by protons. The theory of scattering indicates that the angles of scattering should depend on the spins of the particles involved and their relative orientation at the time of collision. When a neutron and proton combine to form a deuteron they might presumably combine with spins parallel or with spins antiparallel. The latter turns out to be an unstable state, and in the stable deuteron the neutron and proton combine in such a way that the spins are parallel and the magnetic moments are in effect antiparallel, since the neutron has a negative magnetic moment (§16-1). The parallel mechanical spin of the neutron and proton in the ground state is confirmed by observations which show the observed spin for the deuteron to be unity, the sum of $\frac{1}{2}$ for the neutron and $\frac{1}{2}$ for the proton. Experimental evidence shows also that the magnetic moment of the deuteron is very close to the difference between the magnetic moments of the proton and neutron.

The scattering experiments are performed by directing a beam of neutrons toward a target containing hydrogen atoms, as, for instance, a block of paraffin. The number of neutrons deflected through various angles is then measured for different neutron energies. The information obtained is of particular value since neutrons have no net electric charge and are not affected by the electric field about the proton. The angles of scattering consequently would appear to depend only upon the short-range nuclear forces, which act between a neutron and a proton, and upon relative spins.

The experimental results confirm the idea that proton-neutron forces are independent of the charge on the proton and that they do depend on relative spin. The theory of the scattering can be worked out by an applica-cation of the wave-mechanical theory, in which instead of thinking of the scattering in terms of particle-like collisions and rebound the results are in terms of waves according to the wave theory.

Proton-proton scattering experiments have been performed by many people, and these experiments furnish information concerning proton-proton forces. The scattering in this instance is due in part to Coulomb repulsion of like charges. To obtain the effects due to the short-range charge-independent forces of attraction, the effects of Coulomb repulsion must be subtracted as a correction. Such experiments lead to the idea that binding forces between protons, called *p-p* forces, are similar to those between protons and neutrons, called *p-n* forces.

Information about neutron-neutron (*n-n*) forces, obtained from neutron-neutron scattering experiments, would be of great interest, but the experimental difficulties that must be overcome are discouraging.

14-8. Meson Theory of Nuclear Forces: Exchange Force

To try to explain the strong short-range forces within a nucleus we now resort to quantum mechanics and the so-called *exchange forces* for an answer. The idea of an exchange force comes out of quantum-mechanical analysis, and represents an attempt to give a physical interpretation to certain terms in the mathematical equations. It has no counterpart in classical physics. The interpretation is usually based on the concept of an actual exchange of some type of particle between nucleons. At first it seemed that the electron might be such a particle, but computation showed that the electron as an exchange particle is too small to come even close to accounting for the forces that must be present in the nucleus.

In 1935, Yukawa in Japan proposed that exchange forces could account for nuclear forces if the exchange particles were considerably more massive than an electron but less massive than a proton. Yukawa reasoned that if the force between nucleons is an exchange force due to the exchange of some kind of quantum, the quantum responsible for this force will travel a distance between nucleons less than the diameter of the nucleus between emission by one nucleon and absorption by another. This distance would be the range of the nuclear force. Assuming that the quantum travels with the velocity of light c, he arrived at an equation for the rest mass m_0 of the quantum in terms of the range R of the nuclear force where

$$m_0 = \frac{h}{2\pi Rc} \qquad [14\text{--}5]$$

Since the range of the nuclear force could not be accurately specified the rest mass of the exchange particle was in some doubt but it was most likely somewhere near 200 electron masses and the electron itself was thereby ruled out as the exchange particle.

The discovery of a "heavy electron" or *meson* (§17-3) possessing a mass of 207 electron masses seemed at first to be direct confirmation of Yukawa's theory. However, it was soon found that the first kind of meson to be discovered, the *mu meson* (μ-meson) now called the *muon*, had little interaction with atomic nuclei even though plentiful numbers of mu mesons of both positive and negative charge were found. A little later the situation was reversed when it was found that the first-discovered meson, the mu meson, was actually a decay product of a somewhat heavier meson, the pi meson (π-meson) also called the *pion*, which did interact strongly with nuclei.

If the π meson were the particle chiefly responsible for the strong nuclear force the charge independence of these forces could be readily explained since both positive, negative and neutral pi mesons were found. The positives and negatives possessed masses of about 273 electron masses and the neutral pi meson is now known to possess a mass of 264 electron masses. Both pi and mu mesons in free space are unstable particles and decay by emission of electrons and neutrinos, although the neutral pi meson usually decays by gamma-ray emission (§17-4).

The pi meson now seems to be direct fulfillment of Yukawa's prediction, but whether it is complete confirmation of his theory of nuclear exchange forces is not entirely settled. The theory that nuclear binding forces depend largely on exchange of mesons between nucleons is very attractive, and there is no rival theory. A more detailed account of the discovery and properties of mesons including their modes of decay will be given in Chap. 17.

A complete theory of the forces involved in the nucleus must be able to cope with many phenomena such as radioactive decay, nuclear energy levels, resonance absorption, nuclear fission, and the effects described by "magic numbers," which seem to involve completed shells or groups of nuclear particles within the nucleus.

14-9. Nuclear Models

In the attempt to explain nuclear structure a number of different models have been suggested each with its successes and its inadequacies. The existence of energy levels in the nucleus was first indicated by the fine structure of alpha rays. To explain these it was suggested that nuclear particles were in orbits or shells inside the nucleus much like the electrons outside the nucleus. This early *shell model* ran into difficulties and was displaced for a time by the *liquid drop model* of Niels Bohr, which had considerable success especially in describing the fission of a heavy nucleus. Since then we have had the *single-particle shell model*, and various other models such as the *collective model* and the *optical model* to be discussed in what follows.

14-10. Liquid-Drop Model of Nucleus

In 1936 Bohr proposed that the nucleus with its particles might be expected to behave very much like a droplet of some liquid in which the forces of attraction and repulsion between particles in the liquid are balanced. In such a "liquid droplet," the nucleons are presumed to be closely packed together and in a state of continual thermal agitation, moving in various directions with random motions. Emission of nucleons from such a nucleus is then considered similar to evaporation of molecules from a liquid droplet. If a high-energy particle has been captured by the nucleus, the nucleons in the newly formed *compound nucleus* (§15-2) quickly share the energy. For any nucleon to then escape, a considerable portion of this shared energy must be reconcentrated on it.

On the basis of this model of the nucleus it has been possible to account fairly well for the total binding energies of nucleons. As a first approximation we may write an equation for the binding energy E

$$E = k_1 A - k_2 Z^2 A^{-1/3} - k_3 A^{2/3} \qquad [14\text{--}6]$$

where the k's are proportionality constants. The first term $k_1 A$ is the part of the energy resulting from the attraction between nucleons. It is taken to be proportional to the number of nucleons A (the mass number) or, what amounts to the same thing, the volume of the nucleus. In the second term the effect of Coulomb repulsion of protons is negative and is approximately proportional to Z^2, the square of the number of charges. Actually it is proportional to the number of proton pairs $Z(Z-1)/2!$. It is also inversely proportional to the diameter of the nucleus which is known to vary approximately as $A^{1/3}$.

The third term $k_3 A^{2/3}$ represents the effect of "surface tension." It is proportional to the area of the nucleus or to $A^{2/3}$, and it is also negative, representing a decrease in binding energy, because surface particles on the average interact with only half as many particles as those inside the nucleus. In a more complete equation other terms may be required to take account of the surplus of neutrons over protons and of the effect of an odd or unpaired nucleon. Because Eq. 14–6 is derived neither wholly from theory nor wholly from experiment it is called a semi-empirical formula.

If we divide both sides of Eq. 14–6 by the number of nucleons A in a nucleus we find that the average binding energy per nucleon is

$$\frac{E}{A} = k_1 - k_2 Z^2 A^{-4/3} - k_3 A^{-1/3} \qquad [14\text{--}6a]$$

The first term on the right is approximately constant regardless of atomic number A. This is plotted as the upper dashed line of Fig. 14-7 for different atomic numbers. The other two terms of Eq. 14–6 are negative (plotted below the zero axis of Fig. 14-7) and tend to reduce the net binding energy

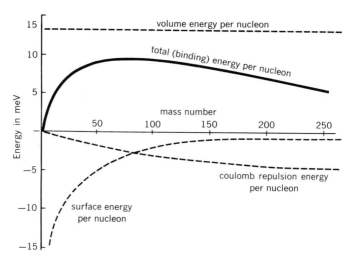

Fig. 14-7. Energy per nucleon in an atomic nucleus as a function of atomic number.

per nucleon. The Coulomb term acts to decrease binding energies as the atomic number increases. The surface energy term on the other hand is of greatest importance for low values of atomic number where the ratio of surface to volume is largest and may account in part for the low average binding energy at the lower end of Fig. 14-7. Adding the ordinates of the three curves gives the full line in the figure which represents the total energy per nucleon. Except for minor deviations this curve gives a fair approximation to the experimental curve of Fig. 14-6.

One of the most useful applications of the droplet model is to the phenomenon of nuclear fission, where a nucleus divides into two more or less equal parts in very much the same way as a droplet of water or other liquid, if set vibrating with sufficient energy, becomes unstable and breaks into two or more droplets (§16-7). However, for higher-energy nuclear reactions, of a few hundred meV or more, the liquid-drop model, together with the idea of the compound nucleus, becomes less and less useful. A high-speed particle, for example, may pass through the nucleus and hit only one or two nucleons in the process, or none at all. Such a picture is radically different from what would be expected to happen at lower energies. Furthermore, the properties of excited states or energy levels in the nucleus are not easy to explain by means of the liquid-drop model. These difficulties have led to the development of another nuclear model.

14-11. The Shell Model of the Nucleus

It is difficult if not impossible to give a satisfactory explanation of excited states of nuclei and of sharply defined energy levels in terms of nuclear particles which are assumed to be closely packed together and to have random energy distributions, as in the liquid-drop model. This led to a revival of an earlier shell model in a newer form. Maria G. Mayer of the University of Chicago and J. D. H. Jensen and coworkers of Heidelberg in 1950 independently showed that a revised shell model called the *individual particle model* could be constructed to successfully explain a surprising number of experimental facts with very few discrepancies. For their success the two were named Nobel Prize winners in 1963.

The *individual particle model* was so called because the particles were assumed to be sufficiently independent of one another that a particle might stay on an "orbit" for an appreciable length of time without being interfered with by its neighbors. One reason to believe it would not suffer too much from collisions was because it was assumed that in the ground states the lower energy levels are filled. Hence by the Pauli exclusion principle the particle could only be excited to some vacant higher energy level.

The validity of many aspects of this model is now generally accepted. For one thing, it is certainly simpler to think of excited states of nuclei in terms of nucleons being raised from one energy level, represented by one shell, to a higher energy level represented by another shell, the idea being borrowed directly from the common picture of extranuclear electronic behavior.

But there is another feature of the shell model the basic idea of which was borrowed from external electronic structure of the atom. Several lines of evidence indicate that nuclei possessing 2, 8, 20, 28, 50, 82, or 126 nucleons of the same kind (either protons or neutrons) are more stable than those having different numbers; for instance helium with 2 each of neutrons and protons is an extremely stable particle. So is the common isotope of oxygen O^{16} with 8 of each. Tin, the nucleus of which has 50 protons, has more stable isotopes than any other element. The relative abundances of the elements in nature (except for helium) also indicate which are the most stable. Apparently the numbers in the series just given have a special significance and suggest that they might represent something like completed shells or subshells. But the attempts to apply the Pauli exclusion principle and compute the energy levels in the nucleus did not give the right results. On the particular assumption that the potential well of the nucleus had rounded edges instead of a rectangular cross section it is true that the energy levels appeared in groups more like shells, but the completed groups came at the numbers 2, 8, 20, 40, 70, 112 and 168 and this was the wrong answer.

The problem was now solved very beautifully by the founders of the new theory when it was noted that if a nuclear particle were in an actual orbit its energy would depend on whether it was spinning on its axis in the same direction as its orbital motion or in the opposite direction. This interaction between spin and orbital motion (*spin-orbit coupling*) although small for an extra-nuclear electron turns out to be relatively large in the nucleus. Indeed it is just enough to split the energy levels and put in large energy gaps at just the right places, that is after the completed groups having numbers 2, 8, 20, 28, 50, 82 and 126. Before this the importance of the numbers was so puzzling that they were called "magic numbers." Now they come logically out of the theory.

Despite the successes of the liquid-drop model and the shell model of the nucleus there remain many problems and neither theory is in any real sense complete. In fact each undoubtedly overemphasizes the features it represents, and in addition the nucleus is far too complicated to surrender to such a degree of simplification. The small size of the nucleus would seem to deny the possibility of large-scale orbital motion with nucleons widely separated in the nucleus as in the electronic structure of the atom. But with the droplet model, the difficulty is how to account for nuclear energy levels and nuclear shells. Here the two theories are in conflict. Where the droplet theory assumed a cluster of particles with random motion, the shell model must assume something like a central potential field. On either model the nucleons must be close together, but even if they are not widely separated in space they must somehow be separated into definite energy groups.

The spins of the various nuclei and their magnetic moments are simply explained by the shell model. It is assumed that usually protons and neutrons each tend to pair off with another proton or neutron of opposite spin. If there is an odd number of either protons or neutrons the odd particle revolves around a core of neutron and proton pairs. Since the core has no spin the spin and magnetic moment of the nucleus (if these are not zero) are accounted for by the odd particle. Magnetic moments of nuclei computed on this assumption are reasonably close to the experimental values.

It is convenient to classify nuclei according to whether the total number of particles in a nucleus is even or odd and whether the numbers of protons and neutrons, respectively, are even or odd. An even-odd nucleus, for instance, usually means a nucleus with an even number of protons and an odd number of neutrons. The mass number is consequently odd. At present about 20 per cent of known nuclides are stable. They are classified in Table 14-1, and it is seen that nuclei having odd numbers of both protons and neutrons are especially unlikely to be stable.

The individual-particle model accounts for the angular momenta of nuclei in a simple manner. In classes I or II, where there is an odd proton or odd neutron, the angular momentum is presumed to be the vector sum of orbital and spin momenta. Since the spin angular momentum of either proton or neutron is $\frac{1}{2}$, and the assumed orbital angular momentum is integral, the sum will be half-integral, 1/2, 3/2, 5/2, or 7/2, etc. depending upon the number of unpaired states of the nucleons. In Class III any two odd particles with half-integral angular momenta, 1/2, 3/2, etc. will couple in such a way that the momenta add vectorially to give a resultant represented by integral values. When there are even numbers of both protons and neutrons (Class IV) the nucleons according to this model are assumed to pair off and couple their angular momenta in such a way that the resultant nuclear angular momentum is zero.

Although the shell theory of nuclear structure and the liquid-drop theory appear in many ways incompatible, each has it sphere of usefulness. The liquid-drop theory assumes particles to be close together with strong interactions between nucleons. The shell theory assumes that the particles, though all within the walls of a common potential well and perhaps as closely packed, at least have a more definite organization and probably interact with each other only slightly (weak interaction). The two models, however, were proposed to describe different groups of phenomena. The droplet theory deals with the over-all aspects of the nucleus as a whole, whereas the shell theory emphasizes energy levels and individual relations of the nucleons.

Recent experiments have revealed still greater complexities among the possible energy levels in a nucleus including evidence for rotational and vibrational states of the nucleus similar to such states found long ago in the behavior of molecules. The attempts at harmonizing these conflicting elements have led to other models which try to preserve the best features of the previous two.

14-12. Other Nuclear Models; Resonance Absorption

A number of phenomena have been accounted for by the *collective model* (or *unified model*) of Aage Bohr and B. Mottelson of Copenhagen, who have had considerable success in attempting to combine essential elements of the liquid-drop and shell models. This model assumes that the last nucleon moves around an inner core which has some of the properties of a liquid drop. In particular its shape is assumed to be deformed by the nucleon moving around it as if the nucleon were a "moon" producing a tidal wave. The deformation or bulge of the nucleus would affect the rotational inertia and make various rotational energy states possible. This has permitted successful calculations of rotational energy levels of some deformed nuclei.

Much significant work in recent years has been concerned with attempts to probe the nucleus by bombarding it with high-energy neutrons and electrons (see §14-13). For instance, the way in which bombarding neutrons are absorbed by the nucleus led to what has been called the *optical model* of Weisskopf in which the nucleus was described as a kind of "cloudy crystal ball" and in which entering neutrons are supposed to travel at least for a time in regular orbits. In itself the picture of a "cloudy crystal ball" would be an obvious oversimplification, but in addition to the matter of orbits (or as part of the problem) one of the important questions has been to find if the nucleus behaves as if it has its own concentrated nuclear center or perhaps a more uniform distribution of matter, and whether or not the boundary is sharp or fuzzy. The results, of course, depend in part on what particles are used as a probe, what their energies are, and whether the particles in the probing beam have a narrow energy spread (nearly "monochromatic") or a wide spread.

An important set of nuclear data comes from experiments showing that neutrons possessing any one of a large number of sharply defined energies in the low-energy range are more strongly absorbed (captured) than neutrons with intermediate energies. This kind of absorption is called *resonance absorption* and a number of these are represented as vertical lines in Fig. 14-8. Regions of intense absorption are called *giant resonances*. In some cases wide regions of absorption are made up of separate sharp resonances which are "blurred" together (Fig. 14-8) when a nucleus is bombarded with particles in the lower energy ranges where sharp separation of energies is not attained. For a nucleus to show such sharp resonances it is believed that the entering neutron must travel at least for a time in a regular orbit representing a definite energy level and such facts are believed to reflect direct information of nuclear structure.

14-13. Probing the Nucleus With High-Energy Electrons

It had long been the desire of physicists to probe the structure of the nucleus with something as small as an electron but this was not feasible until further development of electron accelerators. Early experiments of this kind by Lyman, Hanson and Scott in 1951 using 15.7 meV electrons confirmed that nuclear radii are closely proportional to the cube root of the atomic number and that the radius r_0 is given to a fair approximation as

$$r_0 \simeq 1.40 \times 10^{-13} A^{1/3} \text{ cm} \qquad [14\text{--}7]$$

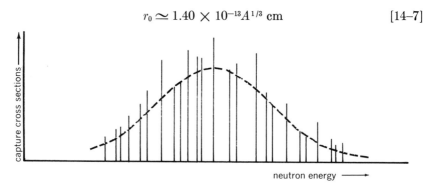

Fig. 14-8. Type of a "giant resonance" (dashed line) in the low energy range of neutrons bombarding a nucleus. Vertical lines represent close group of ordinary resonances at sharply defined energies of bombardment.

Since 1953 much higher energy electrons have been available and some of the most exciting work has been carried on by R. Hofstadter and coworkers for which Hofstadter received the Nobel Prize in 1961.

Hofstadter's experiments were carried out first with electrons having energies of 190 meV, later increased to as much as 1 beV (10^9eV). The experiments consisted of measuring the number of electrons scattered at different angles in much the same manner as that in which Rutherford performed his earlier experiments on the scattering of alpha particles. On the simplifying assumption that the force of interaction when the incident electrons are scattered is only electromagnetic it is possible to compute "form factors" relating the nuclear charge density to the distance from the center of the nucleus. The heavier atoms show charge distributions in the nucleus like gold (Au) (Fig. 14-9) with fairly constant densities up to a certain "skin" region, at the surface, in which the density falls off rapidly. The great exception to this is the proton (p) for which the charge density rises at its center to nearly 15 times that for heavier nuclei. The alpha particle (α) also has a high central charge density but nothing like that of the proton.

Similar experiments to bombard neutrons with electrons cannot be performed so directly but scattering of electrons by deuterons gives results for neutrons (after the effect of the proton in the deuteron is subtracted) which may be interpreted with some difficulty. The results indicate many similarities between the neutron and the proton and have also suggested the existence of a new heavy neutral meson.

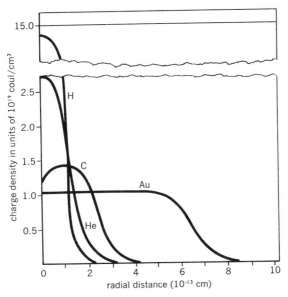

Fig. 14-9. Variation of charge density in the nuclei of hydrogen (H), helium (He), carbon (C) and gold (Au) by electron scattering (after Hofstadter).

From such studies it becomes clear that protons and neutrons cannot be considered to be point charges or point masses. They are complicated structures and one of the leading problems of physics will be to find out more about these structures and the particles of which they consist. At present the same charged clouds of mesons appear in both protons and neutrons and lead to a new picture of both particles. In the proton the charged clouds apparently do not cancel but add together whereas in the neutron they cancel and give the effect of zero charge.

14-14. Nuclear Spins; Nuclear Magneton

Nuclei are now recognized as having resultant angular momentum (spin and orbital) represented by $\sqrt{I(I+1)}\hbar$ where I is the resultant quantum number for the nucleons in any nucleus and it may have integral or half-integral values including zero.

The possible nuclear orientations in a magnetic field (at which precession may occur) are such as have projections on the field direction which are integral multiples of $\hbar$, equal to $m_I\hbar$ where m_I can have any integral values between $+I$ and $-I$. For radiation or absorption of energy, only transitions between adjacent states are allowed, that is $\Delta m_I = \pm 1$. Although the resultant spin as represented by I is usually $I = 0$ or $I = \frac{1}{2}$ it may be larger and for $_{83}\text{Bi}^{209}$ it is $\frac{9}{2}$.

Nuclei also have magnetic dipole moments which are presumed to be associated with resultant nuclear spin as if there was circulation of electric charge along with spin. Notably in even-even nuclei where resultant spin is zero, the magnetic moment is also zero. When not zero it is usually measured in terms of the *nuclear magneton* which must now be defined.

Since the magnitude of angular momentum of a proton (spin $= \frac{1}{2}\hbar$) is the same as for the electron it might, at first thought, be expected that the nuclear magnetic moments would be similarly related. However, the mass of the proton is so much larger that for the same amount of angular momentum it will spin much more slowly and the magnetic moment of such a spinning charge would then be proportionately less. Reasoning partly by analogy we can define the *nuclear magneton* by putting the mass of the proton M_p into Eq. 9–1 (instead of the mass of the electron) giving

$$1 \text{ nuclear magneton} = \frac{eh}{4\pi M_p} = 5.05 \times 10^{-27} \text{ joule/(web/m}^2)$$

This is $1/1836$ the magnitude of the Bohr magneton.

Surprisingly enough, the proton, instead of having a dipole moment of one nuclear magneton is found to have a moment μ_p of nearly three and it is a fractional number at that.

$$\mu_p(\text{proton}) = +2.7928 \text{ nuclear magnetons}$$

The positive sign indicates that the magnetic moment points in the same direction as the angular momentum (along the axis of spin) as if there were circulation of positive charge. The neutron on the other hand, although it has no detectable net charge, does possess a magnetic moment (−1.9128 nuclear magneton, see §16-1) pointing in a direction opposite to its spin. These fractional numbers of nuclear magnetons also indicate that the proton and neutron are not simple structures but are complex.

14-15. Nuclear Magnetic Resonance

The most direct experimental methods for measuring nuclear magnetic moments are the methods of *magnetic resonance* and of *nuclear resonance absorption*.

The first accurate measurements by magnetic resonance were made by Rabi and his coworkers, who developed to a high degree of precision a method based on the Stern-Gerlach (§9-8) experiment and known as *molecular beam* magnetic resonance. A beam of molecules from a small furnace or oven enters the region of nonuniform magnetic field of magnet A and follows a curved path passing through a slit S_1 (Fig. 14-10). This field must be nonuniform, as a uniform magnetic field would exert zero net deflecting force. The magnet C then produces a nonuniform field which bends the paths of the molecules back again so that they pass through slit S_2 and are detected. Magnet B produces a uniform field which of itself has no effect, but in the region of the uniform field a high-frequency electric current produces a magnetic field at right angles to the uniform field.

The molecules passing through the uniform field have a definite quantized space orientation and precess like a spinning top about the direction

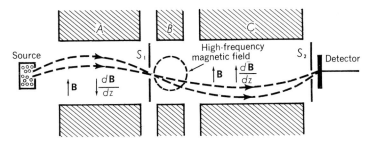

Fig. 14-10. Molecular-beam method of measuring nuclear magnetic moments. Magnets A and C give nonuniform magnetic fields in the same direction but with opposite gradients. Magnet B furnishes a constant field in the same direction, upon which a high-frequency field at right angles to that of B is superposed on that of B. The molecules are focused on the detector. When the frequency of the high-frequency field is adjusted to resonance with the precessional frequency of the nuclei, they will fail to focus, giving a dip in the curve of number recorded.

of the field. When the frequency of the electric current is varied until it equals the frequency of precession, energy will be absorbed and the molecules take up a different quantized space orientation. They are then deflected by the field of magnet C either too little or too much to pass through slit S_2. The diminution in number of molecules passing through S_2 then marks the finding of the precessional frequency, which depends on the magnetic moment and the intensity of the uniform central field. By this method the magnetic moment can be obtained.

In the method of *magnetic nuclear resonance absorption* of Purcell, Torrey, and Pound, and the closely related method of *nuclear resonance induction* of Bloch and his coworkers, no beams of molecules are used. A solid or liquid sample is placed in a uniform magnetic field, and upon this field a high-frequency alternating field is superposed at right angles. Protons or other simple nuclei precessing about the direction of the uniform field will have their quantized angles of space orientation suddenly changed by absorption of energy when the alternating field is tuned to resonance with the precession frequency. This absorption can be detected, and magnetic moments can be computed.

Such methods have been so perfected and have become such powerful tools that they have superseded other methods.

SOME COMMON NUCLEAR TERMS

Nucleons   Neutrons or protons in a nucleus.

Nuclide   A particular type of nucleus. Different nuclides have different numbers of protons or neutrons or both.

Isotope   One of a group of nuclides having the same number of protons but different numbers of neutrons.

Isobar   One of a group of nuclides having the same mass number.

Isomers   Nuclides having the same number of neutrons and protons but able to remain for an appreciable time in different energy states.

Mirror nuclides   Two nuclides for which the numbers of protons and neutrons of one are the reverse of the other.

Problems

Note. Nuclear masses are obtained from atomic masses by subtracting the masses of the external electrons belonging to the atom.

1. What is the mass deficit of O^{16}? Of C^{12}? What is the average mass deficit per nucleon? Which would you expect to be the more stable element? The masses are $O^{16} = 16.0000$ amu and $C^{12} = 12.00380$ amu for the atoms (not the nuclei).

2. Compare the mass deficits per nucleon of Al^{27} and Zn^{64}. Which would you expect to be the more stable? The atomic masses (not the bare nuclei) are $Al^{27} = 26.99014$ amu and $Zn^{64} = 63.94880$ amu.

3. Compute the average binding energy per nucleon for a U^{238} nucleus in joules and in meV. The mass of U^{238} is 238.125 amu for the atom (not the nucleus) and it is composed of 92 protons and 146 neutrons.

4. Compute the average binding energy per nucleon for a U^{235} nucleus in joules and in meV. The mass of U^{235} is 235.117 amu for the atom (not the nucleus).

5. The dissociation energy of a potassium chloride molecule (KCl) is 4.40 eV. This is the energy given off when the molecule was formed from the two separate atoms. How much loss of mass does this represent in atomic mass units? Is it appreciable when adding atomic masses to get the molecular mass?

*6. In Hofstadter's work protons were bombarded with electrons of as much as 1 beV energy. What is the de Broglie wavelength of such electrons? (Use relativistic mass and the approximation $v = c$.)

7. Could a nucleus be "taken apart" by supplying the average binding energy per nucleon to each nucleon in succession? Give reasons for or against.

8. Approximately how many times larger is the radius of a U^{238} nucleus than a helium nucleus?

9. Approximately how many times larger in diameter on the average is the chlorine nucleus in a NaCl cubic lattice than the sodium nucleus? Is this a pure cubic lattice?

10. Compute the energy required to remove a single proton from a nucleus of $_8O^{16}$. The atomic mass of $_7N^{15} = 15.00488$ amu. Why may this be different from the average binding energy?

11. Compute the binding energy of the "last" proton in a nucleus of $_6C^{12}$ if the mass of the $_6C^{12}$ atom is 12.00382 amu and the mass of the $_5B^{11}$ is 11.01281 amu.

*12. Protons may have their spins oriented in either of two directions in a magnetic field. The energy difference in joules between the two orientations is a linear function of the magnetic field and is equal to kB. Compute the value of k if B is in web/m².

*13. In *nuclear magnetic resonance* the nucleus absorbs radiation of sufficient energy to make the nucleus "flip" from one orientation to another. Using the results of the previous problem, compute the photon energy and wavelength required to make the proton "flip" from one position to the other if $B = 0.2$ web/m².

14. Upon what factors does the relative abundance of isotopes in nature depend? Consider stable and unstable isotopes.

15. Tritium ($_1H^3$) undergoes radioactive decay to form helium 3 ($_2H^3$). The mass of a tritium atom is 3.017005 amu and the mass of the helium 3 atom is 3.016986. What particle would be emitted in the decay process and with what kinetic energy in electron volts?

16. Find the "top" of the Coulomb potential barrier around a radium nucleus as "seen" by an approaching proton. Take radius of radium to be given by $r = 1.4 \times 10^{-15} A^{1/3}$ meter where A is the atomic number.

*17. Find the width of the nuclear Coulomb potential barrier for the emission by a radium nucleus of an alpha particle of 4.88 meV energy. This is the width through which the alpha particle of this energy must "tunnel." Assume the nuclear radius is 10^{-12} cm and that the alpha particle at the barrier is in a field produced by a central charge of $(Z - 2)e$.

*18. Imagine an experiment in which two proton beams each consisting of 10^{12} particles per second are in direct collision. If the proton beams have a cross section of 1 mm², show that the chance of collisions between protons is far too small to make the experiment practicable. Refer to §15-5.

Recommended Reading

Elton, L. R. B., *Introductory Nuclear Theory*. New York: Interscience Publishers, Inc., 1960.

Kaplan, I., *Nuclear Physics*, 2nd ed. Reading, Mass.: Addison-Wesley Publishing Co., Inc., 1963.

Evans, R. D., *The Atomic Nucleus*. New York: McGraw-Hill Book Company, Inc., 1955.

Halliday, D., *Introductory Nuclear Physics*, 2nd ed. New York: John Wiley & Sons, Inc., 1955.

Green, A. E. S., *Nuclear Physics*. New York: McGraw-Hill Book Company, Inc., 1955.

Mayer, M. G., and J. H. D. Jensen, *Elementary Theory of Nuclear Shell Structure*. New York: John Wiley & Sons, Inc., 1955.

Bethe, H. A., and P. Morrison, *Elementary Nuclear Theory*, 2nd ed. New York: John Wiley & Sons, Inc., 1956.

Gamow, G., and C. L. Critchfield, *Theory of Atomic Nucleus and Nuclear Energy Sources*. Oxford: Clarendon Press, 1949.

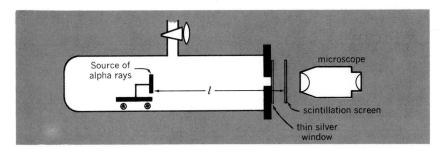

Within the circle: **15**

Nuclear Processes

15-1. Early Experiments in Transmuting Atoms

In 1919 Rutherford produced the first nuclear transmutation by artificial means when he bombarded ordinary nitrogen with high-speed alpha particles emitted by RaC′. He knew that such alpha particles had a range in air of about 7 cm, consequently they should have about the same range in nitrogen gas. Nevertheless, by means of a fluorescent screen he detected particles which had a range of as much as 40 cm (Fig. 15-1). Since the nitrogen atom itself is considerably more massive than an alpha particle, it could in no way be knocked so far by an ordinary collision.

Rutherford then concluded that some less massive particle must have been ejected from the nitrogen nucleus. By applying the laws of conservation of energy and momentum (and also by attempting a magnetic deflec-

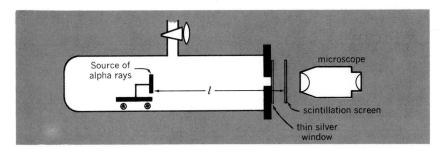

Fig. 15-1. Schematic diagram of Rutherford's first nuclear reaction experiment.

tion experiment) he decided that the ejected particle was most probably a proton. This conclusion was later confirmed by bombarding the nuclei of other elements. Such nuclear events, however, were relatively rare because only about one alpha particle in a million made a close enough collision to dislodge a proton. When observations were made in a cloud chamber, tracks were visible for the dislodged proton and the recoiling nucleus together with the incident alpha particle but no alpha-ray track showed after a collision. From this Rutherford concluded that the alpha particle did not rebound after collision but was absorbed by the nucleus. The new nucleus would then be formed by gain of an alpha particle and loss of a proton. Such a transformation is now called an alpha-proton (α, p) reaction, and is represented symbolically in the following manner when nitrogen $(_7N^{14})$ is irradiated:

$$_2He^4 + {}_7N^{14} \rightarrow {}_8O^{17} + {}_1H^1 \qquad\qquad [15-1]$$

This reaction states that when a nitrogen nucleus $(_7N^{14})$ is hit by an alpha particle $(_2He^4)$ a proton $(_1H^1)$ is ejected leaving an oxygen nucleus $(_8O^{17})$. Thus Rutherford transmuted ordinary nitrogen into a rare isotope of oxygen. Similar experiments were performed on other light elements, and it was found that protons could be knocked out of the nuclei of all the light elements from boron to potassium, though carbon and oxygen at first resisted attempts to disrupt them. A considerable number of light elements was thus studied by Rutherford himself, and this work was later extended by others who confirmed nearly all his work. However, the highest energy alpha particles from a radioactive substance could not produce detectable effects when the heavy atoms with higher potential barriers were bombarded. This led to a search for either a different method or for means of artifically accelerating particles to still higher energies.

In 1930 Cockroft and Walton in Cambridge, England devised a new source of high voltage and tried the effects of bombarding nuclei with high-speed protons. They thus produced the first nuclear disintegrations by charged particles accelerated electrically. Their generator consisted of a number of capacitors arranged in what is called a voltage-multiplier circuit, so that they could be automatically charged in parallel and discharged in series. They used protons accelerated first by 100,000 volts and later by 700,000 volts to bombard lithium 7. The product nucleus was believed to disintegrate into 2 alpha particles, as follows:

$$_3Li^7 + {}_1H^1 \rightarrow ({}_4Be^8) \rightarrow {}_2He^4 + {}_2He^4 \qquad\qquad [15-2]$$

This assumption was beautifully confirmed by observations in a cloud chamber, which clearly indicated the tracks of two alpha particles diverging from the point of collision.

The highest energies used by Cockroft and Walton were considerably below those of the top of the potential barrier of even the lightest elements, but they hoped to prove the wave-mechanical hypothesis that the barrier of the nucleus might be penetrated by particles of energy too low to surmount it. Success attended their efforts, and they not only obtained a $(p, 2\alpha)$ reaction in lithium but similar reactions with several other light elements, thus proving barrier penetration. They even obtained occasional transmutations of lithium with proton energies of 100,000 eV and lower.

These experiments with electrically accelerated particles aroused intense interest and stimulated the demand for means of accelerating charged particles to higher and higher energies. In 1931 E. O. Lawrence, who had recently invented the cyclotron (§18-2), built one to give protons 1.2 meV energy. By the end of World War II a greatly improved cyclotron had produced protons of nearly 300 meV and alpha particles of 384 meV. Van de Graaff meanwhile was developing his electrostatic generator (§18-1) with which he obtained several million volts constant potential difference and more intense beams of particles than could be obtained with the cyclotron. In the years since World War II accelerators (Chap. 18) have gone from the million- to the billion-volt class, and particles having billions of electron volts energy are now available. With such high-energy particles many new and surprising discoveries have been made, and the end is not in sight.

15-2. The Compound Nucleus: Typical Nuclear Reactions

Bohr put forth the idea of the *compound nucleus* in 1936 and it has been very fruitful in correlating many observed phenomena connected with nuclear processes. He described how an atomic projectile entering a nucleus may be thought to remain in the nucleus long enough to put the nucleus into an excited state, after which emission of one or more particles (or a gamma ray) occurs, and a resultant nucleus is formed. When an incident particle enters the nucleus, its excess energy is assumed to be quickly shared by the other nucleons, and thus the *compound nucleus* is a transitional state between the initial state before bombardment and the final state.

The energy contributed to the nucleus is made up of two parts, the kinetic energy of the incident particle and the energy equivalent of the mass that it loses in becoming part of the compound nucleus. If the energy becomes concentrated again on one nucleon such a particle will be likely to escape from the nucleus. If the emitted particle carries away all of this energy the residual nucleus will be in its lowest energy state or ground state. If it does not carry away all of this energy, the product nucleus will be in an *excited state* and will return to its *ground state* by gamma-ray emission.

The compound nucleus is believed to last a length of time which is very short by laboratory standards but may be very long in terms of nuclear processes. If the nucleons are assumed to be moving about inside the nucleus, then, after having been put into a state of greater agitation by capture of an energetic particle, they will move faster. A simple computation shows that the time for a nucleon to move from one side of the nucleus to another may be as little as 10^{-20} sec. The compound nucleus might last a thousand or even a million times longer than that and still break up very quickly by ordinary standards. If it only lasts that long it is long enough that it can have no "memory" of how it was formed, and consequently the manner of decay will be independent of the way in which the compound nucleus was formed. The manner of decay of the compound nucleus is then presumed to depend on various possibilities called *exit processes*, which are in competition with one another, and also to depend on the energy brought to the nucleus by the incident particle.

Nuclear reactions which occur when the bombarding particles have very high energies, 100 meV or higher, may be quite different in character. The compound nucleus may not have time to form, and an effect called *spallation* may occur. A number of particles or groups of particles such as helium, lithium, etc., nuclei may be knocked directly out of the nucleus. These groups represent a major fragmentation or disruption of the nucleus.

The reaction symbolized in [15–1] will now be rewritten to show the formation of the compound nucleus represented as the intermediate state in parenthesis

$$_2\text{He}^4 + {_7}\text{N}^{14} \rightarrow ({_9}\text{F}^{18}) \rightarrow {_8}\text{O}^{17} + {_1}\text{H}^1 \qquad [15\text{--}3]$$

The assumption is made here that the nitrogen atom first captures the alpha particle to form momentarily a compound nucleus of mass number $14 + 4 = 18$ and charge $7 + 2 = 9$, which shows it to be an isotope of fluorine. The ejection of the proton then leaves the nucleus with a mass number 17 and a nuclear charge 8, equal to the sum of the charges of the nitrogen nucleus plus the helium nucleus, diminished by the charge carried away by the proton. The nuclear charge of 8 identifies the product nucleus as an isotope of oxygen.

Many types of reaction have been added to the alpha-proton (α, p) reaction of Rutherford's first experiment and to the first $(p, 2\alpha)$ reaction of Cockroft and Walton. Not only alpha particles and protons, but deuterons, neutrons, and high-energy gamma rays have also been used to bombard nuclei. Some common reactions and their symbols are listed below.

Alpha-proton (α, p)
Alpha-neutron (α, n)
Proton-neutron (p, n)
Neutron-proton (n, p)
Gamma-proton (γ, p)
Proton-gamma (p, γ)

To represent a particular reaction, as for instance a deuteron bombarding nitrogen (N^{14}) to produce N^{15} and a proton, the following abbreviated symbols are sometimes used:

$$_7N^{14} \ (d, \ p) \ _7N^{15}$$

Similarly

$$_9F^{19} \ (p, \ \alpha) \ _8O^{16}$$

represents the effect of proton bombardment on fluorine 19, with ejection of an alpha particle and the formation of oxygen 16.

There follow some typical nuclear reactions of the many now known. The most important neutron-induced reactions will be discussed in the next chapter.

PROTON-INDUCED REACTIONS

Reactions induced by proton bombardment were the first to be produced by artificially accelerated particles (§18-1). A typical reaction occurs when aluminum 27 is bombarded with protons. It is a $(p, \ \alpha)$ reaction, in which an alpha particle is emitted.

$$_{13}Al^{27} + {}_1H^1 \rightarrow ({}_{14}Si^{28}) \rightarrow {}_{12}Mg^{24} + {}_2He^4 \qquad [15\text{--}4]$$

An interesting reaction is the bombardment of boron 11, in which the compound nucleus breaks up into three alpha particles $(p, \ 3\alpha)$.

$$_5B^{11} + {}_1H^1 \rightarrow ({}_6C^{12}) \rightarrow {}_2He^4 + {}_2He^4 + {}_2He^4 \qquad [15\text{--}5]$$

Many other reactions are observed in which neutrons $(p, \ n)$, gamma rays $(p, \ \gamma)$, and deuterons $(p, \ d)$ are produced by proton bombardment.

DEUTERON-INDUCED REACTIONS; STRIPPING REACTION

Deuterons may readily be speeded up by a particle accelerator and may produce many types of transformation. The variety and interesting character of deuteron reactions results largely from the unusual character of the deuteron itself. The two protons and neutrons of which it is composed are very loosely bound, the binding energy being only 2.22 meV in comparison with a binding energy for the average nucleon in an atom of 7 or 8 meV. Furthermore the deuteron is very unsymmetric since the center of charge (the proton) and the center of mass are quite different.

If the deuteron is captured as a whole by a nucleus, reactions such as the two that follow when carbon ($_6C^{12}$) is irradiated could occur.

$$_6C^{12} + {}_1H^2 \rightarrow ({}_7N^{14}) \rightarrow {}_7N^{13} + {}_0n^1 \qquad [15\text{--}6]$$

or

$$_6C^{12} + {}_1H^2 \rightarrow ({}_7N^{14}) \rightarrow {}_6C^{13} + {}_1H^1 \qquad [15\text{--}7]$$

However, if the compound nucleus is formed, the first would be much more probable than the second since the Coulomb barrier would oppose emission of the proton but not the neutron. Quite different reactions may occur in which the picture of the deuteron being included in the compound nucleus is not correct. If the kinetic energy of the deuteron is not large the Coulomb field of the nucleus may in effect turn the proton back while the neutron proceeds onward and is captured. At higher energies both particles *may* be captured but a new effect may also occur. If one of the deuteron's two particles makes a more direct hit on a nucleus than the other, it may be captured while the other proceeds onward pretty much in the direction of the original beam. This is called a *"stripping reaction"* because either a proton or neutron is stripped from the deuteron by the target nucleus. The types of reaction which the nucleus may undergo depend then on which particle is captured.

PHOTON-INDUCED REACTIONS

The disintegration of an atomic nucleus by high-energy gamma-ray bombardment is called photodisintegration. Of the various ways in which photodisintegration of a nucleus may occur, a single example, that of aluminum 27 $(\gamma, 2p)$, is here given.

$$_{13}Al^{27} + \gamma \rightarrow (_{13}Al^{27})^* \rightarrow _{11}Na^{25} + _1H^1 + _1H^1 \qquad [15\text{-}8]$$

The star indicates that the intermediate nucleus is in an excited state since it is still $_{13}Al^{27}$ but it has now absorbed the energy of the gamma ray and one or more nucleons must be raised to higher energy levels.

A reaction such as 15-8 can only take place when the gamma-ray has energy equal to or greater than the *threshold energy* for the reaction. This threshold is the minimum energy required to produce the particular reaction and this minimum must supply the required separation energy (binding energy) of any particle ejected. Of such reactions perhaps the most interesting of all is the photodisintegration of the deuteron. The threshold energy for this reaction is the important quantity, the binding energy of the neutron to the proton. It has been determined with high precision by measuring the neutron yield for different gamma-ray energies and projecting the curve so obtained to the point of zero yield.

Although (γ, n) reactions would be expected to be far more probable than (γ, p) reactions because of the Coulomb barrier which opposes proton emission, it so happens that more (γ, p) reactions have been observed than expected. One explanation of this is that in some instances the compound nucleus is not formed but photodisintegration may take place immediately with the energy of the gamma ray acting directly to eject a proton.

Studies of the readily obtainable (γ, n) reactions have been made on many isotopes and the binding energies of the "last neutron" so obtained show significant drops in binding energy just after isotopes possessing 20, 28, 50, 82 and 126 neutrons. These results were among the first to indicate the unusually high stability of isotopes with these numbers of neutrons (§14-11).

INDUCED RADIOACTIVITY

Many of the nuclei produced in nuclear reactions are unstable and undergo radioactive decay in a manner similar to natural radioactive nuclei decay. This is called *induced radioactivity*, sometimes called *artificial radioactivity*. It was discovered in 1933 by Irene Curie and her husband Frederic Joliot and for this they received the Nobel Prize in 1935. At the time there were only some forty naturally radioactive elements known. Since then it has been possible to induce radioactivity (that is, to form unstable isotopes) in every known element not already radioactive, even including hydrogen.

The Curie-Joliots were studying the emission of positrons from light elements bombarded with high-speed alpha particles. They observed that sometimes the bombarded atoms continued to emit positrons after the alpha-ray bombardment had ceased. This emission of positrons was observed to decrease in time after the manner of natural radioactive decay. However, no naturally radioactive substance had been observed to emit any other than alpha, beta, and gamma rays. Half-life periods were measured for boron and aluminum for which the values 14 min and 3.25 min, respectively, were obtained. They then suggested that the effect of the bombardment of boron was to dislodge a neutron, leaving the nucleus of nitrogen 13 according to the following scheme:

$$_5B^{10} + _2He^4 \rightarrow _7N^{13} + _0n^1 \qquad [15\text{--}9]$$

where $_0n^1$ represents the dislodged neutron. The nitrogen nucleus produced by this reaction they surmised to be unstable and suggested that it might decay from nitrogen 13 to carbon 13 by the emission of a positive electron, or positron as follows:

$$_7N^{13} \rightarrow _6C^{13} + _{+1}e^0 \qquad [15\text{--}10]$$

where $_{+1}e^0$ represents the positron. This surmise was later confirmed although more accurate measurement of the half-life proved it to be slightly less than 10 minutes.

In a similar manner the bombardment of aluminum (Al^{27}) was found to produce by neutron emission an isotope of phosphorus, which was also unstable, giving rise to positron emission and the production of silicon (Si^{30}):

$$_{13}Al^{27} + _2He^4 \rightarrow _{15}P^{30} + _0n^1 \qquad [15\text{--}11]$$

$$_{15}P^{30} \rightarrow _{14}Si^{30} + _1e^0 \qquad [15\text{--}12]$$

Later it was found that the atoms of some elements thus made artificially radioactive may decay by negative electron emission, and if the resultant nucleus is not formed in the ground state in either case gamma rays will also be emitted.

15-3. Nuclear Resonance Radiation, Mössbauer Effect

A number of attempts had been made to show that gamma radiation from an excited nucleus could be absorbed by a similar nucleus in what is called a *resonance* effect just as in the optical realm light from excited sodium atoms may be absorbed by resonance by other sodium atoms which then become excited. The existence of this kind of *nuclear resonance radiation* was detected in a series of experiments involving different methods between 1950 and 1955 by Moon and also by Metzger and their respective co-workers. These results were experimentally confirmed by R. Mössbauer in 1958 at Heidelberg. At the same time he found a new effect to which his name is attached and which has been descriptively called "recoilless" or "recoil-free" radiation. For this he was awarded the Nobel Prize in 1961. Much of the importance of this work lies in the opening up of new fields of investigation.

The gamma-ray frequencies produced by different transitions in a nucleus represent lines in the gamma-ray spectrum just as frequencies in the optical region represent spectral lines. Ordinary spectral lines are not ideally narrow but are broadened, for one thing, by the Doppler effect resulting from random thermal agitation, some of the atoms moving toward the observer and some moving away at any instant. So also are the lines in a gamma-ray spectrum broadened and one of the chief causes of the broadening is the energy loss a gamma-ray photon sustains by recoil of the emitter.

According to the law of conservation of momentum, if a gamma-ray photon is emitted in one direction with a particular amount of momentum, the emitter should recoil in the opposite direction with the same amount of momentum. The energy of recoil comes from the energy of excitation of the nucleus and thereby diminishes the energy (and the frequency) of the photon. Since there are various ways in which recoil may take place the energy of recoil may vary and this leads to a spread of gamma-ray energies and consequent broadening of the line representing a particular energy transition of the nucleus.

If the emitting nucleus is part of a crystal arrangement of atoms the recoil might be taken up by the crystal as a whole but if so the small velocity of recoil would carry off a negligible amount of energy. If the recoil is taken up by the nucleus itself then presumably lattice vibrations would be set up in the crystal and appreciable energy would be drawn from the photon. If the lattice vibrations are quantized then quantum physics predicts that a certain minimum amount of energy would be required to set up the lowest vibrational energy state. If a photon of sufficiently low energy (frequency) could be found, it was believed possible that it might be below the amount required to set up lattice vibrations and in that case no appreciable energy would be taken from the photon. The emitted frequency would then give a "very sharp line" representing with great precision the energy change of the nucleus.

As a source of gamma radiation Mössbauer used the 129 keV transition of iridium Ir^{191} and measured the absorption by similar unexcited nuclei in another sample of the same material. The resonance between emitter and absorber was so sharp that the gamma-ray line could have no more energy width than 4.6×10^{-6} eV and this could only be if no appreciable energy were lost in recoil of the absorber or emitter. If both absorber and emitter were relatively at rest the absorption was a maximum. If the emitter was moved toward or away from the absorber at speeds of only a few cm/sec the Doppler shift changed the frequency of the photon enough that it was no longer in resonance with the absorber and absorption dropped quickly to zero.

Aside from the direct value of the discovery, the possible applications have aroused great interest. In addition to investigating nuclear spectral lines or their fine structure it may be possible to investigate hyperfine structure and thereby learn more about the nucleus itself. In a striking application Pound and Rebka (1960) were able to detect and measure the effect of the earth's gravitational field on emitted radiation. This is the gravitational "red shift" predicted by the general theory of relativity. Some idea of the supersensitivity of this method can be gained by recalling that in the past this had been one of the most difficult effects to measure and the results had been in some doubt even for light radiated by the most massive stars.

15-4. Energy Balance, Q; Isotopic Masses from Nuclear Reactions

Although reactions 15-1 and 15-2 are written in such a way that mass numbers balance before and after, and total electric charge balances before and after, the energies involved do not balance as the reactions are thus written. According to the law of conservation of energy, the total energy after the reaction, including any which is released or absorbed, should be equal to the total before the reaction. This, of course, includes the relativistic energy equivalent of the masses involved, and not the mass numbers but the actual masses. If there is a net decrease in mass after the reaction, the energy equivalent of that loss of mass is released and goes into kinetic energy of the products, including the energy of possible gamma radiation.

Such a reaction is said to be *exothermic* (or *exoergic*), and if the mass is increased with attendant absorption of energy the reaction is said to be *endothermic* (or *endoergic*).

The amount of energy required to balance any reaction is designated by Q and is frequently spoken of as the Q *value*. When the Q value of a reaction is positive the amount of energy represented by Q has been released and is divided between the products of the reaction in the form of kinetic energy of motion. The complete symbolic representation for any reaction, including conservation of energy and mass, must include the symbol Q or its actual value in amu or meV. For instance, to indicate energy-balance, reaction 15-1 should now be written

$$_2He^4 + {}_7N^{14} \rightarrow {}_8O^{17} + {}_1H^1 + Q \qquad [15\text{-}13]$$

The precise measurement of Q values has made it possible to determine isotopic masses of many of the lighter elements with much precision from a knowledge of the energies and masses involved in various nuclear reactions. This serves as a valuable check on mass spectrographic measurements such as those given in Table 3-1.

The Q value of a reaction may be determined best from measurements of the energies of incident and emerging particles by magnetic or electrostatic deflection. Beginning with the known Q value of a reaction involving oxygen 16, if the masses of the incident and emergent particles are known, the mass of the product nucleus may easily be determined. However, if a complete evaluation is to be made by nuclear processes the masses of incident and emergent particles may not be known. It is then necessary to find enough independent reactions so as to set up as many energy-mass equations as there are unknown quantities. The equations may then be solved for the unknowns. In the determination of the mass of the proton by this method Li, Whaling, Fowler, and Lauritsen in 1951 made use of the Q values of 14 reactions. One of the most important results of this method is that masses may be determined for nuclei that do not lend themselves to the methods of the mass spectroscope. A few examples of the results of such measurements are given in Table 15-1. The agreement with mass spectroscopic measurements is particularly good for the lighter nuclei.

TABLE 15-1. SOME ISOTOPIC MASSES DETERMINED
BY NUCLEAR REACTIONS

(compared with measurements by mass spectrograph)

Isotope	By Nuclear Reactions	By Mass Spectrograph
Helium 4	4.003873 (± 15)	4.003860 (± 12)
Oxygen 16	16.0000000 (standard)	16.0000000 (standard)
Lithium 7	7.018223 (± 26)	7.018180 (± 12)
Carbon 12	12.003804 (± 17)	12.0038167 (± 8)
Neon 20	19.998777 (± 21)	19.997771 (± 12)

15-5. Cross Sections for Nuclear Processes

The term cross section is frequently used in describing the efficiency of a nuclear process or rather the probability of its occurrence. If the diameter d of a nucleus could be obtained by direct measurement, the projected area of the nucleus would be called its *geometrical cross section* and would be given by the simple geometrical formula: area $= \frac{1}{4}\pi d^2 = \pi r^2$. If there is 1 nucleus per cm^3 in a volume, the projected area of which facing the bombarding particles is 1 cm^2, the probability that a bombarding particle crossing the region will hit the single nucleus is merely the ratio of the projected area πr^2 of that nucleus to the projected area 1 cm^2 of the entire region. If n nuclei are exposed to bombardment per cm^2 the probability of a hit is n times larger, assuming that there are not enough particles for their projected areas to overlap appreciably. The probability of a hit on some nucleus, when a particle strikes a given area, is then simply the ratio of the total projected areas of the nuclei to the total area (Fig. 15-2). On account of the small area of cross section of a nucleus, the probability of a hit is extremely small unless very large numbers of nuclei are present, and to assure many hits it is necessary to have intense beams of bombarding particles. Even under favorable conditions only one hit in a hundred thousand may occur.

The bombardment of nuclei may result in many different effects such as elastic or inelastic scattering, transmutations of various kinds, or the splitting of a nucleus (fission). Instead of speaking of the relative probabilities of such events, it is customary to speak of the relative cross sections of a given nucleus for such events. The cross sections are computed from observed probabilities. Since the square centimeter is an awkwardly large unit with which to measure anything so small as the cross section of a nucleus, a more appropriate unit has been chosen. It is 10^{-24} cm^2 and is called the *barn*. The story is that for certain processes this area was humorously referred to as being "as big as a barn," and the name persisted, an interesting commentary on scientific jargon and the growth of language.

For a type of event that occurs readily, the computed cross section is relatively large and may be as much as a thousand barns or more. For a

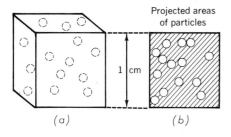

Projected areas of particles

(a) (b)

Fig. 15-2. Probability that a particle entering an area of 1 cm^2 will hit a particle in the volume indicated at a is the ratio of total projected cross-sectional area of the particles shown at b to the total target area of 1 cm^2.

rarer type of event the cross section is small and may be much less than a thousandth of a barn. In ordinary elastic collision of gas molecules the cross sections are referred to as "geometrical" since they depend essentially on what we think of as "ordinary geometrical cross sections." The cross section of a particle for other types of events is defined as the effective projected area which would account for the frequency of the event if it depended only on the geometrical dimensions. But when the probability of occurrence is much larger or much smaller the cross sections are hardly geometrical in the ordinary sense and may involve complex factors.

15-6. Release of Nuclear Energy by Fusion: Heat of Stars

Two nuclear processes of outstanding interest are those of *fusion* of nuclei and *fission* of nuclei. It had long been thought to be impossible by any man-made laboratory method to obtain large-scale release of nuclear energy by conversion of some fraction (if not all) of nuclear mass to energy according to the energy-mass relation, $E = mc^2$. However, with the discovery of *nuclear fission* (next chapter) and the development of the uranium or plutonium fission bomb the situation was abruptly and dramatically changed. Although only a fraction of the nuclear mass is converted into energy the scale of the energy release is now well known to all.

From Fig. 14-6 it is evident that not only could there be in theory such an energy release, if the more massive nuclei could be split into nuclei of intermediate mass, but also a similar if not larger energy release would accompany the *fusion* of nuclei of low mass at the other end of the atomic series into more massive nuclei. But this it was believed could only occur under the extreme condition of high pressure and high temperature existing in the stars.

After the development of the "hydrogen bomb," which is a *fusion* bomb (to be carefully distinguished from a *fission* bomb) this process too became a reality and many efforts have been made to control the process and slow it down so that the energy release could be used for peaceful purposes. However, the difficulties of doing this have indeed been formidable. To bring the nuclei of two atoms close enough together for them to start to interpenetrate and fuse into a single nucleus means that the nuclei must not only be brought close together by high pressure but their thermal motions must then bring them within fusing distance. In the hydrogen bomb this is accomplished by using a uranium or plutonium *fission* bomb to start the *fusion* chain reaction by simulating the high temperature and pressure of a star. Unlike the fission bomb there is no upper limit to the size of a fusion bomb. After the intense fusion flame has been started it can spread throughout any mass of material.

To start the fusion process on a smaller scale and control the rate many methods have been tried, particularly those involving the *plasma* or fully ionized region of an electric discharge in a gas or vapor. Exceedingly intense plasmas have been produced where a discharge carries a large current in a restricted region, and temperatures of several million degrees along with very high pressures have been attained for very brief periods of time. Attempts to contain these plasmas by magnetic fields, rather than by material substances which could not stand such temperatures, have resulted in such intriguing names as "magnetic bottle," "magnetic mirror," "stellarator," etc. which space does not permit us to describe. For one thing, since the products of fusion are in general not radioactive, the fusion process could result in the elimination of radioactive waste which is such a serious problem with present nuclear reactors. For another thing the supplies of hydrogen and other light elements are almost limitless compared to supplies of uranium.

The source of the heat of the sun and the stars had been a great mystery before 1900 and even after the discovery of radioactivity the theories were recognized as being inadequate to account for the large amounts of energy involved. With the recognition of energy release by fusion the situation was completely changed and several different processes have been suggested. One of these called the *carbon cycle* was suggested by Bethe and it is one of the more probable ways in which nuclear energy is released from the sun and the stars. The process involves carbon nuclei and hydrogen nuclei, helium being formed in the process and the carbon acting as a kind of catalyzer. The series of reactions is given as follows:

$$_6C^{12} + {}_1H^1 \rightarrow ({}_7N^{13}) \rightarrow {}_6C^{13} + {}_{+1}e^0 \qquad [15\text{--}14]$$

$$_6C^{13} + {}_1H^1 \rightarrow {}_7N^{14} \qquad [15\text{--}15]$$

$$_7N^{14} + {}_1H^1 \rightarrow ({}_8O^{15}) \rightarrow {}_7N^{15} + {}_{+1}e^0 \qquad [15\text{--}16]$$

$$_7N^{15} + {}_1H^1 \rightarrow ({}_8O^{16}) \rightarrow C^{12} + He^4 \qquad [15\text{--}17]$$

In effect the carbon nucleus captures four successive protons. After first ejecting two positrons the four remaining particles group themselves together as an alpha particle which is then thrown off by the compound nucleus leaving carbon as at the start of the cycle. About 25 meV of energy is thereby released for every alpha particle formed.

Another probable process is called the *proton-proton cycle* in which 4 protons are fused by three steps into an alpha particle plus 2 protons with approximately the same energy release as in the carbon cycle.

$$H^1 + H^1 \rightarrow H^2 + e^+ + \nu \qquad [15\text{--}18]$$

$$H^2 + H^1 \rightarrow He^3 + \gamma \qquad [15\text{--}19]$$

$$H^3 + He^3 \rightarrow He^4 + 2H^1 \qquad [15\text{--}20]$$

The only requirement, for the temperature to remain constant, is that the stellar object consume sufficient mass every day to release energy equal to that lost by radiation in the same length of time. The sun, for instance, could apparently retain its temperature constant by a decrease in mass of about 400 million tons per second. However, the total mass of the sun is so large that even at this rate it would take about 1 million million years (10^{12}) for the sun to use up $1/16$ of its mass.

15-7. Properties of Nuclei and Conservation Laws for Nuclear Reactions

The chief properties of nuclei are mass, size, electric charge, spin, dipole magnetic moment, statistics and parity. Most of these properties have already been discussed in more or less detail. For some purposes other characteristics become important such as quadrupole electric moment.

Every nucleus that possesses angular momentum (spin) also possesses a dipole magnetic moment as if along with mechanical spin there is circulation of electric charge. If the spin is zero the magnetic moment is also zero. However, there is no evidence that nuclei have dipole electric moments. Every nucleus possesses a positive charge and if the charge is not central (or spherically symmetric) then it will have an uneven spatial distribution. This distribution is characterized as a nuclear *quadrupole electric moment* (or some higher multipole) and its effect may sometimes be observed in the very-fine splitting of some spectral lines. The distribution of charge therefore is an important characteristic of nuclei.

Certain properties of nuclei are conserved in any nuclear reaction and these are the "rules of the game" which apply to all such reactions and by which an analysis of a reaction can be made. Some of the most important conservation rules have been borrowed directly from the macroscopic world of common phenomena and we have found them completely dependable.

First and foremost are the laws of conservation of energy and conservation of linear momentum and angular momentum. The latter is particularly important since it has to do with the spin and also the possible orbital motion of nuclear particles. All experimental evidence indicates that electric charge is conserved in the atomic realm as it is in the everyday world. To these are added conservation of *statistics* and conservation of *parity* which have no classical counterpart. In dealing with some of the new particles (Chap. 17) we may also find "strange" particles and a quality of "*strangeness*" that may be conserved. Thus the physicist always looks for some type of *permanence* to which he can relate phenomena. The chief conservation laws for atomic and nuclear phenomena are as follows.

1. Conservation of energy (including equivalent mass)
2. Conservation of linear momentum

3. Conservation of angular momentum (spin and orbital)
4. Conservation of charge
5. Conservation of statistics
6. Conservation of parity (except for weak interactions)

CONSERVATION OF STATISTICS

The conservation of statistics is one of the important rules "obeyed" in any nuclear transformation. The correlation of statistics with the wave functions of nuclear particles was mentioned at the end of §11-5. It was stated there that Fermi statistics apply to single particles or to groups in the nucleus when the number of nucleons is odd. Bose statistics apply when the number of nucleons is even.

If Fermi and Bose statistics are represented symbolically by -1 and $+1$, respectively, the statistics of a group of particles are determined by the product of the symbols for each. For instance, if an electron and positron annihilate each other, before annihilation the statistics of the system are $-1 \times -1 = +1$. After annihilation the statistics of the system, according to conservation of statistics, should still be $+1$. Since we have agreed to represent the statistics of photons (Bose statistics) by the symbol $+1$, and since two photons are formed by pair annihilation, the two photons have statistics represented by $+1 \times +1 = +1$, and the law of conservation of statistics is obeyed.

With these rules of conservation, *allowed* and *forbidden reactions* may be predicted, and by application of one or more or all of these principles the character of the reaction may be more completely described.

15-8. Parity: Not Conserved in Weak Interactions

Parity is a mathematical concept which describes the kind of space symmetry of physical phenomena. The test of this symmetry is to "reflect" the wave function ψ in its space coordinates. This merely means changing the signs of the x, y, and z coordinates from plus to minus (excluding coordinates representing spin). This is equivalent to changing from a right-hand coordinate system to a left-hand system. If the sign of the wave function as a whole does not change, it is said to represent even $(+)$ parity.

$$\psi(-x, -y, -z) = +\psi(x, y, z) \qquad [15\text{--}21]$$

If the sign of the function does change, it is said to represent odd $(-)$ parity.

$$\psi(-x, -y, -z) = -\psi(x, y, z) \qquad [15\text{--}22]$$

The parity of a system of particles is determined by the product of the parities of the separate particles. All fundamental particles and all atomic and nuclear energy states possess either even or odd parity. This concept was proposed by Eugene Wigner (Nobel Prize, 1963).

If parity is conserved the new equations after reflection will be equally valid wave functions for the physical phenomenon that they describe. Since a glove for the left hand is a mirror reflection of a glove for the right hand, it has been said that if parity is conserved "Nature does not know her right hand from her left." If parity is not conserved she does.

Until 1956 it was generally believed that parity was conserved in all nuclear transformations. Direct experimental evidence was then obtained showing that in the case of phenomena involving the *weak interaction force*, parity is not conserved. The overthrow of such an apparently well-established conservation law even in exceptional cases is an unusual occurrence and created much excitement in the scientific world. The conservation of parity was called into question when two types of mesons (then called *tau* and *theta* but now called *K* mesons) were found to be indistinguishable except that one decayed into three pi mesons whereas the other decayed into two. It was concluded that the two mesons could actually be one and the same particle, but if so only one mode of decay would be permitted if parity was always conserved. If such a particle could undergo either one or other of these two modes of decay, parity could not be conserved. Two theoretical physicists, T. D. Lee and C. N. Yang, pursued the idea that parity might not be conserved in the "weak interactions" involved in the radioactive emission of beta particles. Their work set the stage for a full-scale experimental test and led them to the Nobel Prize for 1957. The problem was how to make such a delicate test.

The critical experiment which showed that parity is not always conserved was performed in December, 1956, at the National Bureau of Standards, Washington, D. C., by C. S. Wu of Columbia University and her collaborators at the Bureau under E. Ambler. They cooled radioactive cobalt 60 to a temperature of less than 1° above absolute zero. At this temperature it was possible to obtain alignment of the nuclei of the cobalt atoms in a magnetic field so that the magnetic moments of the nuclei nearly all pointed in one direction. When the beta-ray emission from the nuclei was measured it was found to occur predominantly in one direction. This was direct evidence that the emission is not mirror-symmetrical and that parity is not conserved in beta-ray emission.

Other experiments were soon performed confirming the work of Wu and Ambler. Using methods of great refinement it was proved that the neutrino always spins in one direction viewed along the direction of motion, and the antineutrino always spins in the opposite direction. Thus they represent two different kinds of helicity (§17-6), right-hand and left-hand. Parity is not conserved in these instances and for weak interactions apparently Nature does distinguish her right hand from her left.

Problems

1. Write the energy-balanced reaction for the formation of a deuteron by the combination of a proton and a neutron. What is the mass deficit? Find the Q value in meV.

2. A carbon C^{12} nucleus (atomic mass = 12.00390 amu) captures a neutron to form a C^{13} nucleus (atomic mass = 13.00755 amu). Is this reaction endoergic (energy absorbed) or exoergic (energy released)? What is the Q value for the reaction in meV?

3. Show that although $_4Be^8$ has a positive binding energy of 56 meV and does not tend to disintegrate into neutrons and protons, it will spontaneously disintegrate into two alpha particles. What is the Q value for this reaction? Is it positive or negative? Would you expect to find $_4Be^8$ in nature? The atomic mass of $_4Be^8$ is 8.00785 amu.

4. A nucleus of fluorine $_9F^{19}$ could be formed of how many neutrons and how many protons? Find the Q value for such a reaction in meV. Is it positive or negative? What is the average binding energy per nucleon? The atomic mass of $_9F^{19}$ = 19.00446 amu.

Note. In nuclear reactions energy-mass is conserved and momentum is conserved. The equation for conservation of energy must include the rest-mass energy of the particles. For a target nucleus of mass M_x initially at rest and a bombarding particle of mass m_a and kinetic energy E_{ka}, the conservation of energy-mass requires that

$$M_x c^2 + m_a c^2 + E_{ka} = M_y c^2 + E_{ky} + m_b c^2 + E_{kb}$$

where M_y is the mass of the resultant nucleus (product nucleus), m_b is the mass of the ejected particle, and E_{ky} and E_{kb} are the kinetic energies of M_y and m_b after the reaction takes place. When M_y is large compared to m_b, its kinetic energy and its momentum may be neglected without too much error.

5. Show that the Q of a reaction given by the above equation is

$$Q = (M_x + m_a - M_y - m_b) c^2 = E_{ky} + E_{kb} - E_{ka} \cong E_{kb} - E_{ka}$$

6. A target nucleus is hit by a particle having a kinetic energy of 5 meV. The ejected particle has an energy of 4.5 meV. Is the reaction endoergic or exoergic? What becomes of the energy difference?

7. An experimenter is puzzled to find particles emitted from a target nucleus possessing more energy than the bombarding particles. Explain.

8. Compute the minimum kinetic energy which a neutron must possess to eject a proton of 5 meV energy from a nitrogen nucleus initially at rest. Assume the neutron is captured by the nucleus. The mass of the nitrogen atom $_7N^{14}$ is 14.007526 amu. The mass of the product atom is 14.007692 amu. What is it?

9. A nitrogen $_7N^{14}$ nucleus is hit by and captures an alpha particle of 7 meV and a proton is ejected. What is the energy of the proton if the mass of the product atom is 17.004537 amu?

10. An experiment is set up to detect neutrinos [actually antineutrinos ($\bar{\nu}$) see Chap. 17] by the reaction in which a proton, when capturing an antineutrino, ejects a positron (antielectron) and becomes a neutron according to the reaction

$$p + \bar{\nu} \rightarrow n + e^+$$

What minimum energy of the antineutrino is required to make this reaction energetically possible?

11. If an alpha particle inside of a nucleus possesses kinetic energy of 2 meV, approximately how many times per second according to classical theory could it cross a diameter of the nucleus and collide with the nuclear barrier surface? Take diameter of nucleus to be 10^{-12} cm.

12. In the uranium series of radioactive elements a radium nucleus emits an alpha particle and becomes emanation which also emits an alpha particle and becomes polonium which in turn emits an alpha particle and becomes a radioactive isotope of lead. Why are the three alpha particles not emitted as a single $_6C^{12}$ nucleus?

13. Find the Q value of the reaction by which carbon 14 is formed in the earth's atmosphere from nitrogen by an n,p reaction. Assume the neutron is of thermal energy.

14. Assume a fast neutron is captured by a heavy nucleus and that the following reactions are possible, (n, α), (n, γ) and (n, p). Write these in the order of their probability of occurrence if the probability is determined only by the potential barrier.

15. In every instance of radioactive decay the emission of a particle results in the recoil of the product nucleus in the opposite direction if momentum is to be conserved. When a radium nucleus emits an alpha particle the total energy released (Q value) amounts to 4.88 meV. Assuming free recoil of the product nucleus, how much energy is carried off by the product nucleus?

Recommended Reading

Halliday, D., *Introductory Nuclear Physics*, 2nd ed. New York: John Wiley & Sons, Inc., 1955.

Segré, E., ed., *Experimental Nuclear Physics*, Vol. 1. New York: John Wiley & Sons, Inc., 1953.

Lapp, R. E. and Andrews, H. L., *Nuclear Radiation Physics*. Englewood Cliffs, N.J.: Prentice-Hall, Inc., 1954.

Nuclear Data, compiled by K. Way, L. Fano, M. Scott, and K. Thew. Washington, D.C., National Bureau of Standards, Circular 499 (1950) (and Supplements).

Pollard, E., and Davidson, W. L., *Applied Nuclear Physics*, 2nd ed. New York: John Wiley & Sons, Inc., 1951.

Morrison, P., "Nuclear Reactions," in *Experimental Nuclear Physics, Vol. II*. ed. by E. Segré., New York: John Wiley & Sons, Inc., 1953.

Morrison, P., "The Overthrow of Parity," *Scientific American*, Vol. 196, No. 4, p. 45 (1957).

Bishop, A. S., *Project Sherwood, The U. S. Program in Controlled Fusion*. Reading, Mass.: Addison-Wesley Publishing Company, Inc., 1958.

Neutron Physics

16-1. The Neutron

The discovery of the *neutron* was the culmination of a sequence of experiments by investigators in several countries and aptly illustrates the fact that science knows no national boundaries. In Germany in 1930, Bothe and Becker found that a very penetrating radiation is emitted when high-speed alpha particles strike beryllium or boron. The penetration of the radiation led them to assume that it was high-energy gamma radiation although it was more penetrating than any known gamma rays.

Irene Curie, and her husband Frederic Joliot, in France found to their surprise that putting a block of paraffin (Fig. 16-1) as an absorber in the path of the unknown rays increased by a factor of 2 the readings of the detector (an ionization chamber) instead of decreasing them. Absorption tests showed the rays could not be electrons but were most probably protons. However, if they assumed that protons were knocked out of the paraffin by gamma rays in Compton collisions, the gamma-ray energies would have to be unreasonably high. Since the absorption measurements indicated the emitted protons had energies of 4.5 meV, an application of the theory of Compton collisions showed that the gamma ray, to give a proton this energy, must have about 50 meV of energy although no such gamma ray was then known.

The grand climax came when Chadwick in England made more extensive experiments. He measured the range of protons knocked out of hydro-

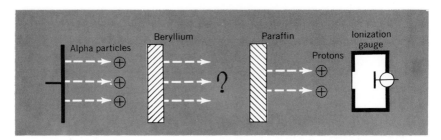

Fig. 16-1. The experiment of Curie and Joliot, showing protons dislodged from paraffin by unknown rays from beryllium bombarded by alpha particles. Chadwick demonstrated that the rays were neutral particles (neutrons).

gen by the unknown rays and found the range to be as much as 40 cm indicating energies up to 5.7 meV requiring gamma rays of perhaps 60 meV energy. He also measured the ranges of recoil particles from a number of other light elements. In his famous paper in 1932 he pointed out three things: 1, that no conceivable reaction could produce such high gamma-ray energies; 2, that gamma rays could not by any known means produce even a thousandth as many recoil particles; 3, that all difficulties disappeared if it was assumed that the unknown rays were a new kind of particle of about the same mass as the proton but zero charge. To this particle the name *neutron* was given. The existence of such a particle had been suggested by Rutherford a number of years earlier but no one had then been able to detect it.

MASS OF NEUTRON; MAGNETIC MOMENT

Chadwick could not measure the mass of the neutron directly since he could not deflect it by electric or magnetic fields. He did conclude correctly, however, from application of the law of conservation of momentum to his collision experiments, that the mass of the neutron must be slightly larger than that of the proton.

The mass of the neutron may now be quite accurately determined. One way is by first determining the mass of the deuteron (m_D) by magnetic deflection. This is 2.014194 atomic mass units (amu). But the deuteron is a neutron plus a proton and the proton mass (m_H) is

$$m_H = 1.007593 \text{ amu}$$

Since the binding energy of the proton and the neutron in the deuteron is 2.220 meV $= 0.002384$ amu (1 meV $= 1.07500 \times 10^{-3}$ amu) the mass of the neutron is

$$m_n = m_D - m_H + 0.002384$$

$$= 1.008985 \text{ amu}$$

Although neutrons possess no detectable net electric charge, experiments by Dunning and others showed that they possess a magnetic moment. Bloch and Alvarez measured the magnetic moment the value of which is now accepted as

$$\mu_n(\text{neutron}) = -1.9128 \pm 0.02 \text{ nuclear magnetons}$$

The negative sign indicates that the magnetic moment of the neutron points in a direction opposite to the angular momentum as if there were circulation of negative charge. For particles which possess a net charge it is easy to conceive of the magnetic moment as due to circulation of that charge, but in the case of the neutron which has no detectable net charge this explanation seems at first to break down. However, as previously mentioned, with the discovery of mesons, and the assumption of positive and negative meson clouds in the neutron, there may be a *net circulation* of meson charge even though the *net charge* is zero.

16-2. Production and Detection of Neutrons

Chadwick assumed that when alpha particles bombard beryllium the neutrons are produced in the following manner. When a beryllium nucleus $_4\text{Be}^9$ is hit by an alpha particle $_2\text{He}^4$ the neutron carries away 1 unit of mass and zero charge, thus leaving a nucleus of charge $2 + 4 = 6$ and of mass $9 + 4 - 1 = 12$, identified as an isotope of carbon. The symbolic representation of the reaction is

$$_2\text{He}^4 + _4\text{Be}^9 \rightarrow _6\text{C}^{12} + _0n^1 \qquad [16\text{--}1]$$

or

$$_4\text{Be}^9 (\alpha, n) \, _6\text{C}^{12}$$

where $_0n^1$ or just n is the symbol representing the neutron.

Neutrons are now produced in great abundance in the fission of heavy atoms in nuclear reactors, and intense streams of neutrons may be obtained from a suitable opening in the reactor shielding. They may in theory be ejected from any atom possessing them, but particularly from atoms rich in neutrons if such atoms are bombarded by sufficiently energetic particles. They are obtained especially by the bombardment of the lighter elements such as beryllium, boron, and lithium by alpha particles. They are produced in the upper atmosphere by cosmic-ray bombardment of air molecules.

The detection of neutrons, as distinct from other particles, was at first quite a problem. Since they possess no net electric charge they produce no appreciable ionization of a gas through which they pass and consequently leave no track in a cloud chamber, nor do they produce directly any ions in a G-M tube by which they may be detected. They may occasionally make head-on collisions with protons or other charged particles, imparting to them such speeds that they in turn produce ionization and are detected. This method has been adopted for fast neutrons, the counter being surrounded by a layer of paraffin or other material rich in protons.

A method more common for slow neutrons is that of lining the inside of a G-M tube or ionization chamber with a layer of something containing nuclei which may readily absorb neutrons, with the provision that the nucleus after absorption must be unstable and disintegrate by emitting an ionizing ray that can be detected (Fig. 16-2). A commonly used substance is boron trifluoride, containing B^{10}, which emits an alpha particle after capture of a neutron according to the following reaction:

$$_0n^1 + {_5}B^{10} \rightarrow {_2}He^4 + {_3}Li^7 \qquad [16\text{--}2]$$

Since the alpha particle is strongly ionizing it is easily detected. The method is particularly successful when the neutrons have speeds for which the probability of capture is large. The boron may also be contained in the gas in the tube.

16-3. Neutron Decay, Half-Life

Since the neutron (an uncharged particle) possesses more mass than the proton (a charged particle) it was suspected that a free neutron might be unstable. Early attempts to detect neutron decay were handicapped by the difficulty of procuring strong neutron beams and of controlling and detecting them. In 1948 it was estimated that the half-life was less than 30 minutes. In 1951 Robson, working with an intense beam of neutrons from the Chalk River (Canada) reactor, obtained a value of 12.8 minutes. As stated in §13-12 (reaction 13–17) a free neutron decays by beta emission and in the process an antineutrino is emitted.

16-4. Neutron Diffraction

One of the tests of the de Broglie hypothesis, that elementary particles have wavelengths given by the formula $\lambda = h/mv$, was made with neutrons.

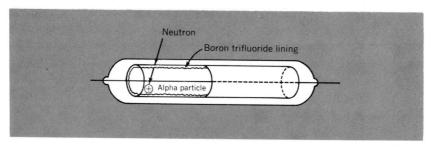

Fig. 16-2. Cut-away of G-M tube, showing boron trifluoride lining for neutron detection.

The equation predicts that neutrons having energies of the order of 1 eV would have wavelengths similar to ordinary x-rays and might show Bragg or von Laue diffraction by crystals, just as electrons do. The first experimental confirmation was obtained by Mitchell and Powers in 1936. With the development of intense neutron beams from nuclear reactors it became possible to obtain photographs of the reinforcement spot pattern by the method of von Laue (Fig. 16-3), as well as by the method of the Braggs. If the energy of a neutron is given in electron volts where V is the number of volts, the de Broglie formula with the numerical values of the constants gives for the neutron wavelength in angstroms (in the non-relativistic range below 100 meV)

$$\lambda \, \overset{\circ}{\text{A}} = \frac{0.286}{\sqrt{V}} \qquad [16\text{--}3]$$

From this it is evident that neutrons having energies in the thermal region have wavelengths of the order of magnitude of atomic spacings in crystals and that neutrons of some meV energy have wavelengths in the range of nuclear dimensions.

In addition to confirming the validity of the de Broglie equation in its application to neutrons, the results are of much interest because neutron

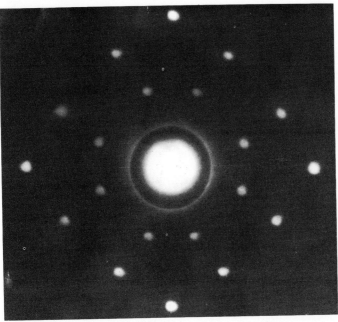

Fig. 16-3. Neutron diffraction by a crystal. Spots indicate reinforcement (in agreement with the de Broglie wavelength) similar to that of von Laue's experiment with x-rays. (Photo by Wollan and Shull. Courtesy, Oak Ridge National Laboratory.)

diffraction affords a valuable method for the study of the structure of matter. Whereas the scattering ability of the lighter elements is relatively small for x-rays, it is relatively large for neutrons, and neutron diffraction can be used to locate hydrogen and other light elements in molecular groupings. Techniques have now advanced to the point where many types of diffraction studies (similar to those in the field of x-rays) are made such as by reflection, transmission, the powder method, etc.

16-5. Neutron-Induced Reactions: Transuranic Elements

In 1934 particle accelerators were in their infancy and quite unable to produce particles of sufficient energy to disrupt the nuclei of the heavier atoms. In that year Fermi in Italy tried to produce nuclear transmutations by neutron bombardment. Since there is no appreciable nuclear potential barrier for neutrons, it was reasoned that even slow neutrons might enter a nucleus and be captured.

When uranium U^{238} was subjected to neutron bombardment it was found that radioactivity was induced, and that the product was a beta-ray emitter, whereas U^{238} is an alpha-ray emitter. This was interpreted to mean that neutrons had penetrated uranium nuclei and had produced an unstable isotope of U^{238}, presumably U^{239}. It was this *product nucleus* that was apparently radioactive and decayed by electron emission. Such emission would change a nucleus of atomic number 92 to one of atomic number 93, and this would represent the production of an atom of higher atomic number than any known natural atom. But the results were confused because a quite different and unsuspected phenomenon was also occurring, the splitting or *fission* of the uranium atom (§16-7). After World War II, and the discovery of fission, Fermi's belief that he had produced transuranic elements was amply confirmed. Now not only have many elements beyond uranium (Table 16-1) been produced by one type of reaction or another but many

TABLE 16-1.   TRANSURANIC ELEMENTS

Atomic Number	Element	Symbol
93	Neptunium	Np
94	Plutonium	Pu
95	Americium	Am
96	Curium	Cm
97	Berkelium	Bk
98	Californium	Cf
99	Einsteinium	Es
100	Fermium	Fm
101	Mendelevium	Md
102	Nobelium	No
103	Lawrencium	Lw

more isotopes of these elements have been produced although the high degree of instability of some makes them difficult to work with. Two elements, *neptunium* and *plutonium*, are of such importance that they will be described in more detail when the reactions in which they are involved are considered (§16-11).

Since Fermi's first experiments more reactions of transmutation have been produced by means of neutrons than by any other means. Low-, intermediate-, and high-energy neutrons have been used to bombard all types of light and heavy nuclei, and many hundreds of different reactions have been observed. Two typical neutron-induced reactions, both with aluminum 27, are shown below. In the first, neutron capture results in gamma-ray emission (n, γ).

$$_{13}Al^{27} + {}_0n^1 \rightarrow ({}_{13}Al^{28}) \rightarrow {}_{13}Al^{28} + \gamma \qquad [16\text{--}4]$$

In the second reaction (n, α), the capture of a higher energy neutron by the same nucleus results in alpha emission.

$$_{13}Al^{27} + {}_0n^1 \rightarrow ({}^{13}Al^{28}) \rightarrow {}_{11}Na^{24} + {}_2He^4 \qquad [16\text{--}4a]$$

The energies involved determine the probabilities of the results.

16-6. Resonance Capture of Neutrons

Low-energy neutrons are generally more likely to be scattered by elastic collisions after the manner of billiard balls than to be captured by a nucleus, but for certain quite sharply defined energies of the incident neutron the probability of capture is greatly increased, sometimes a thousandfold or more. This is called resonance capture, and has been explained by Breit and Wigner as being due to the neutron having exactly the right amount of energy corresponding to an excited state of the nucleus. At this energy the neutron is much more likely to produce excitation and remain in the nucleus than to pass through it. The cross section (§15-5) for such resonance capture is then said to be relatively large and may be hundreds or even many thousands of barns.

When low-energy neutrons are captured by light nuclei the most likely way for the compound nucleus to return to the normal state is by emission of a gamma ray. When low-energy neutrons are incident upon heavy nuclei the probability of capture is generally much larger, but either elastic scattering or capture with consequent gamma radiation may occur. Fig. 16-4 shows resonance absorption peaks in rhodium and silver for low-energy neutrons. Fig. 16-5 shows resonance absorption peaks for cadmium at higher energies and the broad absorption region for lower energy neutrons which makes cadmium almost opaque for neutrons in the thermal region. This is why it is often used as a neutron absorber.

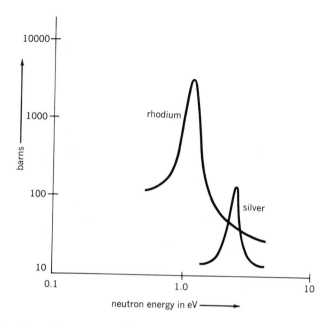

Fig. 16-4. Absorption cross section curves of rhodium and silver for low energy
neutrons showing sharp resonance absorption peaks for rhodium at 1.26 eV and for
silver at 5.2 eV.

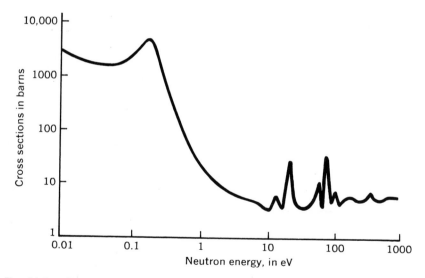

Fig. 16.5. Capture cross sections of cadmium for neutrons. Peaks represent resonance capture, and curve shows the very-high capture probability of cadmium for
slow neutrons.

Figure 16-6 illustrates the difference between strong resonance absorption and weak absorption in terms of the wave function of the neutron. At (a) only a small part of the amplitude of the ψ wave gets in to the nucleus, the remainder being presumably reflected. At (b) the absorption probability is so high that practically the whole amplitude of the ψ wave enters the nucleus. One of the early wave-mechanical theories of resonance absorption was developed by Breit and Wigner. By means of the Breit-Wigner formula a number of resonance absorption cross sections were successfully computed. The one for rhodium (Fig. 16-4) checked closely with experimental measurements.

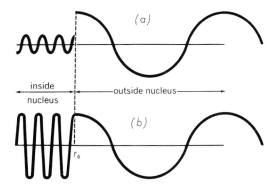

Fig. 16-6. The wave functions (ψ waves) outside and inside the nucleus for a neutron: a, small capture probability; b, large (resonance) capture probability.

16-7. Nature of Fission: Energy Release

When other investigators repeated Fermi's experiments on the transmutation of uranium by neutron capture, they were confronted with results that were puzzling. There seemed to be too many kinds of beta-ray emission and too many kinds of product atoms. In particular, Hahn and Strassmann in Germany worked with meticulous care, and finally succeeded in 1938 in separating by chemical means a tiny amount of an element only about half as heavy as uranium which they were sure had not existed before the experiments were started. Although there was scarcely enough to permit a chemical test, the tests that they did perform gave indications that the substance was barium. Later they concluded that krypton had been formed at the same time, along with the barium. This suggested that the uranium atom had been split into two more or less equal parts, the phenomenon that we now call *fission*. See Plate 2.

Early predictions were soon verified that the products of fission of uranium would be driven apart with total kinetic energies of nearly 200 million electron volts. To grasp the magnitude of this energy release we need only compare it with the most violent chemical explosives known to man, such as TNT, where the total energy released is not more than a few electron volts per molecule. It was at once evident that the fission of uranium releases nearly 100 million times as much energy per atom as any common explosive.

It had been known from the work of Dempster with the mass spectrograph that U^{238} possesses a rare isotope U^{235}. Ordinary uranium is composed of U^{238} for the most part, only 0.7 per cent of the atoms being U^{235}, or approximately 1 in every 143 atoms. There are also other possible isotopes of uranium. Early in the study of fission the question arose as to which of the isotopes of uranium underwent fission. The separation of very tiny samples of U^{238} and U^{235} by A. O. Nier made the first test possible, and later work proved that U^{238} nuclei would undergo fission only when subjected to bombardment by fast neutrons. U^{235} nuclei, on the other hand, would undergo fission by absorption of slow as well as of fast neutrons. Apparently the energy of a slow neutron is sufficient to give the U^{235} nucleus more than the activation energy, but it is not sufficient to give the U^{238} nucleus as much as its activation energy. Consequently slow neutrons would induce fission only in U^{235} nuclei, and fast neutrons would induce fission in U^{238} as well as in U^{235}.

Looking back at the curve (Fig. 14-6) for the average binding energy of nucleons in the nucleus, it is seen that the heaviest nuclei have less binding energy per nucleon than the nuclei of middle weight into which they would be split when fission occurs. Consequently the excess of energy over that required by these middle-weight atoms must be released when fission occurs. This release of energy by fission of a massive nucleus into two middle-weight nuclei must be carefully distinguished from the release by *fusion* described in §15-6, which occurs at the other end of the atomic series.

In U^{235} the actual kinetic energy of the separate particles released in fission has been measured by a delicate calorimetric method and has been found to be about 177 meV. To this must be added the energy of the emitted gamma rays, amounting to something like 23 meV. This brings the total close to 200 meV, as predicted. If the masses of all the particles before and after fission were known accurately, it would be a simple matter to compute the energy released by converting the loss in mass occurring during fission to energy according to the Einstein energy-mass relation. The nature of fission can be described in terms of the liquid-drop model of the nucleus. In an ordinary droplet of liquid, the total energy of the particles in the droplet is not usually adequate to overcome the forces holding the particles together in droplet form. However, if energy is added to the droplet in such a way as to set the droplet in vibration, it will alternately elongate and shorten until, if the amplitude of vibration is large enough, it may divide into two droplets. On the basis of the liquid-drop model, something like this is pictured as happening in the nucleus.

According to Eq. 14–6a the forces of repulsion between positive charges in the nucleus (Coulomb repulsion) are balanced by the binding forces between nucleons, but also there is a kind of surface effect similar to surface tension in the liquid droplet. The net binding energy E of a nucleus owing to the three factors given in Eq. 14–6a may be written:

$$E \text{ (net)} = E \text{ (volume)} - E \text{ (coulomb)} - E \text{ (surface)}$$

In a complete formulation other terms may be needed, and in particular in the fission of uranium a term that depends on whether the mass number is even or odd turns out to be of importance. It need not, however, be considered here. What is important here is to note that, if the nucleus is deformed, there will be a decrease in net binding energy owing to increase in the surface area, and if sufficient energy is added to the nucleus to produce such distortions or vibrations these may be sufficiently violent to disrupt the nucleus (Fig. 16-7).

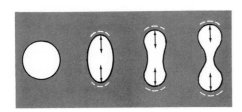

Fig. 16-7. Vibration of nucleus leading to fission, according to the droplet theory.

BOHR-WHEELER THEORY

Bohr and Wheeler in 1939 made a detailed mathematical study of what can happen when energy is added to the drop causing oscillations and distortion. In a first approximation it appears that the volume energy remains unchanged when the drop is distorted and the energy of electrostatic repulsion decreases. The decrease is more than balanced by the effect of increased surface. In this connection it should be remembered that in all phenomena, where both surface and volume relations are involved, surface effects increase in proportion to volume effects for smaller and smaller spheres or droplets. The reason is that the ratio of the surface of a sphere to its volume is

$$\frac{4\pi r^2}{4/3\ \pi r^3} = \frac{3}{r}$$

From this it is seen that, as a sphere is made smaller, the ratio of surface to volume increases in inverse proportion to the radius.

Bohr and Wheeler derived the following formula for the net gain in surface energy E_s for a small deformation of a droplet:

$$\text{Gain in energy} = \frac{2}{5} E_s \left(1 - 0.022 \times \frac{Z^2}{A} \right) \qquad [16\text{--}5]$$

where Z is the atomic number and A is the mass number. For nuclei of larger and larger Z, the second term in the parenthesis approaches unity, and would become unity if Z^2/A were to equal 45.4. The parenthesis would then become zero, and the result is taken to be the limit of stability. At this point the nucleus could presumably no longer exist and would perhaps undergo fission or break up into smaller pieces.

For U^{238} the value of Z^2/A is 35.5, and it times 0.022 is 0.78. A small increase in energy of vibration or deformation then could cause fission. Consequently, in any droplet, if large deformations occur the droplet should undergo fission when the energy of deformation is more than the limiting value known as the *activation energy*. In uranium the addition of a neutron to the nucleus may add more than this limit, and fission may then occur. Generally, it may be remembered that the average binding energy of a neutron in a heavy nucleus is in the neighborhood of 7.5 meV. When an extra neutron is introduced into such a nucleus, especially if it is a high-energy neutron, the average binding energy may be so reduced that the nucleus becomes unstable and divides by fission. If in any nucleus the energy received is less than the limiting activation energy, the excess will most likely be removed by gamma-ray emission or other radioactive decay.

According to Bohr and Wheeler, slow-neutron capture produces fission in U^{235} in the following way. They computed the energy required to produce fission in U^{235} and obtained a value of 5.2 meV. The kinetic energy of a slow neutron is negligible, but the energy equivalent of the mass that it loses in the form of binding energy is large. The loss in mass when a neutron is captured by a U^{235} nucleus to form U^{236} is 0.0073 amu. This is equal to 6.8 meV energy, and its release in the nucleus is therefore more than enough to produce fission. In U^{238} the binding energy is less, and not enough energy is released to produce fission unless the bombarding neutron has a minimum kinetic energy of 1.1 meV.

The simple liquid-drop theory does not explain why fission hardly ever produces two nuclei of equal masses. A considerable amount of study has been devoted to the products of nuclear fission, and the curve of Fig. 16-8 illustrates the percentage of products formed in many fissions. Note that the two peaks of the curve denote that in the largest percentage of cases fission occurs with one particle in the neighborhood of mass 94 and the other in the neighborhood of mass 140. The sharp drop at the middle of the curve indicates that uranium divides into equal nuclei in only about 1/100 of 1 per cent of the cases. Sometimes the fragment may be as small as mass number 72 or as large as mass number 158.

There are many known fission reactions. The one that follows is typical and illustrates how the barium (along with krypton) that Hahn and Strassmann first detected was produced.

$$_0n^1 + {}_{92}U^{235} \rightarrow ({}_{92}U^{236}) \rightarrow {}_{56}Ba^{144} + {}_{36}Kr^{89} + 3{}_0n^1 \qquad [16\text{--}6]$$

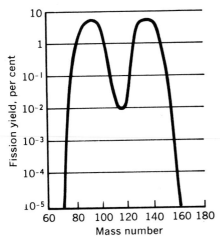

Fig. 16-8. Mass distribution of fission fragments.

Both the barium and krypton isotopes are unstable and give a series of decay products by beta emission as indicated in the following reactions.

$$_{56}\text{Ba}^{144} \xrightarrow{\beta-} {}_{57}\text{La}^{144} \xrightarrow{\beta-} {}_{58}\text{Ce}^{144} \xrightarrow{\beta-} {}_{59}\text{Pr}^{144} \xrightarrow{\beta-} {}_{60}\text{Nd}^{144} \qquad [16\text{--}7]$$

$$_{36}\text{Kr}^{89} \xrightarrow{\beta-} {}_{37}\text{Rb}^{89} \xrightarrow{\beta-} {}_{38}\text{Sr}^{89} \xrightarrow{\beta-} {}_{39}\text{Y}^{89} \qquad [16\text{--}7a]$$

Some evidence in support of the types of fission observed comes from the shell model rather than from the droplet model of the nucleus. The asymmetry of fission has been partially explained by the shell model on the assumption that certain numbers (magic numbers) of neutrons or protons in each "fragment" tend to form closed shells.

The phenomenon of fission is by no means confined to uranium. Most of the very heavy elements have been found to undergo fission under favorable conditions. Of special interest among these is thorium, since there is more thorium in the earth than there is uranium. Fission may also be induced by other methods than neutron capture. Indeed, any method by which the energy given to the nucleus is more than the activation energy can produce fission. Fission has now been obtained by high-energy alpha particles, deuterons, protons, and even by high-energy x-ray photons or gamma rays. In fact, occasional fission of uranium atoms may occur either spontaneously or by the action of cosmic rays.

16-8. Neutron Emission in Fission

It became apparent soon after the discovery of fission that neutrons would most likely be emitted in the fission process, and Fermi suggested that if enough neutrons were emitted so that they themselves in turn produced fission of neighboring nuclei, a *chain reaction* might occur. From the curve of Fig. 14-5, showing relative numbers of protons and neutrons in stable nuclei, it is evident that for stability the heaviest nuclei require more neutrons in proportion than do lighter nuclei. Therefore, when a heavy nucleus splits into lighter nuclei there would presumably be too many neutrons for the lighter nucleus, and some of them could be emitted in the process of fission. Evidence was soon obtained that neutron emission does occur, and that in the fission of uranium between two and three neutrons on the average are emitted per fission [reaction 16–6]. Experimental average values have been obtained of 2.46 neutrons per fission of U^{235} and 2.88 per fission of plutonium Pu^{239}.

PROMPT AND DELAYED NEUTRONS

About 99 per cent of the neutrons emitted in fission of uranium are ejected in a very short space of time, so short as to be almost instantaneous with the fission process. These are called *prompt neutrons*. Later it was found that a few other neutrons are emitted after an appreciable length of time (a matter of some seconds). These are known as *delayed neutrons*, and they originate from the unstable fission fragments that decay by neutron emission before reaching a stable state. The delayed neutrons are of great importance in the control of nuclear atomic reactors (§16-12).

16-9. Neutron Speeds: Reduction by Elastic Scattering

Neutrons possessing energies of 1 meV or more are known as *fast neutrons*. If neutrons are slowed down to speeds comparable to those of gas molecules at normal temperature and pressure they are spoken of as *slow* or *thermal neutrons*. Between these extremes is the indefinite region of neutrons of intermediate speed. Thermal neutrons have energies of approximately 0.03 eV, and sometimes neutrons with energies up to 10 eV are included in the term slow neutrons. Although there is no rigid classification the following is a convenient one:

Neutron Speeds and Energies

Fast	0.1 meV and up
Intermediate	10 eV to 0.1 meV
Slow	0.03 eV to 10 eV
Thermal	0.03 eV (approx.)
Cold	less than thermal

The interaction of fast and slow neutrons with matter is a subject of much importance. Fast neutrons may sometimes pass right through the nucleus of an atom, whereas slow neutrons would much more readily be captured. The slowing down of neutrons then becomes a matter of importance, and at certain speeds the probability of capture may increase enormously (§16-6). On the other hand, fast neutrons may produce effects that slow neutrons cannot.

Neutrons which are not captured by nuclei may be scattered elastically from the nuclei with which they collide. Application of the laws of conservation of energy and momentum show that when a moving particle makes a head-on elastic collision with a free particle of the same mass it will lose all of its speed and the momentum and kinetic energy will be transferred to the second particle. Since random collisions occur at different angles, a particle colliding at random with particles of equal masses loses on the average 63 per cent of its energy per collision.

Because protons possess nearly the same mass as neutrons, a neutron after two collisions with protons would retain on the average only 37 per cent of 37 per cent, or less than 14 per cent of its original energy. A 2-meV neutron can be reduced to the thermal energy of a gas molecule in about 18 collisions in hydrogen and this may occur in less than 0.001 sec. In collision with carbon nuclei, it would take 114 collisions on the average. Thus to slow neutrons down they are passed through a *moderator* material rich either in protons or in nuclei of small mass which are not likely to capture them. Water and paraffin are two of the most easily obtainable and common substances. Heavy water is effective because of its very low capture probability for neutrons. Carbon is often used (§16-12).

Note. If collisions at all possible angles are considered, the number of collisions required on the average to reduce the energy of a neutron from one initial value E_0 to any value E can be shown to be

$$N_{av} = \frac{\ln E_0 - \ln E}{\xi}$$

where ξ (xi) is defined as the average decrease in the logarithm of energy per collision. The classical mechanics of collisions of ideal elastic spheres shows how ξ depends on the atomic mass of the moderating material. Computation gives for hydrogen, $\xi = 1$; for deuterium, $\xi = 0.73$; and for carbon, $\xi = 0.16$.

For many experimental purposes it is desirable to have a "monochromatic" beam of neutrons, that is, a beam of neutrons all having the same speed. Since neutrons cannot be deflected by electric or magnetic fields, this presents quite an experimental problem. One method is that of making use of the wave properties of the neutron.

When a beam of neutrons of different speeds is reflected from the face of a crystal there will be one particular angle for which the de Broglie waves, representing the neutrons, will reinforce, just as in the Bragg method of x-ray diffraction. It will be the angle of maximum intensity for neutrons of just the right speed to have the proper de Broglie wavelength. This is one way of obtaining a beam of neutrons having the same or nearly the same speeds or velocities.

Another method of separating slow neutrons into velocity groups is by the time-of-flight or chopper method. Imagine two slits arranged at opposite extremities of the diameter of a wheel (Fig. 16-9). If the wheel is rotated a narrow beam of light would shine through the slits only when the slits are in line with the source of light. Substitute a neutron source for the source of light, and make the rim of the wheel out of a neutron absorber

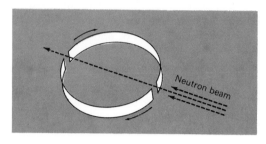

Fig. 16-9. Time-of-flight velocity selector for neutrons. Slits may be aluminum strips imbedded in cadmium absorber.

such as cadmium, with slits in it. The neutrons can only get through the slits when they are in line if the neutrons are moving with a certain minimum velocity, depending on the speed of rotation of the wheel. The slits need not be air gaps but may be slabs of aluminum or another substance through which neutrons pass readily. When a pulse of neutrons passes the slits, the detectors may be so timed as to make measurements on the last neutrons to pass through. These have the known minimum velocity.

16-10. Collisions in Center-of-Mass Coordinates

In many nuclear reactions, such as collisions of neutrons or cosmic ray particles with various nuclei, a considerable simplification results from shifting the coordinate system to which the motions are referred from that of an observer at rest in the laboratory to an imagined observer located at the center of mass of the system and moving with the center of mass. The coordinate system of the latter will be referred to as the C (center-of-mass) system while the former will be referred to as the L (laboratory) system.

Consider the elastic collision of a neutron of mass m with a nucleus of mass M when the nucleus M is at rest in the L-system (Fig. 16-10). The neutron moves from an instantaneous position 1 before collision toward position 2 after collision having lost some of its momentum. At the same time the nucleus M moves from position 3 toward position 4 having gained momentum. A simplification introduced by using the C-system is that the total momentum of the particles with reference to the center of mass is zero before the collision, therefore it must be zero after the collision. Another simplification is that the magnitudes of velocities and momenta of the two particles after collision each remain the same as before collision. Only the direction has changed and since the particles move along the same line

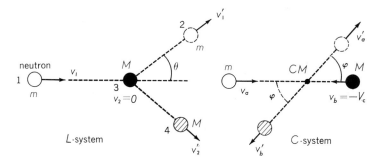

Fig. 16-10. Illustrating the collision of a neutron (m) with a nucleus M in the laboratory system of coordinates (L-system) and in the center-of-mass system of coordinates (C-system).

toward each other before collision they will move directly away from each other along another line in a different direction after collision.

By conservation of momentum it will be seen from reference to Fig. 16-10 that the momentum mv_1 in the L-system before collision must equal the total momentum after collision which is equal to the total mass $M + m$ multiplied by the velocity of the center of mass V_c. From this the velocity of the center of mass is

$$V_c = \frac{mv_1}{M + m} \qquad [16\text{--}8]$$

But this is the velocity with which the center of mass is moving toward the nucleus M in the L-system, therefore in the C-system the nucleus M moves toward the center of mass before collision with a velocity $v_b = -V_c$. The neutron then moves toward the center of mass with a velocity

$$v_a = v_1 - V_c = v_1\left(1 - \frac{m}{M + m}\right) = v_1\left(\frac{M}{M + m}\right)$$

After collision (in the L-system) the neutron moves outward from the center of mass with a velocity v'_1 at an angle θ from its original direction. In the C-system it moves at an angle φ.

The total momentum in the C-system before collision is therefore

$$mv_a + mv_b = m\left(\frac{Mv_1}{m + M}\right) - M\left(\frac{mv_1}{m + M}\right) = 0 \qquad [16\text{--}9]$$

and in the C-system therefore the total momentum after collision must also be zero and

$$mv'_a + Mv'_b = 0 \qquad [16\text{--}10]$$

Conservation of energy requires that

$$\frac{1}{2} m v_a^2 + \frac{1}{2} M v_b^2 = \frac{1}{2} m v'_a{}^2 + \frac{1}{2} M v'_b{}^2 \qquad [16–11]$$

Putting the value of v'_b from Eq. 16–10 into Eq. 16–11 and also the value of v_b from Eq. 16–9 into Eq. 16–11 we find that in magnitude

$$v'_a = \frac{M v_1}{m + M} = v_a \qquad [16–12]$$

Similarly

$$v'_b = \frac{m v_1}{m + M} = v_b \qquad [16–13]$$

which proves that the speeds before and after collision remain unchanged in the *C*-system and only the direction changes. Since the velocities before collision in the *C*-system are oppositely directed they must also be after collision. To find the velocity of either neutron or the nucleus in the *L*-system after collision it is only necessary to take the vector sum of the velocity of the particle in the *C*-system and the velocity of the center of mass.

If the velocity of the neutron is known before and after collision the energy loss can be readily found and for a head-on collision the energy E_2 after collision is

$$E_2 = \left(\frac{M - m}{M + m}\right)^2 E_1 \qquad [16–14]$$

where E_1 is the energy before collision. For a head-on collision of a neutron with a proton at rest, since they are of almost the same mass, the formula shows that the neutron loses practically all of its energy and momentum.

16-11. Applications of Fission: Plutonium

Natural uranium is almost completely composed of the two uranium isotopes U^{238} and U^{235} in the ratio of 143 to 1. When bombarded by neutrons, fission of either isotope may occur, or absorption of neutrons by U^{238} atoms without fission may occur. The probabilities of the occurrence of these events for different neutron energies are represented in Fig. 16-11 in terms of the relative cross-sections for these events. It will be noted that fission of U^{235} occurs for neutrons of any energy but fission of U^{238} occurs only for fast neutrons. The sharp peak of the capture cross-section curve for U^{238} represents the very large probability of resonance capture by U^{238} of slow neutrons having energies in the neighborhood of 5 eV. Both U^{235} and U^{238} have relatively large capture cross sections for slow neutrons but only capture by U^{235} is likely to result in fission.

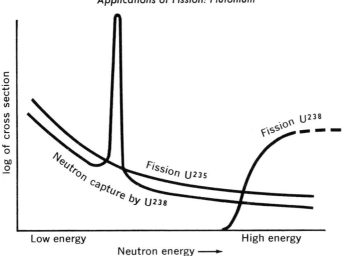

Fig. 16-11. An approximate curve representing the general trend of fission and capture cross sections for uranium.

The high efficiency of slow neutrons for the capture-fission process in U^{235} is what made the first nuclear reactor and the first nuclear bomb possible. To increase the relative number of atoms undergoing fission, natural uranium could be enriched by adding U^{235} to it or else only U^{235} atoms could be used. But U^{235} is relatively scarce and because of their similar chemical properties it was difficult to separate U^{235} from U^{238}. The two chief methods of separation that were tried were based on the small difference in mass between the two isotopes. One of these methods involved either gaseous or thermal diffusion while the other involved magnetic separation as in the mass spectrograph. Both kinds of processes were tediously slow and involved enormous amounts of power to operate great arrays of separators.

While such facilities were being developed at great expense on a grand scale during World War II a sudden revolution in method occurred. It was found that a new and hitherto unknown transuranic element was formed as a product of neutron absorption in U^{238}. This new element was *plutonium* ($_{94}Pu^{239}$) and plutonium was found to undergo fission by slow neutron capture in the same way that U^{235} does and with a similar release of energy. This was a historic break-through since plutonium being a different element could be readily separated from the *parent* uranium (actually the *grandparent* since another new element, *neptunium*, was produced first in the process). The way in which neptunium and then plutonium are produced is as follows.

A U^{238} nucleus absorbs a neutron, thus increasing the mass number by 1, and becomes U^{239}, a heavier isotope of ordinary uranium. U^{239}, however, is unstable and decays, by beta emission with a half-life of 23 minutes, to the new element neptunium $_{93}Np^{239}$. Formation of U^{239} occurs in an excited state with the consequent emission of gamma rays according to the following reaction:

$$_{92}U^{238} + _0n^1 \rightarrow _{92}U^{239} + \text{gamma rays} \qquad [16\text{--}15]$$

The short half-life of the U^{239} nucleus indicates that it is intensely radioactive. The decay process is

$$_{92}U^{239} \rightarrow _{93}Np^{239} + _{-1}e^0 \qquad [16\text{--}16]$$

Neptunium itself is also strongly radioactive and decays, with a half-life of 2.3 days, to plutonium $(_{94}Pu^{239})$.

$$_{93}Np^{239} \rightarrow _{94}Pu^{239} + _{-1}e^0 + \text{gamma rays} \qquad [16\text{--}17]$$

Thus upon capture of a neutron by a U^{238} nucleus the decay processes begin by which plutonium is produced. The plutonium is also radioactive but with a much longer half-life of 25,000 years; consequently it can be stored for long periods of time. Actually plutonium decays by emission of an alpha particle, thus becoming U^{235}. Most important of all from the practical viewpoint is the fact that plutonium is not only a different element from uranium and can be readily separated chemically from uranium and neptunium but also it can be produced by transformation of the common U^{238} nucleus. Whereas in the fission of U^{235} any loss of neutrons by non-fission absorption in U^{238} may impede or even stop the desired self-sustaining chain reaction, in the production of plutonium the absorption of neutrons by U^{238} is just what is desired. Large-scale production of plutonium by nuclear reactor methods was accomplished in a test plant at Oak Ridge, Tennessee and later on at Hanford, Washington where the Columbia River could be used to carry off the enormous amounts of heat released in the process.

16-12. Nuclear Reactors

The first large-scale production of a chain reaction with fissionable uranium was obtained in July 1941 at Columbia University under the guidance of Fermi. The reactor which was then called a *uranium-carbon pile* consisted of about 7 tons of uranium oxide in a cube 8 ft on a side, the containers of uranium being separated by graphite (a pure form of carbon). The graphite was to act as a *moderator* to reduce the speed of the fast neutrons so that they would produce fission of U^{235} without being captured by U^{238}. Since carbon (C^{16}) nuclei are already in a very stable state consisting of 4 pairs of neutrons and 4 pairs of protons it was expected that there would be little loss of neutrons by capture in the graphite.

To start the chain reaction an emanation-beryllium source of neutrons was placed at the bottom of the pile. When put in operation a considerable amount of fission with proportionate energy release was obtained, but the chain process was not self-sustaining. It would gradually die away if neutrons from the outside were not continually injected into the pile because too many of the neutrons released by fission were either lost by diffusion or by non-fission capture in U^{238}. This was described by saying that the multiplication factor k for neutrons effective in producing fission was less than 1.

On Dec. 2, 1942 with improved methods the first self-sustaining nuclear reactor with a multiplication factor $k > 1$ was put into operation at the University of Chicago (later removed to the Argonne National Laboratory at nearby Lemont, Illinois). To control the chain reaction it was arranged to insert movable cadmium rods (Fig. 16-12) into the reactor because cadmium strongly absorbs neutrons (§16-6). Despite these precautions considerable trepidation was felt over the possibility that the chain reaction might run away with itself and release energy in a nuclear explosion. As a matter of fact, if all neutrons in the fission process had been emitted promptly the atomic pile would probably have run away. The saving feature was that, although the delayed neutrons emitted in the fission process are not many in number, they are sufficient to give time to control the process. Of course, if anything should go wrong with such a control system a near-explosion could result and that this has actually happened in a few instances illustrates the imperative need for safe controls.

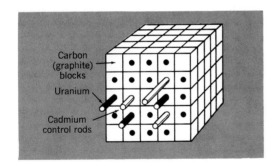

Fig. 16-12. Simplified diagram of reactor, showing cylinders of uranium and control rods of cadmium.

The multiplication factor, k, of a nuclear reactor is defined as follows. Suppose at any instant in a reactor there are N_0 fast neutrons available to produce fission. A few of these may produce fission in U^{238} producing a fractional increase ν. The number available is now $N_0\nu$. To produce fission only in U^{235} these must be slowed down by collision with nuclei of the moderator and to avoid resonance capture by U^{238} they must have energies less than 5 eV. If p is the fraction slowed down the available number is now $N_0\nu p$. Of these the fraction f may succeed in producing fission in U^{235} before being lost by diffusion or absorption in an impurity nucleus. The number of U^{235} nuclei undergoing fission is then $N_0\nu pf$. If for each fission in U^{235} a number ϵ of fast neutrons is produced to start the cycle over again then the total number of neutrons after one cycle, or one generation in the reproductive process, is

$$N = N_0 \nu p f \epsilon \qquad [16\text{--}18]$$

For a self-sustaining chain process to grow requires that $(N/N_0) > 1$ where

$$\frac{N}{N_0} = \nu p f \epsilon = k \qquad [16\text{--}19]$$

For steady operation at any particular power level the cadmium absorbers are adjusted so that $k = 1$ and the reactor is said to be *critical*. If $k > 1$ the reactor is *supercritical* and the fission rate increases. If $k < 1$ the reactor is *subcritical* and the fission rate decreases (Fig. 16-13). The fact that 1 percent of neutrons are not emitted promptly but are delayed (§16-8) gives sufficient time to make control adjustments. If a nuclear reactor were to be too efficient it would become supercritical on prompt neutrons and would be unmanageable.

In a nuclear chain reaction the number of neutrons N available to produce fission in a reactor (or fission bomb) grows exponentially and the rate of liberation of energy grows with it where

$$N = N_0 \epsilon^{\rho t / \tau} \qquad [16\text{--}20]$$

N_0 is the density of thermal neutrons injected into the reactor or the density in it just at the start of a chain reaction, and ϵ is the base of the natural system of logarithms. The quantity τ is the mean lifetime of a neutron in the pile, and ρ (defined as $\rho = k - 1$) represents the fractional increase (or decrease) in the number of neutrons in one neutron generation. Since the average lifetime of a thermal neutron in such a pile is in the neighborhood of a thousandth of a second the neutron density can build up at an enormous rate.

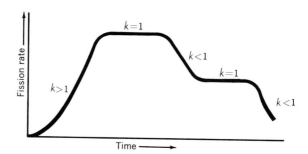

Fig. 16-13. Curve illustrating control of power generated in a nuclear reactor. With control rods in, *k* is less than 1; with rods out it is greater than 1. For steady operation the rods are set for $k = 1$.

A uranium or plutonium bomb (a fission bomb) is actually a reactor designed to be as supercritical as possible. The chain reaction grows at as high a rate as possible and maximum energy is released in minimum time. A reactor (and a fission bomb) also have a *critical size*. If the dimensions are too small too many neutrons escape from the surface by diffusion without producing fission. By increasing the proportion of U^{235} or Pu^{239} to U^{238} the critical size may be reduced. Reactors can be constructed to operate on 10 or 12 lbs of U^{235}. Indeed the secret of detonating a fission bomb is to keep it divided into subcritical sections until the moment of explosion otherwise it might be triggered by a passing cosmic ray.

The chief effects of such a nuclear explosion are: (1) the intense heat, forming thermal waves traveling with the speed of light, causing fatal burns and great damage due to fires; (2) the mechanical shock wave, consisting of a blast of air pressure which in itself can produce death and

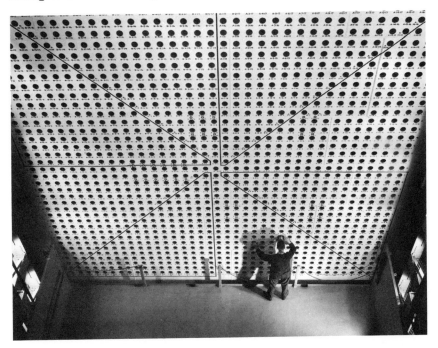

Fig. 16-14.   One face of the Brookhaven experimental reactor. The technician, who is shielded by 5 feet of concrete in front of him, is making observations on the insertion of radioactive fuel elements in the reactor by remote control when the reactor is not operating. Control rods are inserted into the graphite moderator through other openings in the shield and some openings are reserved for experiments such as irradiation of materials by neutrons generated in the reactor. (Courtesy, Brookhaven National Laboratory.)

destruction; (3) radioactivity of the fission products, themselves not only poisonous but emitting dangerous radiations of gamma and other rays.

Of the many hundreds of nuclear reactors in use today many advanced types have been developed and the chief uses are for production of plutonium for military purposes, production of power for peaceful purposes, and scientific research. The "breeder reactor" in Idaho was designed to study the problem of how to produce more fissionable material than is used up in order to conserve our energy sources.

Reactors may be classified as to the type of moderator such as carbon (graphite) (Fig. 16-14) or heavy water. Since heavy water is composed of heavy hydrogen and oxygen each of which has a low absorption for neutrons it is one of the most useful moderators. If the uranium is sufficiently enriched with U^{235} or Pu^{239} the moderator may be dispensed with and fission occurs with fast neutrons. The reactor is then called a *fast reactor*. There is also the possibility of using thorium instead of plutonium with the added advantage that thorium is a more common element. Th^{232} can serve to produce U^{233} and U^{233} undergoes fission with large-scale energy release just as U^{235} does.

Problems

1. A free neutron undergoes radioactive decay emitting a beta particle and then becomes a proton. From the energy-mass relations find the maximum kinetic energy in eV of the emitted beta particle.

2. What fraction of its kinetic energy does a neutron lose in colliding head-on with a deuterium ($_1H^2$) nucleus at rest? How many such elastic collisions must occur for a neutron of 1-meV energy to be reduced to a 1-eV energy or less?

3. What fraction of its kinetic energy does a neutron lose in colliding head-on with a carbon ($_6C^{12}$) nucleus? How many such collisions must occur for a 1-meV neutron to have its energy reduced to 1-eV or less?

4. How many fissions per second of U^{235}, each releasing 200-meV energy, would be required to give 100 kilowatts of power?

5. One pound of coal may be converted into 1.25 kwh of electric energy in a power plant. Find approximately how many tons of coal will give the same energy as that given by the complete fission of 1 gram of U^{235}.

6. Spontaneous fission of U ^{238} may occur with a decay constant of approximately 3×10^{-24} sec^{-1}. What is the average time between such fissions in a milligram of U^{238}?

7. If the neutron flux from an atomic pile is 10^{12} neutrons/cm^2 sec, how does it compare in intensity with a cyclotron beam of deuterons of 10 microamperes (μa)/cm^2?

8. Find three pairs of atoms, any pair of which U^{235} might likely form by fission after absorbing a neutron. Write the symbols for the reactions, assuming that 3 neutrons are emitted at each fission.

9. When a U^{235} nucleus absorbs a neutron it becomes U^{236}. Assume the U^{236} nucleus undergoes fission by dividing into 2 equal parts. Treating these as charged spheres almost touching (distance between centers $= 2 \times 10^{-12}$ cm), what is the coulomb potential energy due to repulsion of their charges? Is this comparable to the energy released in fission?

10. If the average binding energy of the nucleons in the products of fission of U^{238} is 8.7 meV and if the average binding energy of the nucleons before fission is 7.8 meV, find the expected energy release due to fission. (Assume 3 neutrons are emitted in fission.)

11. If a nuclear bomb contains 100 kg of U^{235} and if 0.001 of the atoms undergoes fission in 0.001 sec, what is the approximate horsepower of the bomb if an energy of 200-meV is released per fission?

12. Can fission occur when a U^{235} atom of mass 235.11392 absorbs a neutron of mass 1.00898 with zero kinetic energy? (Take the mass of the U^{236}-atom (compound nucleus) to be 236.11559 and the energy required for fission of U^{236} to be 6 meV.)

13. Electric power production in the U.S. is approximately 100 million kilowatts. If operated at 100 per cent efficiency, 36 gm of U^{235} will give 100 kw for 1 year. How many tons per year of U^{235} would be required to supply all needs if conversion to power is at an over-all efficiency of 30 per cent?

14. Approximately how many tons of radioactive fission products would be produced in 25 years under the conditions of problem 13? How would you suggest that these dangerous products should be disposed of?

15. The capture cross section of Co^{59} nuclei for thermal neutrons is 20 barns. If a thin sheet of Co^{59} having an area of 100 cm^2 and having a mass of 10 grams is subjected to a uniform neutron flux of 10^{16} neutrons/sec for 1 hr, how many Co^{60} nuclei are produced? Could this rate of capture be continued indefinitely?

16. If the capture cross section of cadmium nuclei for slow neutrons is 3000 barns, how many neutrons per million in a uniform beam will get through a cadmium plate 1 cm square and 0.01 cm thick? (Take density of cadmium to be 8600 kg/m^3.) Assume 35 per cent of the nuclei are shielded by other nuclei in front of them.

*17. The fission of U^{239} is 5.9 meV and for U^{236} is 5.25 meV. The binding energy of the last neutron in U^{239} is 5.4 meV and the binding energy of the last neutron in U^{236} is 6.4 meV. What can you deduce from this concerning the possibilities of fission of U^{238} and U^{235} with thermal neutrons?

18. The height of the fission potential barrier of a type of nucleus can be obtained experimentally by finding the energy of a photon required to produce photofission. The required photon energy for photofission of U^{235} is found to be 5.75 meV. To what wavelength in angstroms does this correspond? Why is this not the same as the fission barrier resulting from capture of a neutron by U^{235}?

Recommended Reading

Curtiss, L. F., *Introduction to Neutron Physics*. Princeton, N. J.: D. Van Nostrand Co., Inc., 1959.

Hughes, D. J., *Neutron Cross Sections*. New York: Pergamon Press, Inc., 1957.

Bacon, G. E., and K. Lonsdale, "Neutron Diffraction," in *Reports on Progress in Physics, Vol. XVI*. London: The Physical Society of London, 1953.

Glasstone, S., *Source Book on Atomic Energy*, 2nd ed. Princeton, N. J.: D. Van Nostrand Co., Inc., 1955.

Glasstone, S., and M. C. Edlund, *The Elements of Nuclear Reactor Theory*. Princeton, N. J.: D. Van Nostrand Company, Inc., 1952.

Smyth, H. DeW., *Atomic Energy for Military Purposes*. Princeton, N. J.: Princeton University Press, 1945.

High-Energy Rays
and New Particles

17-1. Cosmic Rays

The study of cosmic rays has been a most fertile field for the discovery of new particles and new nuclear processes. The earth is being continually bombarded from all directions by high-energy rays, called *cosmic rays*, coming from outer space. They pass into our atmosphere where they produce many secondary rays, a considerable number of which reach the surface of the earth. Many of these rays have far higher energies than any rays produced by man or perhaps that can ever be produced by man.

The study of cosmic rays sprang from a very small beginning near the turn of the century, when C. T. R. Wilson and also Elster and Geitel found a small unaccountable leakage of charge in an electroscope which had been carefully insulated. The leakage was more than could be accounted for by any imperfection in the insulation. It appeared to be due to ions formed by some penetrating radiation.

At first it was thought that the radiation came from radioactive material distributed throughout the earth's surface. Yet an amount of shielding that would in effect cut off the rays from all known radioactive substances failed to cut off this penetrating radiation.

In 1910 Gockel in Germany ascended to an elevation of 14,000 feet in a balloon and found to his surprise that the intensity of the radiation did not decrease with elevation, as would be expected if the rays came from the earth; if anything they seemed to increase. The next year Hess in Austria and later Kohlhörster in Germany took electroscopes up in balloons to much higher altitudes and found the intensity of the unknown rays to be as much as 10 times that at the surface of the earth. Hess then proposed that the rays originated from somewhere outside the earth's atmosphere and this led him to be awarded the Nobel prize in 1936 for the ''discovery of cosmic rays.''

The name *cosmic rays* was given to this penetrating radiation by Robert A. Millikan who with a number of co-workers began the study of these rays shortly after World War I. They finally sent sensitive recording instruments in small unmanned sounding balloons to elevations of 100,000 ft or more above the sea level at the same time that Kohlhörster in Europe made similar pioneering measurements. Whereas early measurements had not been able to reach a maximum peak on the cosmic-ray intensity-versus-altitude curve these measurements showed a strong peak followed by a marked decrease in intensity at the higher altitudes (Fig. 17-1). These results were confirmed by others who established new altitude records and

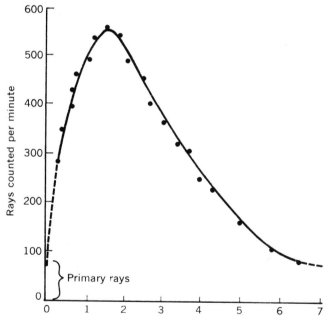

17-1. Experimental curve for variation of cosmic-ray intensity with altitude at one point on earth's surface. Extrapolation of the curve (dashed line) to the top of the atmosphere indicates incoming primary rays. At sea level the absorbing power of the atmosphere is equivalent to 10.33 meters of water.

in 1938 Curtiss, Aston, Stockman and Brown sent a small balloon to 116,000 feet where only one-half of one per cent of the atmosphere remained above the balloon. The limiting altitude for such balloon measurements has now been far surpassed by rockets and satellites.

The attempts to measure variations of cosmic-ray intensity with altitude could hardly have been more successful. The existence of primary radiation is clearly indicated in Fig. 17-1. If the upper end of the curve is extrapolated (dashed line) to zero absorber above the apparatus (top of the atmosphere) it does not fall to zero. The residual intensity at this elevation represents the primary rays which come into our atmosphere from outer space. Although the position of the maximum on the curve was found to depend upon the latitude where the measurements were made, the sharp peak in the curves clearly indicates that the production of secondary rays in the atmosphere reaches a maximum high up in the atmosphere. It also shows that the number of cosmic rays actually filtering down to the surface of the earth, where the absorbing power of the air is equivalent to a little more than 10 meters of water, is very small compared with the intensity in the upper regions of the air. The nature of the primary and the secondary rays then became a problem of first importance.

In 1930 Arthur H. Compton began to organize an intensive study of cosmic rays, and he and Millikan and their groups independently made extensive surveys at many places on the earth's surface, from near the equator to near the poles, and from sea level to high mountain tops. Evidence began to accumulate that the incoming rays were not gamma rays, as had been believed by Millikan, but that they were chiefly positively charged particles. This view was supported by Compton and others and was to receive confirmation later.

Soon the cloud chamber began to supplement electroscope measurements. With the help of the cloud chamber the effects of individual rays could be studied, and the observed tracks indicated the presence of high-speed electrons. However, high-speed electrons could hardly account for the extreme penetrating power of some of the rays. As it later turned out the electrons were not actually primary rays coming in from outside the atmosphere but secondaries formed in the atmosphere itself.

In earlier days it had been supposed that more massive particles would have more difficulty in passing through matter than less massive ones. However, at very high speeds the situation is different. A particle as massive as a proton produces little more ionization than an electron when both travel with speeds approximately that of light, and the tracks may be difficult to distinguish in a cloud chamber until they come close to the ends of their ranges. Also since the momentum of the more massive particle is much greater it is not so easily stopped. At high speeds the loss of energy by ionization may be relatively low, and radiation losses become more important. Yet the radiation loss of a more massive particle is often less than that of a less massive one because it is not so likely to be decelerated. Thus the high penetrating power of some of the rays seemed to require that they have masses greater than an electron.

EFFECT OF EARTH'S MAGNETIC FIELD

The variation of cosmic-ray intensity at the surface of the earth with changes of geographic latitude (the *latitude effect*) was first noticed by Clay of Holland who made measurements on a trip to Java in 1927. This phenomenon was followed up by many investigators including Millikan and Compton and it was established that there was as much as a 10 per cent drop in the intensity of the cosmic rays at the magnetic equator and that the intensity rises to a fairly constant value for latitudes above 40°, as represented in Fig. 17-2. The explanation of this latitude effect is that it is caused by the earth's magnetic field. At the magnetic poles of the earth incoming charged particles can move freely along the magnetic field without deflection or at worst, if moving at a slight angle to the field, they would only follow a spiral path inward (Fig. 17-3, *c* and *d*). But near the magnetic equator incoming rays of a given electric charge, upon crossing the earth's magnetic field, would be bent away from the earth or toward the earth depending on the direction in which they were moving. Some of those bent away from the earth would, of course, miss it altogether. Those bent toward the earth, if possessing enough energy, would hit it as in Fig. 17-3 at *B*. Those possessing less energy would be bent completely around and either just miss the earth, or miss it by a wider margin, as at *A*. Great credit is due Lemaître and Vallarta for developing the theory and computing the orbits of cosmic-ray particles bent by the earth's magnetic field under a variety of conditions.

Consideration of the energies required by particles to enable them to reach the earth indicates that protons of approximately 60 billion electron-volts energy are bent in the equatorial plane of the earth, so that the radius of curvature of path is smaller than the earth's radius; therefore these

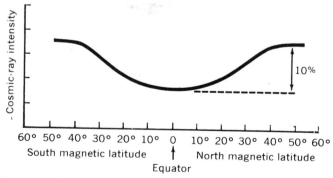

Fig. 17-2. Approximate curve of variation of cosmic-ray intensity with latitude, the result of a number of sets of measurements made with electroscopes.

protons can reach the earth regardless of direction in the equatorial plane. Such particles, with energies of less than 10 billion electron volts, will not be able to reach the earth at all at the equator; those of 10 billion volts or a little more will arrive from a westerly direction if they are positively charged and from an easterly direction if they are negatively charged. If they have energies of 15 or more beV, they can arrive at any angle between the western horizon and the zenith. At the poles particles of any energy can reach the surface of the earth except for losses such as those due to collision, radiation, and ionization. These losses usually amount to about 1.5 beV per particle on the average, another reason why low-energy primary cosmic rays cannot reach the surface of the earth.

More recently the possibility was recognized that many particles unable to reach the earth might be trapped at some elevation such as

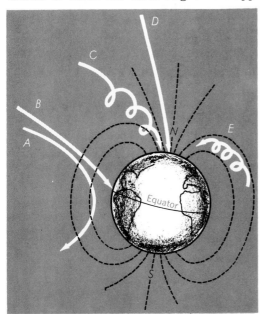

Fig. 17-3. The earth's magnetic field may bend the paths of incoming particles so that at A they miss the earth completely. If the energy of a particle is large enough, as at B, it will reach the earth. Nearer the earth's magnetic pole, lower-energy particles may spiral in, as at C, or move along the lines of force, D, of the magnetic field. E indicates the *Van Allen belt* of high energy rays, formed by particles unable to reach the earth and trapped at some elevation where they spiral back and forth between the earth's poles.

indicated in Fig. 17-3, e where they may spiral back and forth between the earth's poles and form a belt of high energy rays. The existence of such a belt of radiation, called a *Van Allen belt* after its discoverer, has been confirmed by high altitude measurements with rockets and satellites.

The magnitude of the latitude effect indicates that incoming rays are chiefly charged particles. Through the efforts of Johnson and Swann, measurements were made of the relative numbers of cosmic rays arriving from the east and from the west. These measurements indicated that slightly more rays come from the west than from the east. This is known as the *east-west effect* and it indicates that incoming primary rays are mostly positively charged particles. High altitude rocket measurements now give more direct information and confirm that the incoming primary rays are mostly protons with alpha particles next and traces of heavier nuclei in about the same relative abundance as that of the elements in the known universe. Measurable peaks for nitrogen, oxygen, magnesium, silicon, iron and some others have been detected. These may be distinguished by the fact that the more massive particles produce more dense tracks in a nuclear emulsion (Plate 5). The composition of the incoming primaries is believed to be approximately as follows.

Approximate Composition of Primary Cosmic Rays

protons	77 per cent
alpha particles	21 " "
more massive nuclei	2 " "
total	100 " "

Measurements at the surface of the earth show that about 0.5 primary ray per cm² per minute of all energies reaches sea level in our latitude. Although the energies of some incoming rays may run far above a thousand billion electron volts, the average energy of incoming primary rays is believed to be in the neighborhood of 20 beV and the total amount of energy per second received by the earth is estimated to be not more than that of starlight. Despite the fact that something like 10^{18} primary cosmic rays have been estimated to enter the earth's atmosphere every second, and despite the fact that this amounts to a total of something like a million kilowatts of power, the available energy at sea level per unit area is insignificant.

Measurements of the penetrating power have led to traces of cosmic rays being found as far below the surface of the earth as 2000 feet. Although only about 1 in 20,000 of the rays falling on the earth is able to penetrate to this depth, it shows the extraordinary energies of some of the rays, as much as, or more than, 10^{12} eV. This penetration is roughly equivalent to nearly a mile of water or 400 feet of lead. Evidently a ray capable of passing through that much lead could pass through the human body without being noticeably impeded; in fact, it might not hit anything.

SOURCES OF COSMIC RAYS

Investigations of different parts of the sky with a "cosmic-ray telescope" (§13-17) give no indication of a favored source for cosmic rays. They seem to come equally from all directions in space. To answer the question of the source of the rays, one must not only find where they come from but also find a mechanism by which particles of such tremendous energies can be produced. It seems fairly certain that large numbers of the lower-energy particles, which we speak of as cosmic rays, have their source in the sun and are scattered throughout the solar system by means of the magnetic fields of the sun, the earth, and some of the other planets in such a way that they seem to come uniformly from all directions of space.

In times of sunspot activity and solar flares, streams of charged particles are shot off from the sun and may reach the earth, producing "magnetic storms" when sufficiently intense. Confirmation comes from rocket measurements. The production of the higher-energy particles, however, is far more difficult to explain and no satisfactory theory seems possible in terms of any mechanism connected with the sun. Indeed it is difficult to think of any kind of mechanism anywhere that could produce the small number of highest-energy particles a very few of which have energies estimated as high as 10^{19} eV although probably only 10 per cent have energies above 20 meV.

A suggested source of high-energy cosmic rays is the type of star known as a *nova* or *supernova*. In the apparent atomic explosion of such a star, it seems that particles of very high energy might be produced if the nova were surrounded by a time-changing magnetic field enabling it to act as a huge particle accelerator. However, the occurrence of these novae is comparatively rare. Certain pulsating stars may have pulsating magnetic fields and might also act as giant accelerators to speed up such particles.

If there are floating clouds of ionized gas (plasmoids) in interstellar space, repeated collision of charged atomic particles with these clouds over periods of millions of years could conceivably build up high energies. More recently it has been suggested by Hoyle that cosmic ray production may be connected with the formation of the unusually massive stellar objects (far more massive than a star) whose existence seems to be indicated by radio-astronomy.

17-2. Secondary Cosmic Rays

Any rays produced in the atmosphere by action of a primary cosmic ray are called secondary rays. Secondary rays may be produced by a variety of processes, and they may include a number of different types of rays. Measurements of secondaries indicate that there are present in the atmosphere high-speed electrons, positrons, mesons, high-energy gamma rays, and even neutrons, together with many other particles not so well known. The two chief types of event by which secondary rays are produced in our atmosphere when high-energy primary rays collide with air nuclei (mainly oxygen and nitrogen) are *cascade showers*, and the *disruption of nuclei* which give off showers of mesons or other particles. Since mesons decay rapidly they can not be primary particles but must be produced high in our atmosphere.

In a cascade shower there are three chief kinds of event: (1) production of gamma-ray photons (bremsstrahlung) when an incoming primary ray is suddenly slowed down in an encounter with a gas molecule, (2) creation of an electron pair by a gamma-ray photon in the presence of some other nucleus (in order to conserve momentum); and (3) further production of gamma-ray photons by slowing down of these electrons in collisions or nuclear encounters. As this process proceeds and repeats itself, gamma rays, electrons, and positrons multiply as indicated in Fig. 17-4. At the same time many nuclei undergo partial or complete disruption. It is by the latter processes that mesons and other particles as well as protons and neutrons, are ejected from nuclei. Some particles (hyperons) have been detected with masses greater than the proton. Some of the most exciting developments in modern physics have come from the study of such particles, a number of which may now be produced in the laboratory by bombardment of nuclei.

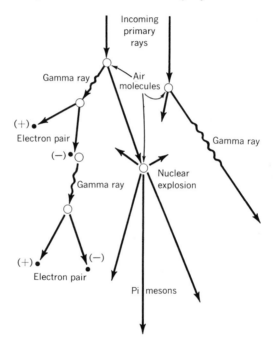

Fig. 17-4. Cascade shower production of secondary cosmic rays in atmosphere by incoming primary rays.

The very penetrating particles in the cosmic rays which reach the surface of the earth in abundance are mu mesons (Fig. 17-5, left). They are particularly penetrating because they do not interact directly with atomic nuclei. Their origin is explained in the next section. Secondary electrons on the other hand suffer many energy losses on the way down through the atmosphere and are the particles which most often produce showers. At the surface of the earth more than half the cosmic radiation consists of mu

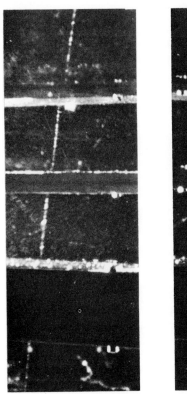 

Fig. 17-5. Early cloud-chamber photographs. Left, a penetrating particle (probably a high-energy mu meson) passes downward and completely through three lead plates 4 mm, 10 mm, and 39 mm thick. Right, a shower-producing particle (presumably an electron) forms a two-stage cascade shower. Nearly all the particles are absorbed in the bottom plate. The two V-tracks may be electron pairs, formed by gamma rays produced when the high-speed particle is slowed down by a lead plate. (Courtesy, Harvard University, Physics Laboratory.)

mesons, the remainder consisting chiefly of the electrons, positrons and gamma-ray photons produced in cascade showers.

When a counter is shielded with a relatively thin layer of lead the counting rate often goes up. The reason was discovered when layers of lead were put into a cloud chamber and it was observed that many rays issuing from the same spot in the lead were produced by a single particle entering the lead at that spot. Thus the particle produces a shower from the lead plate. If the shower particles strike another lead plate they may in turn produce showers, as shown on the right of Fig. 17-5. The maximum intensity of such a shower is usually obtained by a thickness of about 1.7 cm of lead, but it depends on the energy of the shower-producing particle.

Frequently there is an extraordinary multiplication of particles in successive showers, as shown in Fig. 17-6. The bars in the photo are layers of lead of equal thickness inside the cloud chamber and they are separated by gaps where the tracks are visible. Often the shower particles are almost too numerous to count and may number as many as 10,000. Evidently such showers can only be produced by high-energy particles, since the energies of all the shower particles added together cannot be greater than the energy

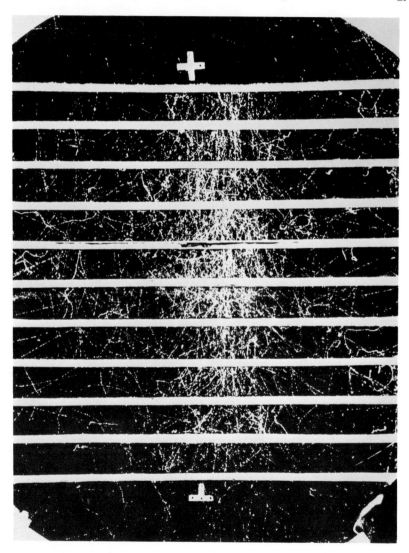

Fig. 17-6.   Intense multiplication of cosmic-ray secondaries by shower process in lead plates in a cloud chamber. (Courtesy, University of California, Berkeley.)

of the incoming particle (or particles) except for relatively small increments due to nuclear processes. Extensive *air showers* are formed by primary rays having energies of 10^{10} eV, and upwards with the upper limit estimated to be as high as 10^{19} eV.

17-3. Mu and Pi Mesons

When particles of intermediate mass between electrons and protons were discovered in cosmic rays in 1937 by Anderson and Neddermeyer, and by Street and Stevenson, they were first called *heavy electrons*, and then *mesons* (from the Greek *mesos* meaning *in-between*) (§14-8). When similar particles of somewhat larger mass were found later, the particles of the first type were called mu (μ) mesons, frequently shortened to *muons*. The closely related but somewhat more massive particles discovered later are called pi (π) mesons, or *pions*.

The mu (μ) meson was discovered from a study of cloud-chamber tracks which showed an occasional track intermediate in character between the known tracks of electrons and protons. Since the differences in observed tracks were small the original identification was made with difficulty. When it was found that this particle did not show a strong interaction with atomic nuclei, as predicted by Yukawa (§14-8), Bethe and Marshak in 1947 suggested that there might be two different kinds of mesons, a heavier meson produced abundantly in nuclear reactions, having a short mean life, perhaps 10^{-8} sec, and a somewhat lighter meson formed by the decay of the heavier one. The heavier particle, it was assumed, might show the expected strong interaction with nuclei which the lighter particle did not show. This was the next particle discovered, the pi meson. Both particles turned out to be unstable, as predicted by Yukawa, and the mu meson was found to result from the decay of a pi meson. Thus the pi meson was considered the primary particle of the two, and it was found to have a strong interaction with atomic nuclei, as implied by the theory. Still other particles have now been discovered and constitute an embarrassment of riches which makes the problem of the nucleus seem more complicated than ever. However, the behavior of the pi meson lends substantiation to the general aspects of the Yukawa theory.

Pi mesons were discovered in 1947 by Lattes, Muirhead, Occhialini, and Powell in England. They used the newly developed nuclear-emulsion plates. Examples of the tracks formed in the emulsions of the plates are shown in Figs. 17-9 and 17-10. These are photomicrographs, and the degree of magnification can be judged from the fact that few tracks of individual particles in the emulsion are more than 500 microns (0.5 mm) in length.

Often incoming cosmic-ray primaries will disrupt nuclei that they encounter in the atmosphere or elsewhere. In these nuclear explosions, numerous types of particles are emitted. When the results of such an explosion are seen on a nuclear-emulsion plate, what is called a *star* is observed, produced by the tracks of particles emanating from a common center and moving in all directions. Sometimes a star shows only a few tracks or "prongs," but it may have as many as fifty or more. See Plate 4.

The pi (π) meson (pion) was discovered through examination of tracks in nuclear-emulsion plates exposed for days at a high altitude. Tracks of mesons were sometimes seen branching at an angle from the ends of other meson tracks that came from a nuclear explosion. The hypothesis was advanced and later confirmed that, in the nuclear explosion, primary or pi mesons somewhat more massive than the mu meson are emitted. After traveling in the emulsion as far as its short life permits, such a pi meson then undergoes spontaneous decay, forming a mu meson. The mu meson then moves in a new direction to a point where the track again suddenly changes direction and appearance, indicating that the mu meson is also unstable and also undergoes decay. These decay processes will be taken up in more detail in §17-4. Such pi-mu *double-decay* tracks are often observed. The hypothesis of pi-mu decay seemed warranted by the early observations, but tracks on which measurements could be made were at first few, and questions arose as to what the modes of decay were and what other particles were emitted.

Direct confirmation of the existence of pi mesons was obtained in 1948, at the University of California, where Lawrence and his co-workers produced pi mesons artificially by bombarding a target with high-energy alpha particles accelerated by the large cyclotron. It had been suspected that mesons might have either positive or negative charges, and there was some evidence suggesting the possible existence of neutral mesons. The experiments in Berkeley settled things neatly. Positive and negative pi mesons could be produced at will. Later the existence of neutral pi mesons was confirmed. See Plate 6.

The experimental arrangement for producing and detecting pi mesons is illustrated in Fig. 17-7. High-energy alpha particles from the cyclotron are directed against a carbon target C. Pi mesons are ejected from the target and enter the region of a deflecting magnetic field, positively charged particles being bent in one direction and negatively charged particles in the opposite direction. To detect the mesons a stack of nuclear-emulsion plates is set on edge in a recess in the shield, and the tracks produced in these emulsions can then be studied after they have been suitably developed. From a knowledge of the bending and the momentum involved, a precise value for the mass of the particle can be obtained. Other estimates of mass are based on such properties as total energy, range, and ionization. Cloud-chamber photographs of the newly discovered pi mesons were also obtained, and the tracks of some of these particles are shown in Fig. 17-8. In the quite remarkable cloud-chamber photograph numerous and different types of

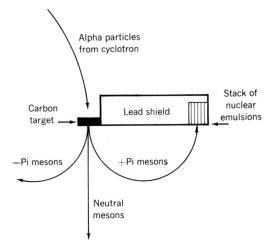

Alpha particles from cyclotron

Carbon target →

Lead shield

Stack of nuclear emulsions

−Pi mesons

+Pi mesons

Neutral mesons

Fig. 17-7. Experimental method developed at the University of California for producing and detecting pi mesons.

tracks are visible. The long thin tracks are mostly electrons. The short thick tracks are more massive particles, presumably protons. The intermediate tracks of mesons are readily discernible.

Both pi- and mu-meson masses have now been determined with considerable accuracy (Table 17-1).

TABLE 17-1.   MASS OF MU AND PI MESONS
(m_e = mass of electron)

Particle	Mass in m_e
$\pi^{\pm}$ meson	273.18
π^0 meson	264.20
$\mu^{\pm}$ meson	206.77

The spin of the pi meson is zero and of the mu meson is $\frac{1}{2}$, therefore pi mesons are describable in terms of Bose statistics, and mu mesons are describable by Fermi statistics.

17-4. Decay of Pi and Mu Mesons

PI-MESON DECAY

When it is possible to follow the track of a pi meson to the point where it apparently ends and a new track begins in a different direction, the event occurring at the branch point very evidently represents the decay of the pi meson (Fig. 17-9). In addition to the visible track of the decay particle, however, it is necessary, in order to conserve momentum, to assume the emission of at least one other particle which does not leave a visible track. Since the mu meson has the same charge as its parent, the pi meson, the other particle must have zero charge. Conservation of spin and statistics

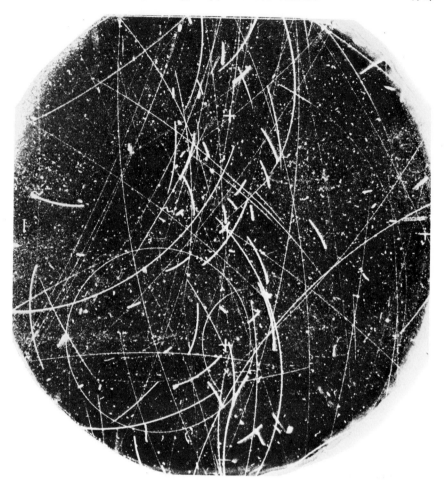

Fig. 17-8. Striking cloud-chamber photograph of tracks of particles expelled from atoms bombarded by high-energy particles from the 184-inch cyclotron at the University of California. The spiral (almost circular) track in lower left-hand part of photo is a positively charged pi meson artificially produced by the bombardment.
(Courtesy, Lawrence Radiation Laboratory, University of California.)

indicate that the particle must have a spin of $\frac{1}{2}$ and that it "obeys" Fermi statistics. This leads to the conclusion that the "mysterious stranger" is a neutrino (ν). The decay is then represented by the following scheme:

$$\pi^+ \rightarrow \mu^+ + \nu \qquad\qquad [17\text{--}1]$$

In the decay of the pi meson the resulting mu meson always has the kinetic energy of 4.1 meV. This is determined from the distance that it travels in the emulsion before it is brought to a stop. The constant energy

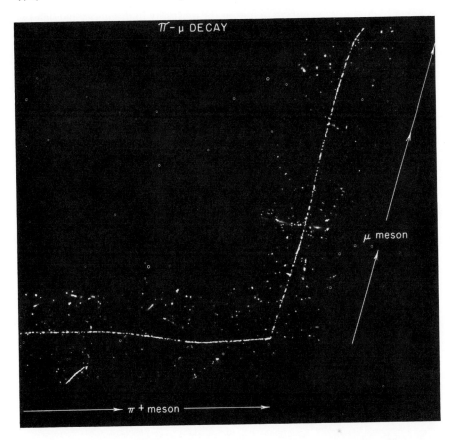

$\pi - \mu$ DECAY

μ meson

π^+ meson

Fig. 17-9. Pi-mu-meson decay track caught in the emulsion of a photographic plate coated with a special nuclear emulsion. Where the track branches suddenly the pi meson underwent radioactive decay and formed a mu meson (muon). (Courtesy, Eastman Kodak Co., and Dr. Sidney Barnes, University of Rochester.)

is taken to be an indication that only a single neutral particle is emitted in pi-meson decay and that its mass may be extremely small or zero, in agreement with the characteristics of the neutrino.

Decay of positive pi mesons is more readily observed than that of negative pi mesons since the positive pi mesons are repelled by nuclei. The negative pi mesons, on the other hand, are so strongly absorbed that the absorption often occurs before they reach the ends of their tracks. However, the evidence for decay of negative pi mesons indicates that they decay in a manner similar to positive pi mesons with the emission of an antineutrino $\bar{\nu}$, that is,

$$\pi^- \rightarrow \mu^- + \bar{\nu} \qquad\qquad [17\text{--}2]$$

When a high-energy negative pi meson (or most any high-energy particle) is absorbed by a nucleus, a nuclear "explosion" may result, forming a "star" in the emulsion. A typical *star* of this kind is shown in Fig. 17-10. The study of such stars yields much information, as, for instance, on the energy of the incoming ray. This is obtained by summing up the energies of all product rays resulting from the explosion.

The fact that pi mesons are rarely observed at sea level in cosmic rays, whereas mu mesons are plentiful, suggests that they are mostly found in the upper atmosphere where high-energy collisions are more frequent. It also suggests that their mean life is much less than that of mu mesons. Measurements indicate that it is probably of the order of a hundredth that of mu mesons, the latter being of the order of a few microseconds. Recent measurements give 2.6×10^{-8} sec for the mean life of a pi meson and 2.2×10^{-6} sec for that of a mu meson.

Pi mesons are now produced by bombardment of a variety of targets with high-energy protons, neutrons, alpha particles, and even gamma rays. For instance, when protons are used as bombarding particles they are

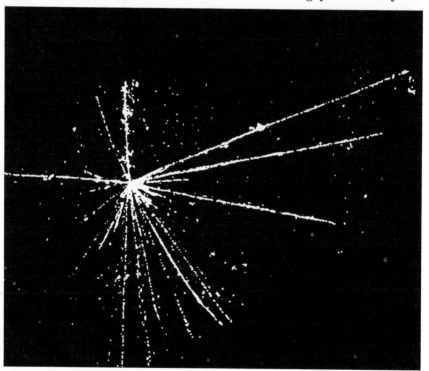

Fig. 17-10. A typical "star" or atomic explosion produced by the absorption of a high-energy ray, presumably a pi meson. (Courtesy, Eastman Kodak Co., and Dr. Bernard Peters, University of Rochester.)

presumed to interact with individual protons or neutrons in a nucleus, and possible reactions are:

$$p + p \rightarrow p + n + \pi^+ \qquad\qquad [17\text{--}3]$$

$$p + n \rightarrow p + p + \pi^- \qquad\qquad [17\text{--}4]$$

These two reactions have been confirmed by bombarding a target with high-energy protons. Since protons and neutrons have half-integral spin it is evident that in order to conserve spin pi mesons must have zero or integral spin.

Although no neutral mu meson has been found the existence of neutral pi mesons has been demonstrated. If pi mesons are responsible for internucleonic forces it may be that neutral pi mesons are involved in the forces between two protons or between two neutrons but their exact role is not clear. As free particles they are found to have an extremely short mean life (10^{-15} sec), and their mass (263.8 electron masses) is unaccountably different from that of charged pi mesons. To conserve charge, spin, and statistics they may decay by either of the following processes:

$$\pi^0 \rightarrow \gamma + \gamma \qquad\qquad [17\text{--}5]$$

$$\pi^0 \rightarrow e^+ + e^- + \gamma \qquad\qquad [17\text{--}6]$$

The first process of decay into two gamma-ray photons has been confirmed experimentally, and the coincident pairs of gamma rays have been detected. In the second process the decay would be into an electron pair, plus a gamma-ray photon.

MU-MESON DECAY

In mu-meson decay emission of two neutrinos (a neutrino ν and an antineutrino $\bar{\nu}$) is required to conserve spin and statistics, and the following decay processes are believed to occur:

$$\mu^+ \rightarrow e^+ + \nu + \bar{\nu} \qquad\qquad [17\text{--}7]$$

$$\mu^- \rightarrow e^- + \nu + \bar{\nu} \qquad\qquad [17\text{--}8]$$

Fig. 17-11 illustrates decay of a pi meson followed by decay of a mu meson.

In the early nuclear-emulsion plates, electrons were difficult to detect because they did not leave satisfactorily observable tracks, but in the more recently prepared emulsions they are now easily detected, and in the decay of a mu meson at the end of its track the path of the particle emitted is very evidently that of an electron. Although it is assumed that in the decay of a mu meson two neutrinos are also emitted, there are no visible tracks. Since the spin quantum number of the mu meson is $\frac{1}{2}$, and since the spin of the electron emitted is $\frac{1}{2}$ there might either be no other particle emitted, or a particle of zero spin, or else two particles the sum of whose spins is zero.

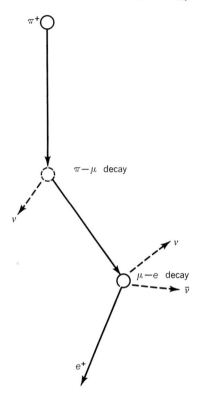

Fig. 17-11. Probable decay of a π^+ meson to a μ meson and a neutrino followed by decay of the μ meson to a positron and 2 neutrinos (a neutrino and an antineutrino).

To account for the great variation of energy of the decay electrons similar to ordinary beta decay, as well as to account for the angles at which they may be emitted, other particles must be assumed to conserve energy and momentum. The assumption that two neutrinos are emitted is then in harmony with the idea of conservation of energy and conservation of spin since the two neutrinos may spin in opposite directions and the sum of their spins may be zero.

In speaking of the half-life of an unstable particle the motion of the particle must be considered. The theory of relativity predicts that moving clocks run slow (time dilation) (§6-7). This means that fast moving particles "live longer" and consequently the half-life of a rapidly moving unstable particle should be longer than the half-life of the particle at rest, or as measured by an observer moving with the particle.

In an experiment by Rossi, Hilberry and Hoag, the mean life t of a group of mu mesons in motion was determined to be 3.2×10^{-5} sec. The energy of the mesons was estimated to be 1.3 beV. From this energy the speed was determined to be about 0.996c. Applying the time dilation formula $t_0 = t \sqrt{1 - v^2/c^2}$ gave the mean life t_0 for μ mesons at rest to be 2.7×10^{-6} sec. The correctness of the time dilation formula was confirmed by measurements on mu mesons which after passing through an absorbing medium were moving more slowly.

17-5. Čerenkov Counter: Velocity Discrimination

One way of distinguishing between various types of high-energy particles is by discriminating between their velocities in a material medium. This may often be done by a *Čerenkov counter* even though the velocities are close to the velocity of light.

Čerenkov in Russia noticed in 1934 that a faint bluish light was given off when an intense beam of high-energy gamma rays was directed into water. The light did not spread out in all directions but was limited to a cone in the forward direction. The explanation was given by Frank and Tamm in 1937 and the three were awarded the Nobel Prize in 1958.

The radiation, called *Čerenkov radiation*, occurs only when charged particles move in a transparent medium with a speed greater than the speed of light in that medium. This is the necessary condition for an electromagnetic "shock wave" formed in a manner similar to the shock wave of sound produced by a projectile in air when it moves faster than the speed of an ordinary sound wave.

The speed of light in a medium of index of refraction μ is c/μ where c is the speed of light in free space. The ratio of c/μ to the speed of the particle v determines the direction of propagation of the wave front, and

$$\cos \theta = \frac{c}{\mu v} \qquad [17\text{--}9]$$

where θ is the angle of propagation with respect to the direction of motion of the particle (Fig. 17-12). The duration of the light pulse is usually only about 10^{-9} sec, but it may be readily detected by means of a mirror system

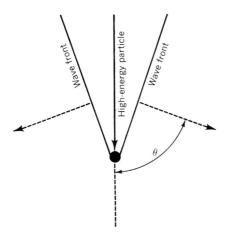

Fig. 17-12. Čerenkov radiation. A high-speed charged particle forms a wave of visible radiation like the bow wave of a boat when moving through a medium with a speed greater than that of light in the medium.

and a scintillation counter which is then called a Čerenkov counter. If the angle of propagation of the wave front is measured, the speed of the particle may be computed.

The Čerenkov counter has become an almost indispensable tool in high-energy physics and it played an important part in the detection of the antiproton (next section). Its most important function is in distinguishing between velocity groups by responding to particles in a narrow range of velocities. For instance in the search for the antiproton these particles had to be separated from pi mesons produced at the same time which were thousands of times more plentiful. The pi mesons were expected to travel faster through a block of lucite than the antiprotons (if they existed) and the angle of the forward cone of light was expected to be about 48° in comparison with 31° for the radiation from the slower antiprotons. Much higher resolving power than this is readily attainable.

17-6. Particles and Antiparticles

Before the discovery of the positive electron and the negative proton the disparity in mass between the smallest negatively charged particle, the electron, and the smallest positively charged particle, the proton, was perplexing. With the discovery of the positron and then the negative proton a new symmetry concept arose in the physics of particles, the concept of the *antiparticle*. It was, of course, known that when an electron pair is created from a gamma-ray photon the two electrons (electron and positron) have the same mass but to conserve charge they must have exactly opposite charges. The positron is therefore now called the *antiparticle* of the electron. In the same manner the negative proton is called the antiparticle of the proton (antiproton). The evidence indicates that there is a symmetry in the world of particle physics such that for every particle there is an antiparticle. The antiparticle for any particle is represented by placing a bar over the symbol. Thus the electron is represented by e^- and its antiparticle the positron is represented by $\bar{e}^+$. To complete the picture of symmetry a neutral particle must then be considered to be its own antiparticle.

A charged particle and its antiparticle always have opposite electric charges. If they are aligned so that their spins point in the same direction (parallel) their magnetic moments will point in opposite directions (antiparallel). Only a particle and its antiparticle can annihilate one another when they are brought together. The word *annihilate* is somewhat misleading. Although they disappear as separate particles the energy they represent goes to form gamma rays and the mass of the particles goes into equivalent energy-mass of the radiation.

If a particle is stable, its antiparticle will also be stable. Since it appears that for every particle there is an antiparticle, it should be possible to build atoms and molecules out of antiparticles. This has led to speculation as to the possible existence of *anti-worlds* and what would happen if worlds and anti-worlds came together in collision!

NEUTRINOS AND ANTINEUTRINOS

Some modes of decay of various particles are given in Table 17-2. In the beta decay of an unstable nucleus the emission of a neutrino was first assumed (in order to conserve energy) and later confirmed by experiment (§13-11). But in general, since beta decay may occur either by *electron* emission or by *antielectron* (positron) emission, it would seem there must be two kinds of neutrinos emitted, one of them the antiparticle of the other. And as will be shown in §17-7 the particle emitted in β^- decay is the *antineutrino*, $\bar{\nu}$.

TABLE 17-2. PRINCIPAL MODES OF DECAY

Muon	$\bar{\mu}^+$	$\bar{\mu}^+ \rightarrow \bar{e}^+ + \nu + \bar{\nu}$
	μ^-	$\mu^- \rightarrow e^- + \nu + \bar{\nu}$
Pion	π^+	$\pi^+ \rightarrow \bar{\mu}^+ + \nu$
(π-meson)	π^0	$\gamma + \gamma$
	$\bar{\pi}^-$	$\rightarrow \mu^- + \bar{\nu}$
K	κ^+	$\kappa^+ \rightarrow 2\pi^+ + \bar{\pi}^-$
Meson	$\bar{\kappa}^-$	$\bar{\kappa}^- \rightarrow 2\bar{\pi}^- + \pi^+$
	$\kappa^0(\bar{\kappa}_0)$	$\kappa^0 \rightarrow \pi^+ + \bar{\pi}^-$
Neutron	n^0	$n^0 \rightarrow p + e + \bar{\nu}$
Lambda	$\Lambda^0(\bar{\Lambda}^0)$	$\Lambda^0 \rightarrow p + \bar{\pi}^-$
		or $\rightarrow n + \pi^0$
Sigma	Σ	various
Xi	Ξ	various

Experiments previously mentioned (§15-8) indicate that for the neutrino the direction of angular momentum (spin) and the direction of linear momentum are opposite (antiparallel). On the other hand for the antineutrino they are in the same direction (parallel), and the spin is clockwise when looking in the direction of motion. This gives the antineutrino a *helicity* or *spirality* like that of a right-hand screw. The spirality of the neutrino is therefore that of a left-hand screw.

In the reactions [17-7] and [17-8] two neutrinos are produced at the same time in the decay of a mu meson, therefore one of these will be a neutrino and the other will be an antineutrino. However, the neutrino problem is not quite so simple as this. Although the neutrinos connected with pi meson to mu meson decay had at first been thought to be identical with those associated with beta emission, certain effects were noticed that seemed to contradict this. In 1962 a beam of high-energy neutrinos associated with muons in pi meson decay were shot at 10 tons of aluminum plates in a spark chamber. Out of an estimated 10^{12} neutrinos 50 were caught in the chamber in a period of six months. In none of these events were energetic electrons produced, implying that muon-connected neutrinos are different from electron-connected neutrinos. Thus it appears that there are two kinds of neutrinos, the ν_e and $\bar{\nu}_e$ which are the electron-connected neutrino and antineutrino, and the ν_μ and $\bar{\nu}_\mu$ which are the muon-connected neutrino and antineutrino. These are indicated in Fig. 17-12.

PROTONS AND ANTIPROTONS

Until 1955 the negative proton was not known to exist. Even the possibility of its existence was still in doubt but ever since the discovery of the positive electron it seemed that to preserve symmetry there might be a negative proton. In that case it should be possible to create a *proton pair* in a manner similar to the creation of an *electron pair* if gamma rays of sufficient energy could be produced (§6-11).

According to the Dirac theory if a proton pair could be created in the same way that an electron pair is created then a negative proton should be formed when a proton is raised to a positive energy state. The negative proton is then the "hole" left in the continuum of negative energy states when the proton is created. Since the rest-mass energy of a proton is 938 meV this would require a minimum gamma-ray energy of $2(938) = 1876$ meV or 1.876 beV. However, for reasons given below the formation of a proton pair at such a minimum energy would not be expected so that much higher energies are required for an experimental test.

Until about this time no particle accelerators were available to produce particles or gamma rays in the billion-volt range. The first of these to become available were the Brookhaven *cosmotron*, the Cornell *electron synchrotron*, and the University of California *bevatron*, and one of the first objectives was to test the creation of proton pairs. Late in 1955 a group at the University of California headed by Segré and Chamberlain announced the discovery of the antiproton, for which these two received the Nobel Prize for 1959. About the same time the creation of neutron-antineutron pairs was also detected. Measurements soon indicated that the negative proton has exactly the characteristics that would be expected of it on a theoretical basis. It is a stable particle; it possesses the same magnitude of charge as the proton; and it has the same mass.

Actually the creation of an electron pair or proton pair with minimum energy would leave the created particles with no kinetic energy of motion and no momentum. Even though energy was conserved the momentum could not be unless the total momentum of the system before creation of the pair was also zero. Although such a process can be imagined as, for instance, having two protons approach each other with the same speeds and each with sufficient kinetic energy that the two could produce a proton-antiproton pair in addition to themselves, it would be difficult to achieve.

There is an even greater relativistic difficulty. A proton which hits another proton at rest can according to classical mechanics transfer all of its kinetic energy to the second proton since both have the same mass. But from the relativistic viewpoint a high-speed proton may have a relativistic mass many times its rest mass. Upon hitting a proton at rest only a fraction of its kinetic energy is available for transfer because both momentum and energy must be conserved and the collision does not bring it to rest. A proton moving with a kinetic energy of 1.876 beV possesses enough energy to form a proton pair but cannot transfer the energy. In order to conserve momentum as well as energy the computed minimum energy to produce a proton pair is not 1.876 beV but over 5 beV.

When proton pairs were created by bombarding a copper target with protons it was found that the bombarding particles required a minimum or threshold energy of only 4.4 beV instead of the computed 5 beV. This was taken to be proof that because of random motion some of the nuclei in the target were moving toward the proton.

In the case of annihilation of an electron pair the energy released is usually not enough to do more than produce a pair of gamma-ray photons but in the annihilation of a proton pair there is enough energy available that particles less massive than protons may be produced as well as photons.

17-7. Classification of Particles: Leptons; Hyperons; Baryons

After the discovery of K mesons which are much more massive than pi mesons it became common to speak of them as "heavy" mesons. However, there are other aspects more important than mere weight. The pi and K mesons interact strongly with atomic nuclei whereas the mu meson, the electron and the neutrino do not. The latter particles are now called *leptons* (light particles) (Table 17-3). If we put only particles having similar properties in the meson group we must exclude the mu meson which is therefore misnamed and it had better be called simply a *muon*. Since that leaves the mesons and photons with zero or integral spin they "obey" Bose statistics and are called *bosons*.

TABLE 17-3.   CLASSIFICATION OF PARTICLES

	Class — Name	Ratio to Electron Mass	Spin	Statistics
Boson	photons	0	1	Bose
Lepton	leptons — neutrino	0		
	electron	1	$\frac{1}{2}$	Fermi
	muon	207		
Boson	mesons — π^0	264		
	$\pi^\pm$	273	0	Bose
	K^0	966		
	$K^\pm$	968		
Baryons	nucleons — proton	1836	$\frac{1}{2}$	Fermi
	neutron	1840		
	hyperons — Λ^0	2182		
	Σ^0	2326		
	$\Sigma^\pm$	2328	$\frac{1}{2}$	Fermi
	$\Sigma^\mp$	2340		
	Ξ^0	2585		
	$\Xi^\pm$	2585		

The discovery of short-lived particles more massive than nucleons further complicated the growing list of particles. They are of three chief types, the lambda (Λ), the sigma (Σ), and the xi (Ξ). The five members of this group with their antiparticles are shown in Table 17-3 and Table 17-4. They are called *hyperons*. The hyperons along with the nucleons (the proton and neutron) all have half-integral spins and are called *baryons*. They, along with the leptons, are *fermions*, "obeying" Fermi statistics and are consequently subject to the Pauli exclusion principle. See Plates 7, 8, 9.

CONSERVATION OF BARYONS AND LEPTONS

The baryons as a group have a distinctive property which is called the *baryon conservation law*. This law enables certain properties to be fitted into a coherent scheme. The *law of conservation of baryons* is as follows: Each baryon is represented by $+1$ and each antibaryon as -1 while other particles are represented by 0. The sum of these numbers is the *baryon number*, B. It is the number of baryon particles minus the number of baryon antiparticles and in any nuclear reaction the baryon number must be the same after the event as before.

TABLE 17-4. FUNDAMENTAL PARTICLES

Name	Symbol and Charge Particle	Antiparticle	Mass — Energy (amu)	Energy (meV)	Average Life (seconds)
Photon	γ	γ	0	0	Stable
Neutrino	ν_e, ν_μ	$\bar{\nu}_e, \bar{\nu}_\mu$	0	0	Stable
Electron	e^-	$\bar{e}^+$	1	0.51	Stable
Muon (mu meson)	μ^-	$\bar{\mu}^+$	207	105.7	2.2×10^{-6}
Pion (Pi meson)	π^0	π^0	264	135	2.3×10^{-16}
	π^+	$\bar{\pi}^-$	273	139.6	2.6×10^{-8}
K meson	K^0	$\bar{K}^0$	966	494	1.2×10^{-8}
	K^+_0	$\bar{K}^-$	968	495	6×10^{-8} 1×10^{-10}
Proton	p^+	$\bar{p}^-$	1836	938.2	Stable
Neutron	n^0	$\bar{n}^0$	1840	939.5	10^3 (approx.)
Lambda	Λ^0	$\bar{\Lambda}^0$	2182	1115	2.5×10^{-10}
Sigma	Σ^0	$\bar{\Sigma}^0$	2326	1191	approx. 10^{-10}
	Σ^+	$\bar{\Sigma}^-$	2328	1189	
	Σ^-	$\bar{\Sigma}^+$	2340	1196	
Xi	Ξ^0	$\bar{\Xi}^0$	2585	1318	
	Ξ^-	$\bar{\Xi}^+$	2585	1318	

In a similar manner in any nuclear reaction it is found that *the lepton number is conserved*. This is obtained by giving each lepton the number $+1$ and each antilepton -1. The sum of all of these is the lepton number. For example consider the radioactive decay of the neutron to a proton by emission of an electron and some kind of neutrino. If conservation of leptons holds true then the neutrino must have a negative lepton number and must therefore be an antineutrino.

$$n \rightarrow p + e^- + \bar{\nu}$$

$$(\text{leptons})\ 0 \rightarrow 0 + 1 - 1$$

In the same reaction there is conservation of baryons as follows.

$$n \rightarrow p + e^- + \bar{\nu}$$

$$(\text{baryons})\ 1 \rightarrow 1 + 0 + 0$$

17-8. "Fundamental Particles": Resonance Particles

Before the discovery of mesons and hyperons, the structure of matter seemed to be much more simple. The nucleus was thought to consist of protons and neutrons, and to form an atom only electrons needed to be added in external shells. It seemed appropriate at that time to speak of protons, neutrons, and electrons as the fundamental particles. However, with the discovery of still more particles, it became increasingly difficult to set up a simple plan of organization describing the structure of matter. Consequently the term *fundamental particle* has lost a considerable amount of significance.

In Table 17-4 there is a total of 34 particles if all antiparticles are counted including photons and the two kinds of neutrinos. This may not be quite fair as antiparticles are only "mirror images" or particles, and the photon and neutral particles are their own antiparticles. There is also growing evidence that according to the earlier suggestion of Heisenberg many of these particles may be considered only as excited states of other particles.

A further complication has arisen in the particle picture. A whole new array of "particles," sixty or more, believed to be temporary or "resonance" associations of longer-lived particles, has appeared on the scene. They are distinguished from the particles of Table 17-4 by an extremely short mean life of the order of 10^{-23} second and they have been called *resonance particles* because they are produced in high-energy bombardment experiments only at certain sharply defined energies of bombardment.

Experiments begun in 1952 by Fermi (et al.) at the University of Chicago showed that when either positive or negative pi mesons of more than 100-meV energy are incident on protons, the collision cross section increases with the energy of the incident particle. When higher energies became available with the Brookhaven *cosmotron*, Yuan and Lindenbaum showed that the cross section reached a distinct peak at 195 meV and then fell off sharply at higher energies. It has been suggested by Brueckner that this indicates a strong *resonance* interaction between a pion and a proton in which the ψ waves of the particles are *in phase*. In that case the particles may perhaps be thought of as forming a temporary association, a Δ "particle" with a total mass-energy of 1237 meV.

In 1960 Alvarez and co-workers at the University of California shot high-energy negative K mesons into a liquid hydrogen bubble chamber and observed in a few instances the production of a neutral lambda, Λ^0, particle plus a pair of π mesons as follows

$$\overline{K}^- + p^+ \rightarrow \Lambda^0 + \pi^+ + \pi^- \qquad [17\text{--}10]$$

In this experiment it appeared that the lambda particle and one of the π

mesons would briefly cling together to form what has been represented as a Σ "particle" with a mass-energy of 1384 meV. The Λ^0 particle was already known and tracks indicating the formation of a pair of these, one being the antiparticle of the other, have been observed.

Soon many other new resonance groupings were found and to even call such temporary groupings *particles* is questionable. Since they are too short-lived as free particles to be studied directly, or to give visible tracks, their existence is only inferred, chiefly by such means as finding resonance peaks on collision cross section curves or by studying their disintegration products.

To bring order out of apparent nuclear chaos, and to organize known particles into a coherent system, new characteristics were sought that are conserved in nuclear changes. Symmetrical relations were also sought. The first fruitful method of classifying the new particles originated with the work of Regge in 1959 and led to plotting particles by groups of states on curves called *Regge trajectories*. Particles in states of higher mass are then found to lie on curves having regularly increasing amounts of half-integral (or integral) spin angular momentum. One of the most successful schemes is that proposed independently by Gell-Mann and Ne'emen in 1961, based on eight quantum numbers (sometimes referred to as "the eightfold way"). It results in arranging all baryons and mesons (not including the muon) in symmetrical groups (multiplets) depending on their charges. The groups may be singlets, doublets, triplets and quadruplets (Fig. 17-13). Five quantities, always conserved in the strong interactions to which baryons and mesons are subject, are involved in the system. They are: 1, atomic mass number; 2, spin angular momentum; 3, parity; 4, isotopic spin; and

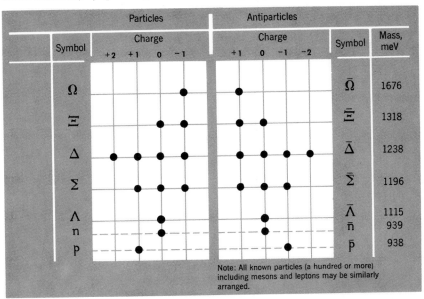

Note: All known particles (a hundred or more) including mesons and leptons may be similarly arranged.

Fig. 17-13.   Symmetrical arrangement of some baryons showing groups of multiplets.

5, strangeness or hypercharge. The first three have been previously mentioned. The last two will be discussed in the next section. Further details may be found in the last recommended reading, p. 419.

A critical test of any such scheme is to see if it enables successful predictions to be made. Gell-Mann and Ne'emen found a glaring vacancy in their system at mass 1676 meV. Different laboratories then began an intensive search for the missing particle, the negative *omega* (Ω) particle, and it was found early in 1964 by Shutt and co-workers at Brookhaven. Such a strong confirmation of the validity of the new classification indicates an important break-through in particle physics, but the search for what is *fundamental* will go on.

17-9. Isotopic Spin; Strangeness; New Quantum Numbers

The term *isotopic spin* represents one of the important factors in classifying particles but it is difficult to define because it has been said to be "neither isotopic nor spin." However, it serves as a connecting link between states of charge and certain other states to be described, and it functions in a manner similar to the representations of angular momentum. It is represented by a set of numbers which are the *isotopic spin quantum numbers* (T). The idea of "spin" comes in because the quantum number T can have integral components T_z along the axis of spin just as angular momentum does. The number of isotopic spin states running from $-T$ to $+T$ is then ($2T_z + 1$) just as for angular momentum quantum states.

For example a proton and a neutron may be thought of as forming a *doublet system* for which $T = T_z = +\frac{1}{2}$ for the proton and $T = T_z = -\frac{1}{2}$ for the neutron. Thus an isotopic spin $\frac{1}{2}$ means a positive charge and a spin of $-\frac{1}{2}$ means zero charge. A pi meson may have 3 charge states and for it $+1$ means positive charge, -1 means negative charge, and 0 means zero charge. Isotopic spin is not merely a designation of charge which is a simple matter by itself, but it is involved along with both the *strangeness* and *baryonic quantum numbers* in attempts to organize the various particles into a logically consistent system.

The K mesons and the hyperons were initially called "strange particles" because of certain anomalies in their behavior. Since both K mesons and π mesons interact strongly with nuclei they are apparently involved with the strong nuclear force that binds nucleons together. Therefore it was expected when K mesons decay to π mesons that the half-life would be relatively short. When it turned out to be relatively long there was no immediate explanation and the behavior was considered *strange*. Although it had been hoped to find a simple relation between the isotopic spin quantum numbers (T) and the baryon numbers, no simple relation was found without introducing still a newer set of quantum numbers (S) for *strangeness*. *Strangeness* (S) is also known as *hypercharge* (Y) and *average charge* ($\overline{Q}$).

According to the classification set up by Gell-Mann neutrons, protons and pi mesons since they are "not strange" are assigned a strangeness quantum number $S = 0$. For K^+ and K^0 mesons, $S = +1$ but for their antiparticles $\overline{K}^-$ and $\overline{K}^0$, $S = -1$. For the hyperons Λ^0, $\Sigma^{\pm}$ and Σ^0, $S = -1$ but for Ξ^- and Ξ^0, $S = -2$.

By this method and the addition of two selection rules a first attempt was made to find order where there had been almost complete lack of it in the relations of many of these particles. The selection and conservation rules are that S is conserved in strong (fast) reactions, that is

$$\Delta S = 0 \quad \text{(strong reactions)}$$

and S is not conserved in weak (slow) reactions but can change only by unity

$$\Delta S = \pm 1 \quad \text{(weak reactions)}$$

By application of the rules of conservation of charge Q, the baryonic number B and strangeness quantum number S, along with isotopic spin T, are related by the formula

$$Q = T_z + \frac{1}{2} B + \frac{1}{2} S \qquad [17\text{--}12]$$

Thus many reactions involving new particles and strange particles could be described.

Problems

1. A primary cosmic-ray proton enters the atmosphere with a kinetic energy of 10^9 eV and forms a cascade shower of gamma rays and electron pairs. What is the maximum number of electron pairs that could be formed by it if no other particles were formed? Assume kinetic energy of each electron pair is equal to its rest-mass energy.

2. A cosmic-ray proton approaches the earth with an energy of 10^9 eV but is deflected away from the earth by the earth's magnetic field. If the most curved part of the path is approximately the arc of a circle of radius equal to the radius of the earth, what is the average magnetic field flux density in that region?

3. The nucleus of an atom in a nuclear emulsion is hit by a high-energy cosmic-ray proton. The nucleus is disrupted and a "star" is formed involving the ejection of a number of particles and the formation of a residual nucleus. Explain how the energies involved and the momenta must be balanced in such a reaction.

*4. A primary cosmic-ray proton of 10^{10}-eV energy enters the solar system and is deflected into the arc of a circle whose radius is one million miles (1.67×10^6 km). What is the average flux density of the magnetic field encountered by the ray? Use relativistic methods.

5. Compute the thickness of a layer of water having approximately the same amount of absorption for cosmic-ray particles as our atmosphere, and also the thickness of a layer of lead.

6. A negative muon is captured by a proton to form a μ-mesic atom. What is the radius of the first Bohr orbit thus formed? Compare this with the first Bohr orbit in hydrogen. What is the binding energy of the two particles?

7. If a pi meson at rest decays to a muon and a neutrino according to the reaction $\pi^+ \rightarrow \mu^+ + \nu$, what is the energy Q liberated? In what way can momentum be conserved?

8. How many more nuclear interactions would be found per centimeter of path in a hydrogen bubble chamber than in a hydrogen cloud chamber at atmospheric pressure? Density of liquid hydrogen $= 0.060$ gm/cm³.

9. Is the reaction $\bar{\pi}^- + p \rightarrow \bar{\pi}^- + p + \pi^+ + \bar{\pi}^-$ possible? Explain.

*10. A π^0 meson approaches the earth with a kinetic energy of 10^9 eV and decays into two gamma-ray photons. Apply laws of conservation of energy and momentum to find the angle between the path of each photon and the initial direction of the π^0 meson. Relativistic methods must be used.

*11. What would be the kinetic energy in meV of a π^0 meson which decays during flight into two gamma-ray photons the paths of which each make an angle of $45°$ with the initial direction of the π^0 meson?

*12. A π^0 meson may decay during flight into two gamma-ray photons. Prove that the angle between the path of each photon and the initial direction of the π^0 meson is given by the surprisingly simple relation $\sin \theta = E_0/E_T$. E_0 is the relativistic rest-mass energy and the total relativistic energy $E_T = E_0 + E_k$ where $E_k =$ the kinetic energy.

13. Show by the formula of problem 12 that for π^0 mesons of 10^{10} eV or more, which decay in flight into two gamma-ray photons, the direction of each photon is nearly the same as the initial direction of the π^0 meson.

14. Show which of the following possible reactions are in agreement with conservation of strangeness ($\Delta s = 0$).

$$\text{(a)} \quad \pi^- + p = K^0 + \Lambda^0$$
$$\text{(b)} \quad\quad\quad = K^0 + \overline{K}^0 + n$$
$$\text{(c)} \quad\quad\quad = 2K^0 + \Xi^0$$
$$\text{(d)} \quad\quad\quad = \overline{K}^0 + \Xi^0 + n$$

15. Which of the three following reactions is allowed according to conservation of charge, spin and strangeness?

$$\text{(a)} \quad K^- + p \rightarrow \Xi^0 + K^0$$
$$\text{(b)} \quad K^- + p \rightarrow \overline{K}^0 + n$$
$$\text{(c)} \quad \pi^- + p \rightarrow \Sigma^0 + n$$

Recommended Reading

Leprince-Ringuet, L., *Cosmic Rays*. New York: McGraw-Hill Book Company, Inc., 1952.

Rossi, B., *High Energy Particles*. Englewood Cliffs, N. J.: Prentice-Hall, Inc., 1952.

Rochester, G. D., and J. G. Wilson, *Cloud-Chamber Photographs of Cosmic Radiation*. New York: Academic Press, Inc., 1952.

Thorndike, A. M., *Mesons, A Summary of Experimental Facts*. New York: McGraw-Hill Book Company, Inc., 1952.

Shapiro, M. M., "Mesons and Hyperons," *American Journal of Physics*, 24, 196 (1956).

Marshak, R. E., "Elementary Particles of Modern Physics," *Science*, 132, 269 (1960).

Gell-Mann, M., and E. P. Rosenbaum, "Elementary Particles," *Scientific American*, July 1957.

Segré, E., "Antinucleons," *American Journal of Physics*, 25, 363 (1957).

Burbidge, G., and F. Hoyle, "Antimatter," *Scientific American*, Vol. 198, No. 4, p. 34 (1958).

Davidson, J. P., "Isotopic Spin," *American Journal of Physics*, 27, 457 (1959).

Chew, G. F., M. Gell-Mann, and A. H. Rosenfeld, "Strongly Interacting Particles," *Scientific American*, Vol. 210, No. 2, p. 74 (1964).

Particle Accelerators

The need to bombard atomic nuclei with particles of higher and higher energies had become apparent by the late 1920's. But attempts to build high-voltage transformers showed that for voltages above a million the difficulties of insulating the windings were practically insuperable and other methods must be found. By 1930 Cockroft and Walton had developed their high-voltage capacitor system (§15-1) for voltages up to 1.4 million volts. At the same time, however, E. O. Lawrence had constructed a model cyclotron based on the idea of cyclic acceleration and about this time Van de Graaff was working on his electrostatic generator. Both of these methods soon succeeded in achieving particle energies in the millions of electron volts. Ever since that time there has been a steady succession of new developments leading to more and more powerful particle accelerators.

In discussing this subject it is necessary to distinguish between particle accelerators that produce high-energy particles by the application of a single high-output voltage and those which operate on some cyclic principle such as repeated accelerations at lower voltage. Devices like the cyclotron and the betatron may produce particles of 100 million-volts energy or more, but they produce these high-energy particles without the requirement of insulation for the high voltages.

Although the cyclotron and the betatron are the prototypes of all cyclic accelerators their inherent limitations led to the development of such machines as the *synchrocyclotron*, the *electron synchrotron*, the *proton synchrotron* and various *linear accelerators* which have achieved energies far beyond their prototypes. To avoid certain complications it is easier to study the earlier accelerators first.

18-1. The Van de Graaff Generator

The Van de Graaff generator followed a very old and simple principle. More than a century earlier a primitive type of electrostatic machine for demonstrating production of visible electric sparks had consisted of a glass-insulating plate, on which electric charges were produced by rubbing. As the plate was made to rotate, the charges on the glass were carried to a metal electrode where continual deposit of charge built up the potential to an amount satisfactory for demonstrations.

In the Van de Graaff generator this principle is pushed to the limit. The moving carrier of charge is an endless belt of silk or other insulating material (Fig. 18-1). Electric charges are sprayed onto this belt by means of sharp-pointed discharge electrodes connected to an electronic generator of sufficient voltage to produce a discharge at the points. The moving belt continually carries electric charge to the inside of a more or less spherically shaped electrode the potential of which continually rises until a limiting value is reached. The limiting value depends on the breakdown point of the insulation surrounding or supporting the large electrode on which the charge collects and also on the rate of leakage of the charge on the moving belt.

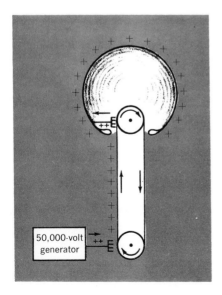

Fig. 18-1. Principle of the Van de Graaff generator. Electric charges are carried continuously to spherical electrode by moving belt.

A simple computation will illustrate the relationship of the quantities involved. The potential V to which any electrode is raised by a charge Q depends upon the capacitance of the electrode and is

$$V(\text{volts}) = \frac{Q(\text{coulombs})}{C(\text{farads})} \qquad [18\text{-}1]$$

For the case of an ideal spherical electrode, the capacitance in rationalized mks units is

$$C(\text{farads}) = 4\pi\epsilon_0 r = \frac{r}{8.988 \times 10^9} \qquad [18\text{-}2]$$

where r is the radius in meters and ϵ_0 is the permittivity of free space. Therefore by Eq. 18-1

$$V = 8.988 \times 10^9 \frac{Q}{r} \qquad [18\text{-}3]$$

If the maximum voltage obtainable is determined by the breakdown of the insulation around the electrode this will be determined by the electric field intensity $\mathcal{E}$ at the surface of the sphere where

$$\mathcal{E} = 8.988 \times 10^9 \frac{Q}{r^2} \qquad [18\text{-}4]$$

From Eqs. 18-3 and 18-4 we have therefore

$$V(\text{volts}) = r(\text{m})\mathcal{E}(\text{volts/m}) \qquad [18\text{-}5]$$

Assuming the insulation is air with a breakdown field intensity of 3×10^6 volts/m (30,000 volts/cm) the maximum attainable voltage V_{max} is

$$V_{\text{max}} = 3 \times 10^6 \times r \qquad [18\text{-}6]$$

If the radius of the sphere is 1.5 meters the maximum attainable voltage for the given specifications is 4.5 million volts.

In the modern design of a Van de Graaff generator the electrode size is often reduced, but to prevent proportionate reduction of output voltage the whole generator is enclosed in a gas-tight housing. The breakdown voltage is then considerably increased by filling the housing with compressed air or some gas such as freon (CCl_2F_2), possessing good insulating properties. Voltages as high as 10 million have thus been attained and currents near a milliampere. The attendant reduction in size has enabled portable units to be developed, and these are now commercially available. More recently two or more Van de Graaff generators have been operated in "tandem" to obtain higher voltages. Twin machines at California Institute of Technology have been used in research to give 12 meV and other tandem sets have been designed to give 20 meV.

The Van de Graaff generator was the first to reach output voltages of several million volts. Although other types of accelerators now far surpass it in ability to produce very-high-energy particles, it is still unsurpassed in its range for convenience, portability, and easy control of output voltage. Furthermore, it has the advantage of giving constant currents of considerable magnitude at high voltage, something that later types of particle accelerators do not do. It also has the advantage that the voltage is controllable to 0.1 per cent so that all the particles in the beam have very nearly the same energies (monoenergetic), a favorable factor for many kinds of precision work. Because of these features it has had many applications not only in research work but in industry and in hospitals, where high voltages are needed for research or for the production of penetrating x-rays.

18-2. The Cyclotron

Following the development of the cyclotron by Lawrence and Livingston a succession of larger models was built until about 1940, just before World War II, a great fixed-frequency cyclotron was built weighing over 200 tons and costing several million dollars (Fig. 18-2). This was the first

Fig. 18-2. View, before shielding wall was built around it, of the large cyclotron built by Lawrence with pole pieces 184″ in diameter. (Courtesy, Lawrence Radiation Laboratory, University of California.)

of many huge machines and the forerunner of improved and larger accelerators to come. With the cyclotron the production of high-speed particles had become big business, with costs in the millions and machines so large that special laboratories had to be built to house them. The cyclotron soon produced particles having energies of 20 million electron volts and by the end of World War II modifications had been made so that by means of frequency modulation (next section) protons of nearly 300-meV energy and alpha particles of 384 meV were obtained. More recent developments in the production of high-speed particles have now left these limits far behind and have opened up many new possibilities for scientific research.

The cyclotron is actually a *magnetic resonance accelerator*. To provide successive accelerations of the particles in a cyclotron they are made to spiral around the interior of two hollow D-shaped electrodes, passing from one to the other twice per revolution (Fig. 18-3). These accelerating electrodes are called "dees" from their shape. The paths of the particles are bent in each dee in a semicircle by the magnetic field at right angles to the dees, produced by the large field magnet. After many circuits the particles may then be brought out through a "window" at the edge of the dees in the form of a high-energy beam by means of deflecting electrodes. The path of a particle is illustrated by the spiral curve shown in the figure, and it is seen that twice per revolution the particle crosses the gap between the dee electrodes. If across this gap an alternating difference of potential of 50,000 or 100,000 volts is impressed, then at each passage of the gap a particle is accelerated in proportion. After revolving through 180° a particle would enter a retarding field except that the potential difference between the dee electrodes has now been reversed. This requires that the potential between the dees be reversed periodically in phase with the motion of the particle. The oscillating potential on the dees is obtained by coupling them to an electronic oscillator, and the frequency of the oscillator is adjusted so that

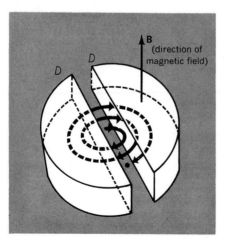

Fig. 18-3. Path of an accelerated positive ion inside the dee electrodes of a cyclotron.

the potential reverses at just the right instant to produce successive forward accelerations. Simple computation indicates that if the energy gained at each crossing of the gap is 100,000 eV the gain per revolution is 2 times that, and in 100 revolutions it would be 20 meV.

The general section of a cyclotron is shown in Fig. 18-4 where the magnet is seen to consist of a large rectangular yoke with poles in the middle. The dee electrodes are located between the poles and are enclosed in an air-tight housing kept at a high vacuum. With an intense magnetic field the path of the particle is approximately a tight spiral of many turns, the change in radius occurring at each increase of velocity when the particle crosses the gap in the dees. The total energy gain of a particle depends on the number of revolutions that it can make before it reaches the outer edge of the dees and the field. This in turn depends upon the size of the magnet and the diameter of the pole pieces. The frequency of the dee oscillator may be in the neighborhood of 12 megacycles/sec if the magnetic field intensity is 15,000 gauss, and a particle starting at the center spirals out to near the edge of the poles in little more than a thousandth of a second. Currents of some hundreds of microamperes may be attained.

It might at first appear to be a difficult problem to adjust the oscillation frequency of the dee potential so as to be in resonance with the passage of the particles between the dees, especially when it is evident that the particle orbit is becoming larger at each revolution. However, elementary analysis indicates that as long as the mass of the particle remains essentially constant, that is, as long as velocities are low enough so that the relativistic change in mass may be neglected, the period of revolution is independent of the radius of path. Thus the oscillator coupled to the dees can have a constant frequency. To show that this is true, consider the equation for the deflection of a particle of charge q in a uniform magnetic field of flux density B (Eq. 2–25), solved for the velocity of the particle.

$$v = \frac{Bqr}{m} \qquad [18\text{–}7]$$

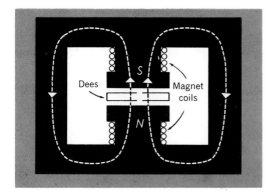

Fig. 18-4. Section plan of cyclotron magnet.

However, the linear velocity of a particle in a circular orbit is also equal to the circumference divided by the period T of revolution, or

$$v = \frac{2\pi r}{T} \qquad [18\text{–}7a]$$

Setting these equations equal to each other we find that the radius r cancels on both sides of the equation, and the period is

$$T = \frac{2\pi m}{Bq} \qquad [18\text{–}8]$$

Evidently if B, m and q are constants the period of revolution and the frequency are independent of the size of the orbit. It is this somewhat surprising result which makes the cyclotron possible in the first place. The frequency of the potential on the dees can be adjusted so that the accelerated particle revolves in *resonance* with it. Eq. 18–8 is the resonance condition for successful operation, or in terms of frequency instead of period $f = 1/T = Bq/2\pi m$.

Evidently this equation can only be applied in the non-relativistic range of speeds where the mass m can be considered constant. The maximum energies of particles attainable in a cyclotron are limited by the relativistic increase in mass of the particles and to take this into consideration Eq. 18–8 becomes

$$T = \frac{2\pi}{Bq} \frac{m_0}{\sqrt{1 - \dfrac{v^2}{c^2}}} \qquad [18\text{–}8a]$$

As the speed v of the particle becomes increasingly appreciable in comparison with the speed of light c the period becomes longer and the resonance condition can no longer be attained. The reason why the cyclotron cannot successfully accelerate electrons becomes evident from this equation. Long before electrons have reached the high energies desired, the relativistic increase in mass increases the period of revolution. This throws it out of step with the oscillating potential on the dees and makes further acceleration impossible.

In accelerating protons or alpha particles, however, speeds equivalent to energies of 20 meV may be reached before relativistic change of mass becomes important enough to seriously affect the operation of the accelerator. To achieve higher energies of some hundreds of meV, a modification of the operation of the cyclotron is necessary, and in the newer form it became known as a *frequency-modulated cyclotron* or *synchrocyclotron*.

18-3. The Synchrocyclotron

The synchrocyclotron or frequency-modulated cyclotron is a cyclotron modified to remove the limitation resulting from relativistic increase in mass of the particles. The cyclotron is arranged so that when the frequency of revolution of the particle begins to slow down the frequency of oscillation of the accelerating potential between the dee electrodes is similarly slowed down. This permits the oscillation frequency on the dees to keep in step or in synchronism with the revolution of the particles, and thus forward acceleration can be carried on to much higher energies. The process is repeated automatically for successive groups of particles, and the cyclotron is then said to be frequency-modulated. Without frequency modulation the high-speed particles would be produced in a steady stream, but with frequency modulation they only come in separate pulsations. Consequently the total current in the beam is considerably reduced, but the gain in energy is worth the sacrifice.

18-4. The Betatron

Although the cyclotron cannot be used to accelerate electrons, the chief function of the *betatron* is the acceleration of electrons. The first successful betatron or electron accelerator was built by Donald R. Kerst at the University of Illinois in 1941. In the betatron, electrons are continuously accelerated all the way around their circular path. In going around the path again, they are again accelerated, and in each successive revolution they receive further acceleration until after having made 100,000 or more complete circuits they have gained energies of a hundred million electron volts or more. Since the acceleration around the circular path is continuous, any change of mass and slowing down of the rate of revolution have no harmful effect. There is no synchronism to be preserved, and the energy of each electron builds up continuously.

The fundamental principle of the betatron involves two separate factors which must act together to produce the desired effect. Consider the simple case of the north pole of a magnet which is moved toward a closed circular loop of conductor. As the magnet approaches the face of the loop the changing magnetic field through the loop generates an emf which acts around the loop in the direction of the arrow (Fig. 18-5a). The conduction electrons in the conductor would move in the direction opposite to the emf since they are negatively charged. An electron passing around the loop once would be acted upon by the emf generated in the loop, and in n round trips it would be acted upon n times. But in the conductor, of course, it is not free to be accelerated indefinitely and because of collisions actually moves very slowly. Now, however, imagine the conducting loop replaced by a ring-shaped hollow tube with a high vacuum (Fig. 18-5b).

Every time an electron makes a complete circuit of the ring it gains energy in eV equal to the emf around its path. Substituting the ring-shaped orbital tube for the conductor, so that the electrons become free to move

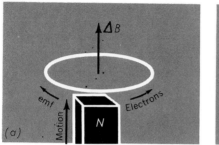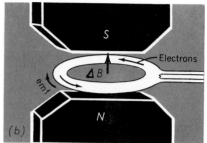

Fig. 18-5. Principle of betatron: *a,* emf induced in conducting ring by approaching magnetic pole; *b,* emf around ring-shaped tube induced by increasing flux density *B* between poles of magnet.

as fast as they can, there would now appear to be nothing to confine them to the circular path. However, since it is necessary to have a changing magnetic field at right angles to the ring-shaped orbital tube to produce the accelerating emf, the possibility arises of making this field of sufficient intensity at each moment to bend the paths of the electrons into the arc of a circle, so that they will remain near the axis of the orbital tube. As the electrons gain speed and move faster the magnetic field must become more intense; consequently it must be an increasing one.

Since it would be out of the question to move a magnet periodically toward the orbital tube, a fixed magnet is used with periodically increasing pulses of current which produce increasing magnetic fields. To operate the magnet a large alternating-current generator to furnish heavy current is required. The magnet is then tuned to resonance with the generator current by means of a large bank of capacitors. This in effect balances the inductive load and improves the power factor, thus reducing the volt-ampere capacity required of the generator. Because in alternating current the current increases to a maximum during one quarter-cycle the high-speed electrons are not produced continuously in the tube but are produced in pulses, one pulse for each cycle of the current (Fig. 18-6). The basic problem in building the betatron was to design the size and shape of the magnet, together with the necessary current-carrying coils, so that the magnetic field would fulfill

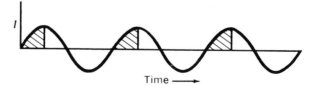

Fig. 18-6. Successive groups of electrons are accelerated in betatron during intervals in which current *I* is rising sharply.

its two functions. The rate of change of the magnetic field must furnish the emf to give the electrons the requisite velocity, and the momentary intensity of the same field must bend their paths so as to make them follow the same paths continuously. The following analysis leads to the fundamental relation that must be satisfied.

The bending of the path of an electron moving in a circular orbit depends upon the magnetic field intensity B_r at the path itself, that is, at the distance r from the center of path, where r is the radius of path. Since in this application the speeds are in the extreme relativistic range, increase in momentum for the highest speeds is chiefly the result of relativistic increase in mass. The momentum mv from Eq. 2–25 for the bending of the path of an electron must now be replaced by the relativistic momentum p, and the equation becomes

$$p = B_r er \qquad [18\text{--}9]$$

Now, tangential force is the rate of change of the tangential momentum, or

$$F_{\text{tan}} = \frac{dp}{dt} = \frac{d}{dt}(B_r er) \qquad [18\text{--}10]$$

Tangential force is also work eV done on the electron in one complete revolution, divided by the distance $2\pi r$,

$$F_{\text{tan}} = \frac{eV}{2\pi r} = \frac{e}{2\pi r}\frac{d\varphi}{dt} \qquad [18\text{--}11]$$

where the emf V is the rate of change of flux φ through the path. Then

$$F_{\text{tan}} = \frac{e \cdot}{2\pi r}\frac{d(B_{\text{av}}\pi r^2)}{dt} \qquad [18\text{--}12]$$

where φ, the flux, is the average magnetic flux density B_{av} times the area πr^2 enclosed by the path. Putting Eq. 18–10 equal to Eq. 18–12, we have

$$\frac{e}{2\pi r}\frac{d(B_{\text{av}}\pi r^2)}{dt} = \frac{d(B_r er)}{dt} \qquad [18\text{--}13]$$

from which, by integrating both sides of the equation, assuming that $B = 0$ at $t = 0$, we obtain

$$\frac{B_{\text{av}}er}{2} = B_r er \qquad [18\text{--}14]$$

and

$$B_{\text{av}} = 2B_r \qquad [18\text{--}15]$$

From this we see that, for the magnetic field to perform its two functions of providing emf by its rate of change and of bending the electron by the proper amount for each instantaneous value of the speed, the average flux density through the loop must be twice the flux density at the orbit. To increase the average flux density of the field the gap at the central part of the field is narrowed by putting a slab of magnetic material there, as shown in Fig. 18-7a.

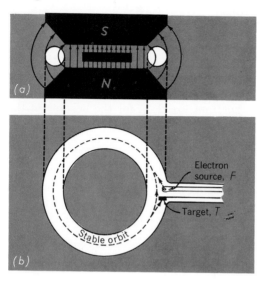

Fig. 18-7. a, Tapered pole pieces and location of orbital tube in betatron. Central magnetic slab increases average field intensity to attain required emf; b, part of electron gun and target, together with the paths of electrons.

The first betatron was designed to give energies of a mere 100,000 eV and was constructed with the technical aid of the General Electric Co. With increased efficiency of design and in response to the demand for higher and higher energies, a betatron with a 400-ton magnet was designed to give 340 million-volt electrons (Fig. 18-8). The circular tube in which the electrons revolve is 9 feet in diameter, and electrons travel 140,000 revolutions in 0.004 second, or more than 700 miles in this short time. In the betatron it is so difficult to bring the beam out of the orbital tube that the target is usually put into the tube. The electrons to be accelerated are injected into the orbital tube at energies up to 1 meV from a linear accelerator, and are pulled by means of the bulging field into a stable orbit (Fig. 18-7b). At the end of each acceleration interval the orbit is quickly expanded by means of an auxiliary field, and the beam is made to strike the target, as indicated in Fig. 18-7b. With the betatron it was possible for the first time not only to use high-speed electrons as bombarding particles but also to produce x-rays so short in wavelength and so penetrating in character as to surpass the gamma rays from radioactive substances and to be comparable with many of the gamma rays present in cosmic rays.

In both cyclotron and betatron the problems of orbital stability loom large; attainment of stability must be assured by proper design. For an electron in the betatron to travel in a stable orbit of constant radius, there must be a restoring force acting inward to prevent the electron from moving to a larger orbit. There must also be a restoring force acting outward to prevent the electron from moving to a smaller orbit. In addition there must be restoring forces to produce vertical stability.

Fig. 18-8. The 340-million-volt betatron at the University of Illinois. Electrons make 140,000 revolutions in a circular tube 9 ft in diameter in 0.004 sec, and thus travel more than 700 miles to gain this energy. The circular orbital tube is placed between the poles of the magnet at the middle of the 400-ton frame. (Courtesy, University of Illinois.)

If the electron wanders into an orbit of larger radius, the required centripetal force mv^2/r for circular motion of that radius is reduced since it is inversely proportional to the radius and the required horizontal restoring force is reduced somewhat. The magnetic flux density must then not decrease as fast as $1/r$ if there is to be a restoring force. This is the condition for horizontal stability. For vertical stability, a component of the magnetic field will act to restore the electron if the field is made to bulge outward. Indeed, both conditions of stability may be satisfied to a certain degree, if the field does not bulge too much, by properly tapering the pole pieces as shown in Fig. 18-9 (exaggerated to show vertical focussing). Since the deflecting force of the magnetic field is at right angles to the field, the force vectors, marked F on the diagram, each have components inward and toward the median plane of the orbit between the poles. Such a slightly bulging field is also feasible for the cyclotron for vertical stability when the particles are near the edge of the field. The limitations of this method of achieving stability and focussing of the beam so as to lose as few particles as possible lead to its being spoken of as *weak focussing* in contrast with newer methods of *strong focussing* to be described later (§18-7).

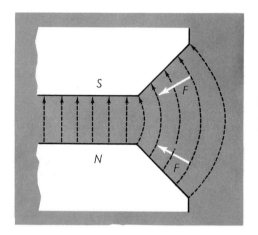

Fig. 18-9. Bulging field at edge of betatron magnet gives both vertical and horizontal stability to electron orbits.

18-5. The Electron Synchrotron; Synchrotron Radiation

For electron energies much over 100 meV the cost of a sufficiently large magnet for a betatron becomes prohibitive, and the efficiency of operation drops rapidly. The attempt to overcome these limitations led to the development of the electron synchrotron. The principle of the synchrotron was suggested at about the same time by Veksler in Russia and McMillan in this country. They showed theoretically that successful operation in stable orbits could be attained.

In the betatron the total energy that an electron acquires depends on the total number of revolutions that it makes before it departs too much from a stable orbit near the axis of the ring-shaped orbital tube. It was obvious that electrons could be made to attain higher energies if they could be kept rotating for a larger number of times. Since the electrons move almost with the velocity of light they do not move appreciably faster as they are accelerated, but they experience rapidly increasing relativistic change of mass. At an energy of 1 meV an electron is traveling with more than 0.9 the speed of light, and its mass has increased to about $2\frac{1}{2}$ times its rest mass. At 100-meV energy it has a speed 0.999 that of light, and its mass has increased to 200 times its rest mass. The increase in mass makes it more difficult for the magnetic field to bend the paths of the electrons into the same orbit, and a magnetic field of greater intensity just at the orbit is needed. Indeed, if an accelerating emf is furnished by some method other than the change of magnetic flux through the orbit, the central part of the field could be omitted and only bending field (guide field) just at the orbit is needed. This bending field, however, has to be increased periodically to enable groups of electrons to be carried to higher energies.

The accelerating emf for synchrotron operation is furnished by having the electron beam pass successively through two cylindrical metal electrodes which are built into the orbital tube (Fig. 18-10). At each revolution the

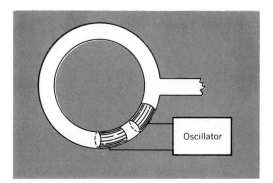

Fig. 18-10. How cylindrical accelerating electrodes are built into orbital tube of betatron for synchrotron operation.

electrons pass the gap between the two cylindrical electrodes where an accelerating potential from an oscillator is applied. As the electron mass increases, the magnetic field which deflects them must similarly increase in synchronism with the accelerating potential. Because the massive central core of the betatron magnet can be omitted and only a ring of magnets around the orbit is required to furnish the bending field, the synchrotron is far less bulky and is more efficient than the betatron (see Fig. 18-11).

The chief difference between the synchrocyclotron and the electron synchrotron is that in the former the magnetic field is held constant while the frequency of acceleration changes. In the latter the frequency is held constant while the magnetic field increases.

A serious limitation on the maximum attainable energies is that an accelerated charge radiates energy, and a limit would be reached when the rate of radiation of energy equals the rate at which energy is put into the particle. This radiation is appreciable at speeds achieved in the betatron but is not appreciable at the lower speeds attainable by the more massive particles in a cyclotron. Although the electrons in a betatron soon reach a speed nearly that of light and further linear acceleration is slight, they are continually accelerated toward the center of path and this acceleration produces radiation. Such radiation is called *synchrotron radiation* (Problem 10) because it was first noticed in synchrotron operation. It is of course also a factor in the upper limit of operation of a betatron.

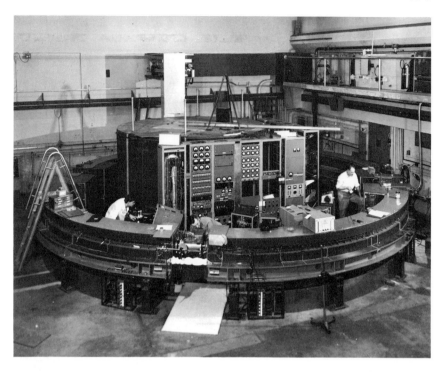

Fig. 18-11.   The Cornell electron synchrotron was the first to use strong focussing. It gives electrons of 1-beV energy. Notice the absence of any central magnet. (Courtesy of Robert R. Wilson, Laboratory of Nuclear Studies, Cornell University.)

In operation, pulses of electrons are first accelerated by a Van de Graaff generator or a linear accelerator to energies of a few million electron volts and speeds approaching that of light. They are then injected into the synchrotron. As the energies of the electrons increase at each revolution the guide field must also increase, and the ratio of the output energy to the input energy may be as much as 500 or more. From earlier limits of some millions of electron volts the output energies have now increased to the billions and the electron synchrotron at Cambridge (a joint project of Harvard and M.I.T.) was designed to give 6 or more beV.

18-6. The Proton Synchrotron

The *proton synchrotron* operates on very much the same principle as the electron synchrotron except that it is designed to accelerate protons. It also has no solid magnetic core but only a ring of guide magnets around the periphery to bend the paths of the particles and keep them in stable orbits of constant radius. Polarities are of course reversed in order to accelerate positive particles.

Just as with electrons, the guide field must steadily increase for each pulse of protons to keep the protons from spiraling outward. However, the frequency of the accelerating field cannot be held constant as in the electron synchrotron and it must be at first increased for each pulse. The reason is that, whereas electrons reach almost the speed of light at about 1 meV and thereafter travel with nearly constant speed, the protons do not settle down to a constant speed approximating that of light until they have reached energies of nearly 5 beV. From this point on the proton synchrotron operates in the same manner as the electron synchrotron.

The Cosmotron at Brookhaven National Laboratory (Fig. 18-12) was the first accelerator to achieve energies as high as 3 beV. It has a 200-ton magnet and the diameter of the orbit is a little more than 60 feet. At Berkeley their *bevatron* was built to give energies of 6 beV. A huge new AG synchrotron (next section) at Brookhaven, 842 ft. in diameter (Plates 10 and 11), and one at CERN (Conseil Européen pour la Recherche Nucléaire) in Geneva, Switzerland have been designed to reach energies of 25 to 30 beV. The one at CERN has an orbital diameter of 650 ft. It was put into operation late in 1959 and furnished a beam of 10^{10} protons per pulse. A similar Russian proton accelerator is said to be designed for 50 beV and the end is not yet in sight.

Fig. 18-12. The Cosmotron ("race-track" accelerator) was the first designed to give a proton of several billion electron volts energy. (Courtesy, Brookhaven National Laboratory, Upton, N. Y.)

The very high energies of particles available from an accelerator are not always as good as they appear since only a fraction of this energy may be available for transfer in a collision process (§16-10). If a low-speed proton hits head-on another proton at rest, the classical laws of conservation of momentum and energy predict that the first proton will transfer all of its momentum and energy to the second particle since they have the same mass. But a high-speed proton has a much larger relativistic mass. For instance, a 6-beV proton colliding with a proton at rest can only transfer about 2 beV or $\frac{1}{3}$ of its energy to the proton.

18-7. Strong Focussing; Alternating Gradient

When a uniform guide field is used around the orbital path of the particles it is difficult to keep the particle beam from spreading out, with severe loss of intensity. The method of Fig. 18-13 first applied to the beta-tron has serious limitations; the greater the bulging of the field the more vertical focussing is attained but the less horizontal focussing. To get both at the same time only weak focussing can be attained. Indeed mathematical analysis shows that if too strong vertical focussing is achieved there will actually be some defocussing in the horizontal direction. However, in the early 1950's a striking new development called *AG strong focussing* occurred which was greatly to be desired because conventional guide magnets had just about reached maximum practical size and mass.

Strong focussing was developed following suggestions of Courant, Snyder and Livingston. The magnet furnishing the guide field was to be

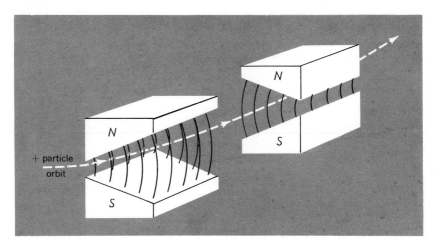

Fig. 18-13. Strong focussing. The guide magnets have pole faces tapered alternately in and out and produce magnetic fields that alternately bulge in and out. These bulging fields give a high degree of orbital stability.

composed of sections with tapered poles such that alternate sections have fields bulging inward or outward, and horizontal field intensity gradients alternately increase and decrease outward (Fig. 18-13). Because the field gradients thus alternate the method is spoken of as *alternating gradient* (*A G*) *strong focussing*. This permits strong focussing vertically for one field and strong focussing horizontally for the next and so on.

In Fig. 18-14 the section drawings show that at *a* there are components of the field inward in the vertical plane that produce vertical focussing, although if the focussing is strong vertically there is actual defocussing horizontally as particles moving outward (to the right) in larger orbits do not find the field strong enough to push them back. On the other hand at *b* in the next section they do experience such a field and are focussed horizontally, though now somewhat defocussed vertically. It might be thought that the net effect of a succession of these fields would only give weak focussing but this is not so. Both theory and practice show that if properly designed there can be a net effect of strong focussing which keeps a larger number of particles in the beam "on the orbit." Indeed the orbital tube may be only a few square inches in cross section whereas for weak focussing to get the same beam intensity it might need to be several square feet in cross section. This enables much smaller and lighter magnets to be used. The newer machines all use one form or another of strong focussing.

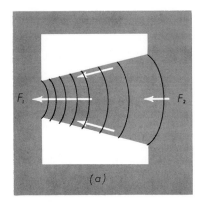
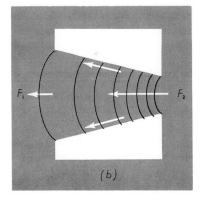

Fig. 18-14. Field intensity at *a* decreases outward from F_1 to F_2 giving horizontal defocussing, but components of the field act inward to produce vertical focussing. At *b* the field intensity increases outward pulling wayward electrons inward horizontally though temporarily defocussing them vertically.

To give an optical analogy of how strong focussing produces the equivalent of a larger aperture for the guide tube in any magnet section, Fig. 18-15*a* shows a tube with a single weak converging lens at the center. The dotted lines show the angle of acceptance for light rays. In the same figure at *b* three stronger lenses (strong focussing) are used and the angle of acceptance is considerably larger. Although successive magnet sections alternately focus and defocus in any one plane (horizontal or vertical) the net effect is to focus as in the optical analogy at *c* of a convergent and divergent lens.

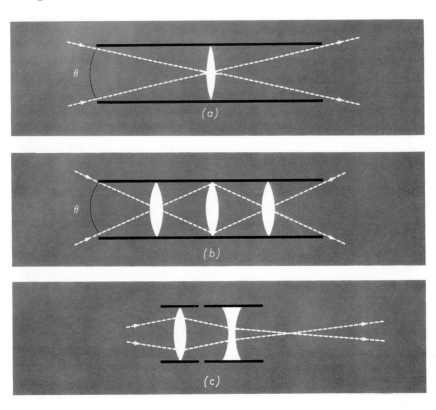

Fig. 18-15. By analogy with *a*, weak (thin lens) and *b*, strong (thick lens) optical focussing, particles being accelerated in any magnet section are accepted through a wider angle (larger aperture) with strong focussing than with weak focussing. The successive magnet sections alternately focus and defocus in any one place (horizontal or vertical) but the combination may still be convergent, as in the optical analogy at *c*.

In the method of strong focussing just described the field intensities must be increased for each pulse in proportion to the increasing energies of the particles as they circle around. A modification of this idea has been applied to the cyclotron. The field is kept constant in time but, by special design of the pole pieces in sectors that spiral outward or are in the form of radial sectors (Fig. 18-16), the field increases with radial distance and permits the use of what is called *fixed field alternating gradient* (FFAG)

Fig. 18-16. The radial-sector type of FFAG (fixed field alternating gradient) accelerator designed by MURA (Midwestern Universities Research Association) in Madison, Wisconsin. In operation since 1962, it accelerates electrons from 0.1 to 50 meV. Built as a pilot model for a still larger machine. (Courtesy, MURA).

focussing. Limitations of space do not permit further discussion of these interesting developments here.

18-8. Linear Accelerators

Although the first linear accelerators were built before the development of cyclic accelerators the necessary power to operate them and reach very high energies was not then available and the lengths required for high energies seemed impractical. After the development of more powerful high-frequency oscillators during World War II the situation changed. Now linear accelerators (often called a *linac* for short) have been developed at many institutions. For the most part they are used to accelerate electrons (*electron linac*) or to accelerate protons (*proton linac*) or even deuterons or alpha particles, but some called *heavy-ion accelerators* such as those at Yale University and the University of California have been especially constructed to accelerate the ions of heavier elements. The linac used to inject protons into the 30 beV Brookhaven accelerator is shown in Plate 12.

There are two closely related, general types of linear accelerators. In one, the voltage is switched from one pair of electrodes to the next pair of

electrodes, so that the particle leaving the region between the first pair of
electrodes enters the second region between electrodes just in time to be
accelerated again (Fig. 18-17). Since the particles are now moving faster,
the drift distance along each electrode must increase if the accelerating
potential is switched at the same rate to successive electrodes, and if speeds
have not approached the speed of light. If the switching process is continued
in step with the particles moving down the tube, there is no theoretical
limit to the energies that might be reached, but there are practical limitations of length of tube and of available power.

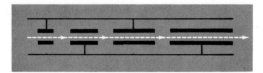

Fig. 18-17. Section of one
type of linear accelerator. Voltages between cylindrical drift
tubes accelerate the particles.

A feature that tends to keep the accelerated particles in groups or
"bunches" so that they do not get lost and thus reduce the beam intensity
is the automatic tendency toward what is called *phase bunching*. This kind
of stabilizing effect is present in any machine operating on the principle of
successive impulses. Let E (Fig. 18-18) represent the accelerating field
encountered by the middle of a bunch of particles passing between the
accelerating electrodes. A particle which is traveling faster than the average
will arrive at an earlier time, before the alternating field has risen to the
value E, and will receive an acceleration by a weaker field as at E_1. Thus it
will slow down and tend to move toward the center of the bunch. On the
other hand, a particle that is traveling at a less than average speed will
reach the gap after the field has risen to a higher value such as E_2. It will
then be accelerated more, tending to make it catch up. This kind of stabilizing effect is an important factor in the successful operation of such
accelerators.

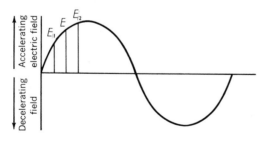

Fig. 18-18. Illustrating phase
stability in a particle accelerator.

Another type of linear accelerator is the *wave accelerator*. During
World War II, methods were perfected of transmitting electro-magnetic
waves through hollow pipes of conducting material, called wave guides. In
a wave guide it is possible to set up various modes of electromagnetic waves,
and in one of these the electric field is parallel to the axis of the tube.

Assume now that in the wave guide (Fig. 18-19) the waves move down the tube. If a stream of charged particles is injected into the tube in the direction of the axis at the right moment, the particles will be accelerated by the electric field of the wave parallel to the axis. The speed of the wave down the wave guide can be controlled by diaphragms as in the figure. In some cases the diaphragms may be little more than circular ridges in the wave guide. If the electric field and the particle move down the guide at the same speed the particle will be continuously accelerated. It is similar to the way in which a surf rider can sometimes ride the crest of a water wave. When the particles have nearly reached the speed of light they do not increase in speed appreciably and the wave can then also travel at constant speed. Since electrons approach the speed of light quickly this type of machine is particularly applicable to acceleration of electrons.

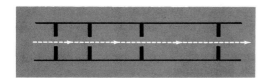

Fig. 18-19. Section of a wave type of linear accelerator. Diaphragms slow wave speed down to that of particles.

In the operation of linear accelerators particles are usually injected at energies of a few meV from a Van de Graaff generator. The required power frequency applied to the drift electrodes in that type of linac may be as much as 20 mc/sec or more depending on the lengths of the drift tubes. Even at a hypothetical gain of 200,000 eV per gap, the number of drift tubes required to reach 100 meV would be nearly 500 and the length of the linac could be unreasonable. This calls for higher frequencies, more voltage gain per gap and shorter drift tubes. At Stanford University the first high-energy electron linac was constructed by Hansen; it was 200 ft long, and produced electrons of 600 meV energy. This is far surpassed by the latest one at the same place, the world's longest linear accelerator, 2 miles in length, designed to give electron energies of 30 to 40 (or more) beV. The first high-energy proton linac was built by Alvarez at the University of California in 1946.

Although the particles accelerated by a linac are produced in bunches, the bunches may come at a very high repetition rate depending on the ability of the system to dissipate the heat energy involved. The power required to operate a 50-meV linac may be 3000 kilowatts and because of lower efficiency at higher energies may rise to 50,000 kilowatts for 200 meV. In the largest linear accelerators the lower energies may be attained by the drift-tube construction, which then changes to diaphragm (or loaded) wave guide for the higher energies. For the most efficient operation of a proton linac it can be shown that the change-over should occur at about 200 meV.

Problems

1. A Van de Graaff generator produces a potential difference of 5×10^6 volts. If it is used to accelerate the bare nuclei of (a) hydrogen, (b) deuterium, (c) helium, and (d) lithium, what energies in eV can be attained?

2. Show by what approximate ratio the frequency of alternating voltage on the dee electrodes would need to be changed if a cyclotron designed to accelerate protons is to be converted to accelerate bare lithium (Li^7) nuclei.

3. A cyclotron has been used for accelerating alpha particles. The magnetic flux density through the dees is 2.0 weber/m² and the dees have a diameter of 1.0 m. The frequency of potential on the dees for alpha particles has been 16 mc/sec and maximum energies of 48 meV have been attained. What change in frequency if any, is needed to accelerate deuterons and what maximum energies may be attained?

4. A cyclotron has a magnetic flux density of 2.0 weber/m² through the dees. If the diameter of the dees is 1.0 m, what frequency of the oscillator voltage on the dees is required to accelerate (a) alpha particles, (b) protons? What maximum energies of each can be obtained?

5. If the radius of curvature of the path of a particle inside one of the dees of a cyclotron is r, and if the number of times the particle has been accelerated by crossing the space between the dees is n, show that r is proportional to $\sqrt{n}$.

6. A cyclotron is to be designed to accelerate alpha particles to a maximum energy of 40 meV. The maximum magnetic flux density obtainable from the iron of the magnet is 1.6 weber/m². How many revolutions must a particle make? What must the diameter of the dee electrodes be if the voltage peak of the oscillatory voltage on the dees is 40 kilovolts? What must the oscillatory frequency be? (Use non-relativistic theory.)

7. An accelerator produces pulses of protons at the rate of two per second. If each pulse contains 10^{12} protons what average current in milliamperes would this represent?

*8. In a synchrocyclotron, proton energies are increased from 1 meV to 200 meV while the orbit expands in a magnetic field of flux density of 1.8 weber/m². Find the initial and final frequencies of rotation.

9. In an electron synchrotron the electrons are injected at an energy of 2 meV and reach an energy of 1 beV. Assume speed is constant and approximately that of light. If the diameter of the electron orbit (circular) is 8 meters, what is the approximate average gain in kinetic energy per revolution if the time of acceleration is 1/120 sec? What is the total length of path in meters and miles?

*10. Find the energy in joules and in eV radiated per revolution by a 1-beV electron rotating in an accelerator in a circular orbit of radius $r = 5$ meters. Use the formula obtained by Schwinger from relativistic theory for particles with speeds near the speed of light, where the energy radiated per revolution in joules is

$$\text{Energy per rev} = 12\pi \frac{e^2}{r}\left(\frac{E_T}{m_0 c^2}\right)^4 \times 10^9 \text{ joules}$$

In this formula m_0c^2 is the rest-mass equivalent energy, E_T is the total energy, that is, rest-mass energy plus kinetic energy, and the charge and radius are in mks units.

*11. Using the formula given in the preceding problem find the energy radiated per revolution by a 10.0-beV proton and also find the energy radiated per second, in joules and in eV.

*12. The electrons in a betatron move in a circular orbit of 4 meters radius with approximately the speed of light. If the average gain in energy per revolution is 20,000 eV, what maximum energy could be attained before radiation loss given by the formula in problem 10 equals energy gained?

13. Electrons of 1 meV energy are injected into a linear accelerator of the drift-tube type having 301 drift tubes. The drift tubes are connected to a 5000-megacycles/sec oscillator so that alternate sections are positive (or negative) at any instant. What maximum voltage is required between drift tubes in order to obtain electrons of 16-meV energy? What would be the lengths of (a) the second drift tube and (b) the next to the last drift tube? (c) What would be the approximate length of the accelerator assuming negligible gap between drift tubes?

14. A drift-tube type linear accelerator 1 mile (1.6 km) long could produce electrons of what approximate energy if the maximum voltage between drift tubes is 50 kV and if the oscillator frequency is 3000 megacycles/sec? Neglect spacing between drift tubes.

Recommended Reading

Van de Graaff, Trump and Buechner, *Electrostatic Generators for the Acceleration of Charged Particles*, in Rep. Prog. Phys., Vol. XI. London: Physical Society, 1946.

Livingston, M. S., *High-Energy Accelerators*. New York: Interscience Publishers, Inc., 1954.

Slater, J. C., "Linear Accelerators," in *Annual Review of Nuclear Science*, Vol. 1. Stanford: Annual Reviews, Inc., 1952.

Haworth, L. J., "Electronuclear Machines," in *Recent Advances in Science*, ed. by Shamos and Murphy. New York: Science Editions, Inc., 1961.

Wilson, R. R., and R. Litauer, *Accelerators*. Garden City, N. Y.: Anchor Books, Doubleday & Co., Inc., 1960.

Of Historical Interest

Sloane, D. H., and E. O. Lawrence, "The Production of Heavy High-Speed Ions Without the Use of High Voltage," *Physical Review*, 38, 2021 (1931).

Kerst, D. W., "The Betatron: Development and Applications," *American Scientist*, 35, 56 (1947).

APPENDIX

1. IMPORTANT PHYSICAL CONSTANTS

Based on the 1963 recommendation of the Committee on Fundamental Constants of the National Academy of Science—National Research Council.

(Masses in amu are in terms of $\frac{1}{16}$ the mass of O^{16}.)

Speed of light in a vacuum	c	2.997925×10^8 m/sec
Planck's constant	h	6.6256×10^{-34} joule sec
		6.6256×10^{-27} erg sec
Avogadro's number	N_0	6.0252×10^{23} atoms/gm-atomic wt
Gas constant	R	8.3143 joule/(gm mole)°K
Boltzmann's constant	$k = R/N_0$	1.38054×10^{-23} joule/molecule°K
Volume of 1 gm-mol wt of perfect gas, normal temperature and pressure		22.414 liters
Faraday		96487 coulombs
Electron charge	e	1.60210×10^{-19} coulomb
		4.80298×10^{-10} esu
Electron volt (eV)	1 eV	1.6021×10^{-19} joule
	1 meV	10^6 eV
	1 beV	10^9 eV
Electron rest mass	m_0	9.1091×10^{-31} kg
		0.51098 meV
Proton rest mass	M_p	1.6725×10^{-27} kg
		1.007593 amu
Neutron rest mass	M_n	1.6748×10^{-27} kg
		1.008982 amu
Ratio of proton mass to electron mass	M_p/m	1836.1
Ratio of H atom mass to electron mass	M_H/m	1837.1
Charge-to-mass ratio of the electron	e/m	1.758796×10^{11} coulomb/kg
		5.272738×10^{17} esu/gm
Rydberg constant	R_∞	$109{,}737.31$ cm^{-1}
	R_H	$109{,}677.58$ cm^{-1}
Radius of first Bohr orbit	r	0.529167 Å
Classical electron radius	$e^2/2\pi\epsilon_0 mc^2$	2.81777×10^{-15} m
Compton wavelength of electron		2.42621×10^{-12} m
Bohr magneton		9.2732×10^{-24} joule (web/m²)⁻¹
Nuclear magneton		5.0505×10^{-27} joule (web/m²)⁻¹
Permittivity of free space (mks)	ϵ_0	8.85434×10^{-12} farad/m
Permeability of free space (mks)	μ_0	$4\pi \times 10^{-7}$ henry/m

IMPORTANT PHYSICAL CONSTANTS—*Continued*

Atomic mass unit	1 amu	1.6598×10^{-27} kg
		931.16 meV
Angstrom unit	1Å	10^{-10} m
Nanosecond		10^{-9} sec
Base of natural system of logarithms	ϵ	2.718

2. COMMON UNITS

Physical Quantity	mks units	cgs units
Length	1 meter (m)	$= 10^2$ centimeters (cm)
Mass	1 kilogram (kg)	$= 10^3$ grams (gm)
Time	1 second (sec)	$= 1$ second (sec)
Force	1 newton (n)	$= 10^5$ dynes
Momentum	1 kg m/sec	$= 10^5$ gm cm/sec
Energy	1 joule (1 newton meter)	$= 10^7$ ergs
Electric charge	1 coulomb	$= 3 \times 10^9$ statcoulombs (esu)
Electric current	1 ampere	$= 3 \times 10^9$ statcoulombs/sec (esu)
Potential	1 volt	$= \dfrac{1}{300}$ statvolt (esu)
Electric field intensity	1 volt/meter	$= \dfrac{10^{-4}}{3}$ statvolt/cm (esu)
Magnetic flux density	1 weber/meter^2	$= 10^4$ gauss (emu)

2A. PREFIXES

milli	$= 10^{-3}$	kilo	$= 10^3$
micro	$= 10^{-6}$	mega	$= 10^6$
nano	$= 10^{-9}$	giga	$= 10^9$
pico	$= 10^{-12}$	tera	$= 10^{12}$

3. GREEK ALPHABET

Alpha	A, α		Nu	N, ν
Beta	B, β		Xi	Ξ, ξ
Gamma	Γ, γ		Omicron	O, o
Delta	Δ, δ		Pi	Π, π
Epsilon	E, ϵ		Rho	P, ρ
Zeta	Z, ζ		Sigma	Σ, σ
Eta	H, η		Tau	T, τ
Theta	Θ, θ		Upsilon	Υ, υ
Iota	I, ι		Phi	Φ, ϕ
Kappa	K, κ		Chi	X, χ
Lambda	Λ, λ		Psi	Ψ, ψ
Mu	M, μ		Omega	Ω, ω

4. PERIODIC TABLE OF THE ELEMENTS

With Chemical Atomic Weights (Chemical Scale)

Period	Group I a	Group I b	Group II a	Group II b	Group III a	Group III b	Group IV a	Group IV b	Group V a	Group V b	Group VI a	Group VI b	Group VII a	Group VII b	Group VIII			Group VIII b
I	1 H 1.0080																	2 He 4.003
II	3 Li 6.940		4 Be 9.013			5 B 10.82		6 C 12.010		7 N 14.008		8 O 16.0000		9 F 19.00					10 Ne 20.183
III	11 Na 22.997		12 Mg 24.32			13 Al 26.98		14 Si 28.09		15 P 30.975		16 S 32.066		17 Cl 35.457					18 Ar 39.944
IV	19 K 39.100	29 Cu 63.54	20 Ca 40.08	30 Zn 65.38	21 Sc 44.96	31 Ga 69.72	22 Ti 47.90	32 Ge 72.60	23 V 50.95	33 As 74.91	24 Cr 52.01	34 Se 78.96	25 Mn 54.93	35 Br 79.916	26 Fe 55.85	27 Co 58.94	28 Ni 58.69	36 Kr 83.80
V	37 Rb 85.48	47 Ag 107.880	38 Sr 87.63	48 Cd 112.41	39 Y 88.92	49 In 114.76	40 Zr 91.22	50 Sn 118.70	41 Nb 92.91	51 Sb 121.76	42 Mo 95.95	52 Te 127.61	43 Tc [99]	53 I 126.91	44 Ru 101.7	45 Rh 102.91	46 Pd 106.7	54 Xe 131.3
VI	55 Cs 132.91	79 Au 197.2	56 Ba 137.36	80 Hg 200.61	57 to 71 Rare earths*	81 Tl 204.39	72 Hf 178.6	82 Pb 207.21	73 Ta 180.88	83 Bi 209.00	74 W 183.92	84 Po 210	75 Re 186.31	85 At [210]	76 Os 190.2	77 Ir 193.1	78 Pt 195.23	86 Em 222
VII	87 Fr [223]		88 Ra 226.05		89 to 102 Actinides†													

* Rare earths: 57 La 138.92, 58 Ce 140.13, 59 Pr 140.92, 60 Nd 144.27, 61 Pm [145], 62 Sm 150.43, 63 Eu 152.0, 64 Gd 156.9, 65 Tb 159.2, 66 Dy 162.46, 67 Ho 164.94, 68 Er 167.2, 69 Tm 169.4, 70 Yb 173.04, 71 Lu 174.99

† Actinides: 89 Ac 227, 90 Th 232.12, 91 Pa 123, 92 U 238.07, 93 Np [237], 94 Pu [242], 95 Am [243], 96 Cm [243], 97 Bk [245], 98 Cf [246], 99 Es [253], 100 Fm [255], 101 Md [256], 102 No [253?], 103 Lw [ ]

Atomic weight in square brackets is of the isotope of longest half-life or in some instances the first one identified.

5. ALPHABETICAL LIST OF THE ELEMENTS

Starred elements have no stable isotope.

Element	Symbol	Atomic Number, Z	Element	Symbol	Atomic Number, Z
Actinium	Ac	89	Gadolinium	Gd	64
Aluminum	Al	13	Gallium	Ga	31
Americium	Am	95	Germanium	Ge	32
Antimony	Sb	51	Gold	Au	79
Argon	Ar	18	Hafnium	Hf	72
Arsenic	As	33	Helium	He	2
Astatine*	At	85	Holmium	Ho	67
Barium	Ba	56	Hydrogen	H	1
Berkelium*	Bk	97	Indium	In	49
Beryllium	Be	4	Iodine	I	53
Bismuth	Bi	83	Iridium	Ir	77
Boron	B	5	Iron	Fe	26
Bromine	Br	35	Krypton	Kr	36
Cadmium	Cd	48	Lanthanum	La	57
Calcium	Ca	20	Lawrencium*	Lw	103
Californium*	Cf	98	Lead	Pb	82
Carbon	C	6	Lithium	Li	3
Cerium	Ce	58	Lutecium	Lu	71
Cesium	Cs	55	Magnesium	Mg	12
Chlorine	Cl	17	Manganese	Mn	25
Chromium	Cr	24	Mendelevium*	Md	101
Cobalt	Co	27	Mercury	Hg	80
Copper	Cu	29	Molybdenum	Mo	42
Curium*	Cm	96	Neodymium	Nd	60
Dysprosium	Dy	66	Neon	Ne	10
Einsteinium*	E	99	Neptunium*	Np	93
Emanation*	Em	86	Nickel	Ni	28
Erbium	Er	68	Niobium	Nb	41
Europium	Eu	63	Nitrogen	N	7
Fermium*	Fm	100	Nobelium*	No	102
Fluorine	F	9	Osmium	Os	76
Francium*	Fr	87	Oxygen	O	8

Note: The Commission on Inorganic Nomenclature of the I.U.P.A.C. (International Union of Pure and Applied Chemistry) has recommended the following changes in symbols: Ar for argon, not A, Es for einsteinium, not E, and Md for mendelevium, not Mv.

ALPHABETICAL LIST OF THE ELEMENTS—*Continued*

Element	Symbol	Atomic Number, Z	Element	Symbol	Atomic Number, Z
Palladium	Pd	46	Strontium	Sr	38
Phosphorus	P	15	Sulfur	S	16
Platinum	Pt	78	Tantalum	Ta	73
Plutonium*	Pu	94	Technetium*	Tc	43
Polonium*	Po	84	Tellurium	Te	52
Potassium	K	19	Terbium	Tb	65
Praseodymium	Pr	59	Thallium	Tl	81
Promethium*	Pm	61	Thorium*	Th	90
Protactinium*	Pa	91	Thulium	Tm	69
Radium	Ra	88	Tin	Sn	50
Rhenium	Re	75	Titanium	Ti	22
Rhodium	Rh	45	Tungsten		
Rubidium	Rb	37	(Wolfram)	W	74
Ruthenium	Ru	44	Uranium*	U	92
Samarium	Sm	62	Vanadium	V	23
Scandium	Sc	21	Xenon	Xe	54
Selenium	Se	34	Ytterbium	Yb	70
Silicon	Si	14	Yttrium	Y	39
Silver	Ag	47	Zinc	Zn	30
Sodium	Na	11	Zirconium	Zr	40

6. ISOTOPIC MASSES

Mass numbers and masses in amu of neutral atoms of the isotopes of the more common elements. Unstable nuclides are marked with an asterisk. Parentheses indicate doubtful values.

Element	Mass number	Atomic mass amu	Element	Mass number	Atomic mass amu
$_0$n	1	1.008 986	$_8$O	14*	14.013 06
$_1$H	1	1.008 143		15*	15.007 784
	2	2.014 742		16	16.000 000
	3*	3.017 005		17	17.004 537
$_2$He	3	3.016 986		18	18.004 875
	4	4.003 874		19*	19.009 620
	5*	5.013 89	$_9$F	17*	17.007 512
	6*	6.020 79		18*	18.006 676
$_3$Li	5*	5.014 00		19	19.004 443
	6	6.017 034		20*	20.006 35
	7	7.018 232	$_{10}$Ne	18*	18.011 20
	8*	8.025 020		19*	19.007 940
$_4$Be	7*	7.019 158		20	19.998 771
	8*	8.007 849		21	21.000 524
	9	9.015 060		22	21.998 329
	10*	10.016 725		23*	23.001 61
$_5$B	8*	8.026 70	$_{11}$Na	23	22.997 091
	9*	9.016 208			
	10	10.016 124	$_{12}$Mg	24	23.992 669
	11	11.012 808		25	24.993 782
	12*	12.018 185		26	25.990 854
$_6$C	10*	10.020 20			
	11*	11.014 939	$_{13}$Al	27	26.990 111
	12	12.003 815			
	13	13.007 490	$_{14}$Si	28	27.985 826
	14*	14.007 692		29	28.985 71
	15*	15.014 40		30	29.983 290
$_7$N	12*	12.022 90	$_{15}$P	31	30.983 613
	13*	13.009 877			
	14	14.007 525	$_{16}$S	32	31.982 238
	15	15.004 878		33	32.981 947
	16*	16.011 20		34	33.978 664
	17*	17.014 00		36	35.978 525

Isotopic Masses—*Continued*

Element	Mass number	Atomic mass amu	Element	Mass number	Atomic mass amu
$_{17}$Cl	35	34.979 972	$_{29}$Cu	63	62.949 604
	37	36.977 657		65	64.948 426
$_{18}$Ar	36	35.978 983	$_{30}$Zn	64	63.949 471
	38	37.974 802		66	65.947 013
	40	39.975 093		67	66.948 419
				68	67.946 458
$_{19}$K	39	38.976 100		70	69.947 576
	40*	39.976 709			
	41	40.974 856	$_{33}$As	75	74.945 54
$_{20}$Ca	40	39.975 293	$_{35}$Br	79	78.943 49
	42	41.971 967		81	80.942 15
	43	42.972 444			
	44	43.969 471	$_{36}$Kr	78	77.944 97
	46	45.968 297		80	79.942 00
	48	47.967 766		82	81.939 50
				83	82.940 42
$_{22}$Ti	46	45.967 241		84	83.938 19
	47	46.966 685		86	85.938 11
	48	47.963 190	$_{37}$Rb	85	84.939 02
	49	48.963 429		87*	86.936 9
	50	49.960 669			
			$_{38}$Sr	84	83.939 9
$_{24}$Cr	50	49.961 931		86	85.936 7
	52	51.957 026		87	86.936 6
	53	52.957 482		88	87.934 0
	54	53.956 023			
			$_{40}$Zr	90	89.932 9
$_{25}$Mn	55	54.955 523		91	90.934 2
				92	91.933 9
$_{26}$Fe	54	53.956 759		94	(93.937)
	56	55.952 725		96	95.939 8
	57	56.953 511			
	58	57.951 736	$_{41}$Nb	93	92.935 2
$_{27}$Co	59	58.951 920	$_{42}$Mo	92	(91.937)
				94	(93.935)
				95	94.934 6
$_{28}$Ni	58	57.953 772		96	95.935 4
	60	59.949 824			
	61	60.950 462		97	96.937 0
	62	61.948 029		98	97.937 1
	64	63.948 284		100	99.938 3

Isotopic Masses—*Continued*

Element	Mass number	Atomic mass amu	Element	Mass number	Atomic mass amu
$_{46}$Pd	102	101.937 3	$_{54}$Xe	124	123.945 52
	104	103.936 3		126	125.944 5
	105	104.938 2		128	127.944 18
	106	105.936 6		129	128.945 7
	108	107.937 8		130	129.944 81
	110	109.939 4		131	130.946 70
				132	131.946 10
$_{47}$Ag	107	106.938 8		134	133.947 99
	109	108.939 2		136	135.950 42
$_{48}$Cd	106	105.939 6	$_{55}$Cs	133	132.947 39
	108	107.938 4	$_{56}$Ba	130	129.947 54
	110	109.938 3		132	131.947 1
	111	110.939 5		144	133.946 83
	112	111.938 6		135	134.948 5
	113	112.940 4		136	135.947 58
	114	113.939 8		137	136.949 06
	116	115.941 8		138	137.948 73
$_{50}$Sn	112	111.940 7	$_{74}$W	180	180.001 7
	114	113.940 1		182	182.003 9
	115	114.939 9		183	183.006 3
	116	115.939 0		184	184.007 4
	117	116.940 3		186	186.009 8
	118	117.939 5	$_{79}$Au	197	197.029
	119	118.941 0	$_{80}$Hg	196	196.028
	120	119.940 3		198	198.030
	122	121.942 2		199	(199.031)
	124	123.944 6		200	(200.032)
$_{51}$Sb	121	120.942 15		201	201.034
	123	122.943 3		202	
$_{52}$Te	120	119.942 6		204	204.039
	122	121.941 66	$_{82}$Pb	204	204.036
	123	122.943 4		206	206.038
	124	123.942 5		207	207.040
	125	124.944 3		208	208.041
	126	125.943 90	$_{83}$Bi	209	209.046
	128	127.946 2	$_{90}$Th	232*	232.112
	130	129.948 26	$_{92}$U	234*	234.115
$_{53}$I	127	126.945 0		235*	235.117
				238*	238.123

ANSWERS TO ODD-NUMBERED PROBLEMS

Chapter 1. Pages 11-12

1. 7.0×10^{-5} cm
3. 10^5 volts/m;
   1.6×10^{-14} newton

9. 6.88×10^{22};
   5.53×10^{-10} m

Chapter 2. Pages 32-34

1. 3.58×10^{-8} sec
5. 1.602×10^{-19} joule
7. 102.6×10^5 m/sec;
   51.3×10^5 m/sec;
   7.8×10^{-10} sec
9. 1.95×10^4 m/sec
11. electron, 1.17 cm;
    proton, 50.2 cm
13. 16.6×10^5 m/sec

15. 5.00 cm
17. 18,700 volts
19. 1.77×10^{-3} joule/m³
21. 1.96
23. 0.7 per cent
25. 0.34 meV
27. 0.31 per cent
29. 1.8×10^{-14} newton;
    left upward at angle 26.5°

Chapter 3. Pages 46-47

1. 1.70×10^4 m/sec;
   2.38×10^4 m/sec
3. 1.67×10^{-27} kg
5. 6.3 cm

7. 10 per cent of A^{44};
   90 per cent of A^{46}
9. 0.22 per cent
11. 338 gauss cm
13. 1.00027

Chapter 4. Pages 73-75

1. 12,390 volts;
   1,239,000 volts
3. 997 watts
5. 8.56 watts
7. 0.1 cm
9. 12.5 cm
11. 688,000

13. 5; 2; 0
15. 3.12 Å
17. 7.3°; 22.5°
19. 4.8 Å
21. 0.085 Å
25. 2.8 cm

Chapter 5. Pages 100-103

1. 6.76×10^{-16} watt
3. 2.6 eV
5. 1.3×10^{15} sec⁻¹
7. 3.64×10^9
13. 6.63×10^{-28} joule;
    4.13×10^{-9} eV

15. 0.0286 Å
17. 7.25×10^6 m/sec;
    149 eV
19. 1.16×10^{-4} cm
21. 6.62×10^{-23} m
23. 3.84 Å

Chapter 5.   Pages 100-103—continued

25. 3.7×10^{-16} joule;
2.6×10^{-23} kg m sec^{-1}
27. 0.0414 Å;
0.241 Å

29. 8.1×10^{7}

31. $v = \dfrac{u}{2}\left(\dfrac{g\lambda}{8\pi}\right)^{1/2}$

Chapter 6.   Pages 132-135

1. The first;
5 min
5. 0.695 m;
59.88°
7. 0.94c
9. 2.83×10^{8} m/sec;
175,000 mi/sec
11. $\dfrac{v}{c} = \left[1 - \left(\dfrac{m_0}{m}\right)^{2}\right]^{1/2}$
15. 484 sec

17. 2.74 min; 2.74 min
21. 0.42 eV
23. 1.41×10^{14} metric tons;
0.7×10^{-13}
25. 11.1 gm
27. 4.41×10^{-36} kg;
$4.85 \times 10^{-4}\ m_0$
29. $2.67\ m_0 c^2$;
$2.18\ m_0 c^2$

Chapter 7.   Pages 157-159

1. 5.92×10^{17}
3. 19.3×10^{-13} cm;
9.65×10^{-13} cm
5. 3.13×10^{-11} cm;
3.08×10^{-21} cm^2
7. 0.529 Å
11. grav. force, 4.05×10^{-47} newton;
elec. force, 9.22×10^{-8} newton;
ratio, 4.4×10^{-40}
13. 122 eV
15. 3.16×10^{-34} kg m/sec
17. 2.42×10^{-19} joule;
1.51 eV

21. zero
23. higher frequency;
1.79 Å longer
25. 6562.8 Å; 4861.3 Å; 4340.5 Å;
4101.7 Å
27. 27,420 cm^{-1};
3645 Å;
3.4 eV
31. 3rd, 5th, 7th, etc. lines for Balmer
type transitions
33. 1.58×10^{5} °C

Chapter 8.   Pages 178-179

1. 20 Å; 10 Å; 6.7 Å; 5 Å; 4 Å
3. 9.4; 84.8; 234; 463 eV
5. 10^{9} eV

13. 1.37×10^{5} escape;
8.63×10^{5} reflected
15. 1.054×10^{-26} joule;
1.6×10^{7} sec

Chapter 9.   Pages 213-215

9. 9.27×10^{-24} joule/(weber/m^2)
11. 54.7°
19. 4.15×10^{4} m/sec^2 (direction of field)

23. 0.20 Å
25. 2.35×10^{-5} eV

Chapter 10.   Pages 232–233

1. 0.039 eV
3. 465 m/sec
5. 13.6 eV
7. 3.55×10^8;
   1.41×10^{-3} cm

9. $\dfrac{\hbar^2}{I}$
11. 0; 0.0055; 0.0165 eV;
    0.224; 0.112 mm

Chapter 11.   Pages 252–253

1. 400 m/sec;
   436 m/sec
3. 410 m/sec

7. 1.23×10^6
11. 12,400 m
13. 8.6×10^{-4} cm

Chapter 12.   Page 275

1. 5.92×10^{28}
3. 1.27×10^7 amp/m²
7. 3.2 eV

9. 5.1×10^{19} amp
11. 6.9×10^{20} amp/m²
13. 0.35 amp

Chapter 13.   Pages 313–314

1. 42; 1.75
3. half-life, 3.46×10^5 sec;
   av. life, 5×10^5 sec
5. 1570 years
7. 15.2 days; 0.17
9. 35 cm³

11. 3.9×10^{12} atoms of emanation;
    2.2×10^9 atoms of polonium
13. 465 days
15. 77.7 per cent
17. 4.84 meV
19. 2.4×10^{-14} coulomb;
    4.8×10^{-3} volt

Chapter 14.   Pages 342–344

1. for O^{16}, 0.1372 amu; 0.00857 amu per
   nucleon;
   for C^{12}, 0.099 amu; 0.0083
   amu per nucleon
3. 1.19×10^{-12} joule; 7.45 meV
5. 4.7×10^{-9} amu

9. 1.15
11. 16 meV
13. 5.64×10^{-27} joule; 35.2 m
15. β^- emission;
    17.7 keV
17. 4.1×10^{-12} cm

Chapter 15.   Pages 361–362

1. 2.38×10^{-3} amu; $+2.22$ meV
9. 5.4 meV;
   $_8O^{17}$

11. 9.8×10^{20}
13. 1.15 meV
15. 0.085 meV

Chapter 16.   Pages 386–387

1. 0.78 meV
3. 0.33; 35
5. 9.1 tons
7. 1.6×10^{-2} as intense

9. 142 meV
11. 1.1×10^{13} hp
13. 132 tons
15. 7.35×10^{17}

Chapter 17.   Pages 417-419

1. 490 electron pairs
5. 10.33 m (water);
   0.94 m (lead)

7. 33.7 meV
11. 56 meV
15. The first one

Chapter 18.   Pages 441-443

1. (*a*) 5 meV;
   (*b*) 5 meV;
   (*c*) 10 meV;
   (*d*) 15 meV
3. No change in frequency; 24 meV
7. 3.2×10^{-4} milliamp

9. 10^4 eV per rev;
   2.5×10^6 meters;
   1560 miles
11. 3.73×10^{-24} joule;
   2.33×10^{-5} eV
13. (*a*) 5.9 cm;
   (*b*) 6.0 cm;
   (*c*) 18.0 m

INDEX